D1535112

Infinite Series

By Earl D. Rainville

Elementary Differential Equations, Third Edition
A Short Course in Differential Equations, Third Edition
Special Functions
The Laplace Transform: An Introduction
Unified Calculus and Analytic Geometry
Analytic Geometry, Fifth Edition
(with the late CLYDE E. LOVE)
Differential and Integral Calculus, Sixth Edition
(with the late CLYDE E. LOVE)
Intermediate Differential Equations, Second Edition
Infinite Series

EARL D. RAINVILLE

The University of Michigan

Infinite Series

The Macmillan Company, New York
Collier-Macmillan Limited, London

Library of Congress catalog card number: 66-23894

THE MACMILLAN COMPANY, NEW YORK
COLLIER-MACMILLAN CANADA, LTD., TORONTO, ONTARIO

Printed in the United States of America

Some material in this book is from
Elementary Differential Equations (3rd ed.), © Copyright 1964 by The Macmillan Company;
Unified Calculus and Analytic Geometry, © Copyright 1961 by The Macmillan Company;
and *Special Functions*, © Copyright 1960 by Earl D. Rainville.

Preface

This book is an elementary treatment of infinite series; it can be read with a background of calculus.

To supplement a standard calculus course, the first eight chapters may be found suitable, even including uniform convergence, a topic usually reserved for advanced calculus.

To supplement an advanced calculus course, or a similar course for engineers, a reasonable selection would be Chapters 1 through 9, plus whatever choice may be made from the essentially self-contained units, Chapters 10 and 11, and one or more of Chapters 12, 13, and 14.

This book is also aimed at providing a simple and sound introduction to series for a short course or for self-study. There are detailed explanations, many illustrative examples and more than 500 exercises. I have stated theorems carefully and have included proofs, except for a Fourier theorem and except in a few instances so simple that proof was left as an exercise. There are additional theorems in the exercises.

The tables of power series and Fourier series at the end of the book are intended to be sufficiently extensive to prove useful to people employing series in their everyday work. The tables can also be used by instructors in constructing additional exercises for class work or for examinations.

There is a feeling, held by most mathematics teachers, that infinite series is the subject least appreciated by all but the very best students. In this book I try to spread outside my own classes my personal war against that situation. Not only are infinite series effective tools in advanced mathematics but the study of them can be esthetically rewarding without applications. They can be fun.

I hope I have not disappointed the many teachers who have encouraged me to write this book. I am grateful for their interest and confidence. I wish to thank Professor Ralph L. Shively of Lake Forest College and Professor Jack L. Goldberg of the University of Michigan for their helpful comments on the manuscript.

EARL D. RAINVILLE

Ann Arbor, Michigan

Contents

CHAPTER 1 *Introduction*

    1. Geometric Series   *1*

    2. The Sigma Notation   *3*

    3. The Index of Summation   *4*

    4. Sum of an Infinite Series   *5*

    5. A Necessary Condition for Convergence   *6*

    6. The Simple Factorial   *7*

CHAPTER 2 *Sequences*

    7. Definition of a Sequence   *10*

    8. Limit of a Sequence   *11*

    9. Basic Properties   *13*

    10. Bounded Sequences; Null Sequences   *14*

    11. Monotonic Sequences   *15*

    12. Subsequences   *19*

    13. Cluster Points   *22*

    14. Cauchy Criteria   *24*

    15. Telescoping Series   *25*

CHAPTER 3 *Positive Term Series*

    16. An Integral Test   *29*

    17. Direct Comparison Tests   *35*

18. Other Comparison Tests   *37*

19. Ratio Tests   *43*

20. Rearrangement of Terms   *47*

CHAPTER 4   *Tests of Kummer, Raabe, and Gauss*

21. Ratio-Comparison Tests   *51*

22. Kummer's Criteria   *53*

23. Raabe's Test   *56*

24. Gauss' Test   *57*

CHAPTER 5   *Series of Constants*

25. Series of Absolute Values   *60*

26. Absolute Convergence   *61*

27. Insertion of Parentheses   *66*

28. Addition of Series   *67*

29. Rearrangement of Absolutely Convergent
    Series   *67*

30. Multiplication of Series   *70*

31. Cauchy Products   *72*

32. Alternating Series Test   *73*

33. Series of Complex Terms   *79*

CHAPTER 6   *Uniform Convergence*

34. Series of Functions   *83*

35. Uniformly Convergent Series   *84*

36. Graphical Interpretation   *90*

37. The Weierstrass M-test   *93*

38. Continuity   *94*

39. Term-by-Term Integration   *98*

40. Term-by-Term Differentiation   *102*

41. Hardy's Test   *103*

CHAPTER 7   *Power Series*

42. Two Fundamental Problems   *108*

43. Convergence of Power Series   *109*

44. Taylor and Maclaurin Series   *114*

45. Some Basic Expansions   *118*

CHAPTER 8 *Operations with Power Series*

46. Addition and Multiplication   *123*

47. Uniqueness   *128*

48. Division   *129*

49. Integration   *133*

50. Continuity; Abel's Theorem   *134*

51. Differentiation   *136*

52. Harmonic Sums   *141*

53. Bernoulli Numbers   *144*

54. Expansion of Tan X *146*

55. Euler Numbers   *147*

56. Expansion of Sec X *148*

CHAPTER 9 *Functions Defined by Power Series*

57. The Factorial Function   *151*

58. The Gamma Function   *153*

59. The Beta Function   *154*

60. The Hypergeometric Function   *156*

61. Two Fundamental Properties   *158*

62. Some Elementary Expansions   *160*

63. A Bessel Function   *163*

CHAPTER 10 *Orthogonal Sets of Functions*

64. Orthogonality and Formal Expansions   *167*

65. Normalization   *170*

66. A Least Square Property   *170*

67. Bessel's Inequality   *172*

68. The Convergence Problem   *175*

69. Even and Odd Functions   *176*

70. Orthogonality of a Set of Sines and
    Cosines   *178*

CHAPTER 11   *Fourier Series*

    71. The Fourier Coefficients   *182*

    72. An Expansion Theorem   *185*

    73. Numerical Examples of Fourier Series   *187*

    74. Fourier Sine Series   *196*

    75. Fourier Cosine Series   *201*

    76. Integration of Fourier Series   *205*

    77. Differentiation of Fourier Series   *207*

CHAPTER 12   *Computations*

    78. Improvement in Rapidity of Convergence   *214*

    79. Numerical Computations   *215*

    80. Summation of Power Series   *219*

CHAPTER 13   *Asymptotic Series*

    81. Two Methods of Approximation   *222*

    82. Definition of an Asymptotic Expansion   *223*

    83. Asymptotic Expansions About Infinity   *225*

    84. Algebraic Properties   *228*

    85. Term-by-Term Integration   *230*

    86. Uniqueness   *231*

    87. Computations with Asymptotic Series   *233*

CHAPTER 14   *Infinite Products*

    88. Definition of an Infinite Product   *236*

    89. The Associated Series of Logarithms   *237*

    90. Absolute Convergence of Products   *238*

    91. Uniform Convergence of Products   *241*

    92. Euler's Product for the Gamma Function   *243*

    93. The Weierstrass Product   *247*

    94. Evaluation of Certain Infinite Products   *249*

    Table of Power Series   *252*

    Table of Fourier Series   *256*

    Index   *261*

Infinite Series

CHAPTER 1

Introduction

1. Geometric Series

A finite geometric series is a sum of terms in which the ratio of consecutive terms remains constant. Consider the sum of the first $(n+1)$ terms of a particular geometric series,

(1)
$$1 + \frac{1}{3} + \left(\frac{1}{3}\right)^2 + \cdots + \left(\frac{1}{3}\right)^n.$$

Let

(2)
$$s_n = 1 + \frac{1}{3} + \left(\frac{1}{3}\right)^2 + \cdots + \left(\frac{1}{3}\right)^n.$$

Then

(3)
$$\frac{1}{3}s_n = \frac{1}{3} + \left(\frac{1}{3}\right)^2 + \left(\frac{1}{3}\right)^3 + \cdots + \left(\frac{1}{3}^{n+1}\right),$$

and it follows from (2) and (3) that

$$\left(1 - \frac{1}{3}\right)s_n = 1 - \left(\frac{1}{3}\right)^{n+1}.$$

Therefore

(4)
$$s_n = \frac{3}{2} - \frac{3}{2}\left(\frac{1}{3}\right)^{n+1}.$$

If we let the number of terms in (1) approach infinity, $(n+1) \to \infty$, we see from (4) that $s_n \to \frac{3}{2}$ because $\left(\frac{1}{3}\right)^{n+1} \to 0$. Indeed, the s_n approaches

$\frac{3}{2}$ steadily; that is, the larger the number of terms taken, the closer s_n is to $\frac{3}{2}$. It is therefore intuitively reasonable to attach to the infinite geometric series

(5) $$1 + \frac{1}{3} + \left(\frac{1}{3}\right)^2 + \cdots + \left(\frac{1}{3}\right)^n + \cdots$$

the sum $\frac{3}{2}$. That sum can be approximated as closely as desired by taking a sufficiently large number of terms of the series (5).

A reader who has not previously encountered the concept of the sum of an infinite series may get a feeling for what is going on here by computing the sum s_n of the finite series (1) for various values of n. The table below exhibits the sum to six decimal places for certain small values of n.

n	0	1	2	3	4	10
s_n	1	1.333 333	1.444 444	1.481 481	1.493 827	1.499 992

For one thousand and one terms, $n = 1000$, the sum differs from 1.5 by less than four units in the 478th decimal place.

To the general infinite geometric series

(6) $$a + ar + ar^2 + \cdots + ar^n + \cdots, \qquad a \neq 0,$$

we attach a sum defined again as the limit of a finite sum as the number of terms approaches infinity. Put

(7) $$S_n = a + ar + ar^2 + \cdots + ar^n.$$

To the infinite series (6) we attach the sum

$$\lim_{n \to \infty} S_n$$

if that limit exists.*

From (7) it follows that

(8) $$rS_n = ar + ar^2 + ar^3 + \cdots + ar^{n+1}.$$

Then (7) and (8) yield

$$(1 - r)S_n = a - ar^{n+1}.$$

---

* The meaning of a limit here is the same as that used in calculus except that the independent variable n takes on only integral values. Section 8, page 11, contains a short review of such limits.

Hence, if $r \neq 1$,

$$(9) \qquad\qquad S_n = \frac{a(1 - r^{n+1})}{1 - r}.$$

If $|r| < 1$, $r^{n+1} \to 0$ as $n \to \infty$. Therefore

$$(10) \qquad \lim_{n\to\infty} S_n = \lim_{n\to\infty} \frac{a(1 - r^{n+1})}{1 - r} = \frac{a}{1 - r}, \qquad \text{for } |r| < 1.$$

Therefore we say that if $|r| < 1$, the sum of the infinite geometric series (6) is $\dfrac{a}{1 - r}$.

If $|r| \geq 1$, S_n does not approach a limit as $n \to \infty$ and we do not attempt to define a sum for the corresponding infinite series (6).

2. The Sigma Notation

A compact notation is needed if infinite series are to be discussed without using excessive space and effort. The symbol most frequently employed to indicate the summation process, finite or infinite, is a capital sigma, $\sum$. We write

$$(1) \qquad\qquad \sum_{k=2}^{6} \frac{1}{k^2}$$

to mean the sum of the terms that are obtained by substituting in $\dfrac{1}{k^2}$ the consecutive integral values of k starting with $k = 2$, as shown below the $\sum$, and ending with $k = 6$, as shown above the $\sum$. Thus

$$(2) \qquad \sum_{k=2}^{6} \frac{1}{k^2} = \frac{1}{2^2} + \frac{1}{3^2} + \frac{1}{4^2} + \frac{1}{5^2} + \frac{1}{6^2}.$$

In (2), $\sum$ is called the *summation sign* and k is called the *index of summation*. Note that k is a dummy index; it is only a tool used to construct the terms to be summed. The right member of (2) does not contain k. A sum is always independent of the index of summation.

The left member of (2) may be read "the sum of $\dfrac{1}{k^2}$ from $k = 2$ to $k = 6$." We refer to $k = 2$ as the lower limit of summation, to $k = 6$ as the upper limit of summation. The function $\dfrac{1}{k^2}$ on the left in (2) is called the *general term* of the series.

In an infinite series the summation index takes on consecutive integral values starting with the lower limit of summation but never stopping. Thus

$$(3) \qquad \sum_{n=4}^{\infty} b_n = b_4 + b_5 + b_6 + \cdots + b_n + \cdots,$$

which may be read "the sum of b_n from $n = 4$ to infinity." The series in (3) is only a formal sum; its significance is yet to be defined.

3. The Index of Summation

The terms of a series may involve one or more parameters. Then the general term will contain not only the index of summation but other parameters. For example, the general term of the series

$$(1) \qquad \sum_{n=0}^{\infty} x^n$$

depends upon x as well as upon n. The terms of the series (1) are functions of x.

We now stipulate that the index of summation takes precedence over all other parameters in the formation of the terms of a series. For example, the symbol in (1) stands for

$$(2) \qquad 1 + x + x^2 + x^3 + \cdots + x^n + \cdots,$$

no matter what the value of x. There is, then, no ambiguity in the determination of the value of the first $(n = 0)$ term when the parameter x takes on the value zero. The above stipulation is, indeed, forced upon us by the fact that the index of summation is a dummy index.

It is frequently desirable to perform what is called a *shift of index* in a series. For instance, in the symbol

$$(3) \qquad \sum_{n=0}^{\infty} \frac{1}{(3n + 1)^2}$$

we may put $n = k - 1$. When $n = 0$, $k = 1$, and as $n \to \infty$, so does k. We may replace (3) by

$$(4) \qquad \sum_{k=1}^{\infty} \frac{1}{(3k - 2)^2}.$$

For many reasons, one of the least being the conservation of letters, it is customary when shifting index to use the same letter for the new index of summation as for the old. For instance, in (3) let us replace n by $(n-1)$. When the old n is zero, the new n is unity and (3) becomes

(5)
$$\sum_{n=1}^{\infty} \frac{1}{(3n-2)^2}.$$

4. Sum of an Infinite Series

Consider the series

(1)
$$\sum_{n=0}^{\infty} a_n.$$

Let S_n denote the sum of the terms of (1) out to and including a_n; that is, let

(2)
$$S_n = \sum_{k=0}^{n} a_k.$$

The S_n of (2) is called a *partial sum* of the series (1).

If, as $n \to \infty$, the limit of S_n exists, we call that limit the sum of the series (1). If

(3)
$$\lim_{n \to \infty} S_n = S,$$

S is the sum of the series (1). This definition of the sum of an infinite series is a direct extension of the idea of the sum of a geometric series as introduced in Section 1.

If the sum (3) exists, we say that the series (1) is *convergent* and that it *converges* to S. If the sum (3) does not exist, we say the series (1) is *divergent*.

Convergent series have many applications in both pure and applied mathematics. Few concepts have had as tremendous an impact on the development of mathematics as the idea of the sum of an infinite series.

Divergent series are not, in general, as well behaved as convergent ones. The use of divergent series is a matter of some delicacy and is ordinarily restricted to advanced mathematics or to rash beginners. We shall make a short study of some divergent series later in the book after we have developed a degree of sophistication.

It is of prime importance to us to determine whether a given series is convergent or divergent. It is usually not feasible to demonstrate convergence or divergence directly by showing that the limit in (3) does, or does not, exist. We therefore devise tests for convergence or divergence.

A test is a theorem which states that the series

$$\sum_{n=0}^{\infty} a_n$$

is convergent (or divergent) if the general term a_n possesses certain specified properties. In the next section and throughout Chapters 3 and 4 we shall concentrate on the development of such tests.

No test for convergence is capable of testing all series. At best, a test will show that certain series converge, that others diverge, but there will remain series for which that test gives no answer.

It is important to realize that convergence or divergence of an infinite series is a property which is a result of the behavior of the general term as the index of summation approaches infinity. Convergence or divergence depends upon nothing else. It does not matter what the first billion terms (or any fixed number of terms) may be; those terms affect the sum of the series, if it has one, but have no effect upon the existence or nonexistence of that sum.

LEMMA 1. *If m is a fixed integer* $\geqq 1$,

$$\sum_{n=0}^{\infty} a_n \text{ and } \sum_{n=m}^{\infty} a_n$$

converge or diverge together.

That is, if either series in Lemma 1 converges, the other series converges; if either series diverges, the other diverges.

Proof of Lemma 1 follows at once from the definition of the sum of an infinite series. The proof is left as an exercise.

5. A Necessary Condition for Convergence

One simple but useful conclusion about convergent series follows at once from the definition of convergence. If the series

(1) $$\sum_{n=0}^{\infty} a_n$$

with the partial sums

(2) $$S_n = \sum_{k=0}^{n} a_k$$

is convergent, there exists an S such that

(3) $$\lim_{n \to \infty} S_n = S.$$

Then also, by a shift in index,

(4) $$\lim_{n \to \infty} S_{n-1} = S.$$

From (3) and (4) it follows that

(5) $$\lim_{n \to \infty} (S_n - S_{n-1}) = 0.$$

Now $S_n - S_{n-1} = a_n$. Hence, if the series (1) is convergent, its general term a_n must approach zero as $n \to \infty$.

THEOREM 1. *If* $\sum_{n=0}^{\infty} a_n$ *converges*, $\lim_{n \to \infty} a_n = 0$.

The above theorem is most useful when reworded as a divergence test.

THEOREM 1a. *If* a_n *does not approach zero as* $n \to \infty$, $\sum_{n=0}^{\infty} a_n$ *diverges*.

EXAMPLE (a). Consider the series

$$\sum_{n=0}^{\infty} \frac{n+1}{7n+3}.$$

Here, $a_n \to \frac{1}{7}$ as $n \to \infty$. Since a_n does not approach zero as $n \to \infty$, the series diverges.

EXAMPLE (b). Consider the series

$$\sum_{n=4}^{\infty} \frac{(-1)^n n^2}{n^2+1}.$$

For this series a_n does not approach a limit as $n \to \infty$. By Theorem 1a, the series diverges.

6. The Simple Factorial

The symbol $n!$ (read factorial n, or n factorial) is used to denote the product of all the integers from 1 to n inclusive:

(1) $$n! = 1 \cdot 2 \cdot 3 \cdots (n-2)(n-1)n.$$

It is convenient to add the definition

(2) $$0! = 1$$

in order to simplify the writing of certain formulas. The factorial enters many infinite series and will be used frequently throughout this book.

In manipulating factorials it is often wise to write the indicated products in detail. For example,

$$\frac{7!}{4!} = \frac{1 \cdot 2 \cdot 3 \cdot 4 \cdot 5 \cdot 6 \cdot 7}{1 \cdot 2 \cdot 3 \cdot 4} = 5 \cdot 6 \cdot 7;$$

$$\frac{(n+1)!}{3!(n-2)!} = \frac{(n+1)n(n-1) \cdot (n-2)!}{1 \cdot 2 \cdot 3 \cdot (n-2)!} = \frac{(n+1)n(n-1)}{1 \cdot 2 \cdot 3}.$$

Exercises

In Exercises 1–11 write the first five terms of the given series.

1. $\displaystyle\sum_{n=0}^{\infty} \frac{(-1)^n}{(n+2)^2}.$ ANS. $\dfrac{1}{4} - \dfrac{1}{9} + \dfrac{1}{16} - \dfrac{1}{25} + \dfrac{1}{36} + \cdots.$

2. $\displaystyle\sum_{n=2}^{\infty} \frac{(-1)^n}{n^2}.$ ANS.   Same as in Exercise 1.

3. $\displaystyle\sum_{n=1}^{\infty} \frac{2n}{2n+1}.$

4. $\displaystyle\sum_{n=0}^{\infty} ne^{-n}.$

5. $\displaystyle\sum_{k=0}^{\infty} \frac{1+(-1)^k}{k^2+1}.$

6. $\displaystyle\sum_{k=0}^{\infty} \frac{2}{4k^2+1}.$

7. $\displaystyle\sum_{n=0}^{\infty} \frac{1}{n+1}.$ ANS. $1 + \dfrac{1}{2} + \dfrac{1}{3} + \dfrac{1}{4} + \dfrac{1}{5} + \cdots.$

8. $\displaystyle\sum_{n=0}^{\infty} \frac{2n^2-5n+6}{6(n!)}.$ ANS. $1 + \dfrac{1}{2} + \dfrac{1}{3} + \dfrac{1}{4} + \dfrac{1}{8} + \cdots.$

9. $\displaystyle\sum_{n=0}^{\infty} \frac{1}{2n^4 - 12n^3 + 22n^2 - 11n + 1}.$

     ANS. $1 + \dfrac{1}{2} + \dfrac{1}{3} + \dfrac{1}{4} + \dfrac{1}{53} + \cdots.$

10. $\displaystyle\sum_{n=1}^{\infty} \frac{1}{n^2}.$ ANS. $1 + \dfrac{1}{4} + \dfrac{1}{9} + \dfrac{1}{16} + \dfrac{1}{25} + \cdots.$

11. $\displaystyle\sum_{n=1}^{\infty} \frac{2n^2 - 9n + 19}{6(n^2 + n!)}$.   ANS. $1 + \dfrac{1}{4} + \dfrac{1}{9} + \dfrac{1}{16} + \dfrac{4}{145} + \cdots$.

In Exercises 12–15, show that each series is divergent.

12. $\displaystyle\sum_{n=1}^{\infty} \frac{3n}{5n+1}$.

13. $\displaystyle\sum_{n=0}^{\infty} (-1)^n n^2$.

14. $\displaystyle\sum_{k=0}^{\infty} \frac{\pi^k}{k+1}$.

15. $\displaystyle\sum_{k=2}^{\infty} \frac{3k-1}{3k+1}$.

16. Show that every infinite arithmetic series (difference of consecutive terms constant) with terms not all zero is divergent.

In Exercises 17–24, show that the given series are identical.

17. $\displaystyle\sum_{n=1}^{\infty} (-1)^{n+1} x^n$ and $x - x^2 + \displaystyle\sum_{n=3}^{\infty} (-1)^{n+1} x^n$.

18. $\displaystyle\sum_{k=0}^{\infty} \frac{y^{k+1}}{k+1}$ and $y + \tfrac{1}{2} y^2 + \displaystyle\sum_{k=2}^{\infty} \frac{y^{k+1}}{k+1}$.

19. $\displaystyle\sum_{n=0}^{\infty} \frac{x^{n+1}}{n+1}$ and $\displaystyle\sum_{n=1}^{\infty} \frac{x^n}{n}$.

20. $\displaystyle\sum_{n=0}^{\infty} \frac{x^{n+2}}{n^2 + 4n + 5}$ and $\displaystyle\sum_{n=2}^{\infty} \frac{x^n}{n^2 + 1}$.

21. $\displaystyle\sum_{n=1}^{\infty} (n^2 - 2n + 3) y^{-n}$ and $\displaystyle\sum_{n=0}^{\infty} (n^2 + 2) y^{-n-1}$.

22. $\displaystyle\sum_{n=2}^{\infty} a_n b_{n-2}$, $\displaystyle\sum_{n=1}^{\infty} a_{n+1} b_{n-1}$,   and $\displaystyle\sum_{n=0}^{\infty} a_{n+2} b_n$.

23. $\displaystyle\sum_{k=0}^{n} a_{k+1}$ and $\displaystyle\sum_{k=1}^{n+1} a_k$.

24. $\displaystyle\sum_{k=1}^{n} \frac{u^k}{(k-1)!}$ and $\displaystyle\sum_{k=0}^{n-1} \frac{u^{k+1}}{k!}$.

25. Prove Lemma 1, page 6.

26. Prove the following theorem:

   If $\displaystyle\sum_{n=0}^{\infty} a_n$ is convergent, $\displaystyle\sum_{n=0}^{\infty} (a_n - a_{n+1})$ is convergent to the sum a_0.
Consider the partial sums of the latter series. The second series in this exercise is called a telescoping series. See also Section 15, page 25.

CHAPTER **2**

Sequences

7. Definition of a Sequence

The elements of a set are said to be denumerable, or countable, if those elements

(1) can be put into one-to-one correspondence with the positive integers,

or

(2) are finite in number.

Consider a set H whose elements are denumerable and not finite in number. Since the elements of H can be put into one-to-one correspondence with the positive integers, such a correspondence can be achieved in an unlimited number of ways. Even the selection of which element corresponds to unity affords that much freedom.

A specific correspondence of the elements of H with the positive integers is an *ordering* of those elements and the ordered set is called a *sequence*, or an *infinite sequence*.

The elements of a sequence may be designated in various ways. When the elements are not explicitly stipulated, a subscript is often used to indicate the position of each element in the ordered set. By a simple adjustment, we may stipulate a sequence by giving a one-to-one correspondence of its elements with the increasing consecutive integers starting with any specific integer, not necessarily starting with unity.

Examples of sequences:

(a) $2 + \dfrac{3}{1}, \; 2 + \dfrac{3}{2}, \; 2 + \dfrac{3}{3}, \; \ldots, \; 2 + \dfrac{3}{n}, \; \ldots \; ;$

(b) $e, \; e^2, \; e^3, \; \ldots, \; e^n, \; \ldots \; ;$

(c) $\dfrac{1}{1^2 + 1}, \; \dfrac{2}{2^2 + 1}, \; \dfrac{3}{3^2 + 1}, \; \ldots, \; \dfrac{n}{n^2 + 1}, \; \ldots \; ;$

(d) $S_0, \; S_1, \; S_2, \; \ldots, \; S_n, \; \ldots \; ;$

(e) $f_2(x), \; f_3(x), \; f_4(x), \; \ldots, \; f_n(x), \; \ldots \; ;$

(f) $a(k, 0), \; a(k, 1), \; a(k, 2), \; \ldots, \; a(k, n), \; \ldots \; ;$

(g) $b(1), \; b(2), \; b(3), \; \ldots, \; b(n), \; \ldots \; .$

In the above examples, n is called the *running index*. The *general term* of each sequence is the element that contains the running index.

A sequence is often designated by writing its general term inside braces. For example, the sequence (d) above may be written as $\{S_n\}$ and the sequence (e) as $\{f_n(x)\}$. In this notation, the initial value of the running index is omitted, although it may be separately stipulated if necessary.

The partial sums of an infinite series form a sequence. On page 5, we defined the sum of an infinite series as the limit of a partial sum as its index approaches infinity. Let us now consider the limit concept implied in that definition.

8. Limit of a Sequence

By the *limit of a sequence* we mean the limit of the general term of the sequence as the running index approaches infinity. The definition of a limit is the definition used in calculus except that the running index is restricted to integral values. That is, we write

(1)
$$\lim_{n \to \infty} b_n = B$$

if and only if, for any given positive ε, there exists a fixed positive number $n_0 = n_0(\varepsilon)$ such that, for all $n > n_0$,

(2)
$$|b_n - B| < \varepsilon.$$

It does not matter whether n_0 is taken to be an integer or not.

EXAMPLE. Show that the sequence with general term

(3)
$$b_n = \frac{12n + 17}{3n + 2}$$

has the limit 4.

First we seek an n_0 such that we can establish the inequality (2) for all $n > n_0$, with b_n and B given their current meanings. Once we have such an n_0, we can proceed to the desired proof.

If (2) is to be satisfied, we must have

(4)
$$\left| \frac{12n + 17}{3n + 2} - 4 \right| < \varepsilon,$$

which reduces to

(5)
$$\left| \frac{9}{3n + 2} \right| < \varepsilon.$$

We reason that the left member of (5) decreases as n increases. If we can find for n a value n_0 such that the members of (5) are equal, then (5) should be satisfied for all n greater than that n_0. From the tentative equality

$$\frac{9}{3n_0 + 2} = \varepsilon,$$

we obtain

(6)
$$n_0 = \frac{9 - 2\varepsilon}{3\varepsilon}.$$

Equation (6) dictates a desirable choice for n_0, except we have stipulated that n_0 be positive, so we replace the right member of (6) by its absolute value.

We are now in a position to prove that

(7)
$$\lim_{n \to \infty} \frac{12n + 17}{3n + 2} = 4.$$

Given any positive ε, no matter how small, choose

(8)
$$n_0 = \left| \frac{9 - 2\varepsilon}{3\varepsilon} \right|.$$

For all $n > n_0$,

$$n > \frac{9 - 2\varepsilon}{3\varepsilon}.$$

Hence $3n\varepsilon > 9 - 2\varepsilon$, so

$$(3n + 2)\varepsilon > 9,$$

from which it follows, since $(3n + 2)$ is positive, that

$$\left| \frac{9}{3n + 2} \right| < \varepsilon,$$

$$\left| \frac{12n + 17}{3n + 2} - 4 \right| < \varepsilon,$$

as desired.

The preceding example is included to emphasize that limits of sequences are to be treated much the same as are the corresponding limits of functions in calculus. The only difference lies in the fact that the running index in a sequence is restricted to integral values. Theorems on limits of sequences corresponding to the limit theorems of calculus are therefore quoted without repeating the proofs.

We avoid tedious repetition by adopting the convention that throughout this book the letters j, k, n are restricted to take on only integral values. Whenever it is desirable to restrict other parameters to integral values, that restriction will be explicitly stated.

9. Basic Properties

It is possible to start with the fundamental concepts of the real number system and from them build a theory of sequences. Such a procedure would occupy a large part of a book as small as this one. We therefore simply state basic properties of sequences and for their systematic development refer the reader to treatises on series.*

THEOREM 2. *If* $\lim\limits_{n \to \infty} a_n = A$ *and* $\lim\limits_{n \to \infty} b_n = B$, *then*

(1)
$$\lim_{n \to \infty} (a_n + b_n) = A + B$$

and

(2)
$$\lim_{n \to \infty} (a_n b_n) = AB.$$

* See, for instance, Konrad Knopp, *Theory and Application of Infinite Series*, Blackie and Son, Ltd., London, 1928, 571 pp.

Theorem 2 is frequently used when the elements of one sequence are independent of n, $a_n = c$. Thus, if $b_n \to B$, then $cb_n \to cB$ and $(c + b_n) \to (c + B)$.

THEOREM 3. *If* $\lim\limits_{n \to \infty} a_n = A$, *if* $\lim\limits_{n \to \infty} b_n = B$, *and if* $B \neq 0$, *then*

$$(3) \qquad\qquad \lim_{n \to \infty} \frac{a_n}{b_n} = \frac{A}{B}.$$

LEMMA 2. *If* $\lim\limits_{n \to \infty} a_n = A$, *then for any fixed integer* k, $\lim\limits_{n \to \infty} a_{n+k} = A$.

By using Lemma 2, we can simplify certain statements in later chapters.

The preceding lemma and theorems are easily proved by employing the same methods as are used in the study of limits in elementary calculus.

10. Bounded Sequences; Null Sequences

If the limit of a sequence exists, the sequence is said to *converge*, or to be *convergent*; if the limit is A, the sequence converges to A. A sequence which is not convergent is called *divergent*.

A sequence that has the limit zero is called a *null sequence*. A null sequence is one that converges to zero. By Theorem 1, page 7, the terms of any convergent series form a null sequence.

If a constant M exists such that for all n

$$(1) \qquad\qquad |b_n| \leq M,$$

the sequence $\{b_n\}$ is said to be *bounded*. If

$$(2) \qquad\qquad b_n \leq M,$$

the sequence $\{b_n\}$ is *bounded above*, or *bounded to the right*. The M in (2) is called an *upper bound* for the sequence. If

$$(3) \qquad\qquad M \leq b_n,$$

the sequence $\{b_n\}$ is *bounded below*, or *bounded to the left*. The M in (3) is a *lower bound* for the sequence.

THEOREM 4. *If* $\{a_n\}$ *is a null sequence and* $\{b_n\}$ *is a bounded sequence, then* $\{a_n b_n\}$ *is a null sequence.*

THEOREM 4a. *If* $\lim\limits_{n \to \infty} a_n = 0$, *and if* $|b_n| < M$, *with* M *independent of* n, *then* $\lim\limits_{n \to \infty} (a_n b_n) = 0.$

Theorems 4 and 4a are the same; the latter is a less sophisticated wording of the former. Each states that the element-by-element product of a null sequence and a bounded sequence is a null sequence. Proof of Theorem 4 is so elementary it is left as an exercise.

The criterion for boundedness, the inequality (1), need be established only for all n greater than some fixed n_0. For any fixed n_0, there exists a constant M_1 such that

(4) $$|b_n| \leq M_1, \qquad \text{for } n \leq n_0,$$

because only a finite number of elements b_n are involved. If a constant M_2 exists such that

(5) $$|b_n| \leq M_2, \qquad \text{for } n > n_0,$$

then the boundedness criterion (1) is satisfied by choosing $M = \text{Max}$ (M_1, M_2). Hence, (1) may be replaced by (5), if it is convenient to do so. If a sequence is bounded from some index on, it is a bounded sequence.

11. Monotonic Sequences

A sequence $\{b_n\}$ is said to be *monotonic increasing* if

(1) $$b_{n+1} \geq b_n,$$

and to be *strictly monotonic increasing*, or *steadily increasing*, if

(2) $$b_{n+1} > b_n:$$

the sequence may exhibit the monotonic behavior described by (1) or (2) for all n, or only for n greater than some fixed n_0.

The sequence $\{b_n\}$ is said to be *monotonic decreasing* if

(3) $$b_{n+1} \leq b_n,$$

and to be *strictly monotonic decreasing*, or *steadily decreasing*, if

(4) $$b_{n+1} < b_n;$$

the elements b_n may satisfy (3) or (4) for all n, or only for $n > n_0$.

In any study of the convergence or divergence of a sequence, all that matters is the behavior of the elements as the index approaches infinity.

For such studies a monotonic characteristic valid for $n > n_0$ is as useful as one valid for all n.

We shall now prove that if a sequence $\{a_n\}$ has an upper bound as defined on page 14, the set of all upper bounds must have a smallest element, called the *least upper bound*. If there is an upper bound, but no least upper bound, then there must be a number Q, not itself an upper bound, such that every number greater than Q is an upper bound for the a_n. For this Q there must be an element $a_m > Q$. But consider the number $\frac{1}{2}(Q + a_m)$. Since

$$\tfrac{1}{2}(Q + a_m) > \tfrac{1}{2}(Q + Q) = Q,$$

$\frac{1}{2}(Q + a_m)$ must be an upper bound for a_n. But

$$\tfrac{1}{2}(Q + a_m) < \tfrac{1}{2}(a_m + a_m) = a_m,$$

so $\frac{1}{2}(Q + a_m)$ is not an upper bound. The assumed existence of Q leads to a contradiction. Hence, a least upper bound does exist.

If a sequence has a lower bound, there must be a greatest lower bound, the existence of which may be demonstrated in a manner paralleling our proof of the existence of a least upper bound.

If a sequence is bounded, it has both upper and lower bounds and the sequence therefore has a least upper bound and a greatest lower bound.

LEMMA 3. *A bounded sequence has a least upper bound and a greatest lower bound.*

THEOREM 5a. *A bounded monotonic increasing sequence converges.*

THEOREM 5b. *A bounded monotonic decreasing sequence converges.*

PROOF. To prove Theorem 5a, let $\{a_n\}$ be a bounded monotonic increasing sequence and M be its least upper bound. For any positive ε,

$$(M - \varepsilon) < M,$$

so there exists an index m for which

$$a_m > (M - \varepsilon),$$

and, since the sequence is a monotonic increasing one,

(5) $$a_n > M - \varepsilon, \quad \text{for all } n > m.$$

We therefore have, recalling also that M is an upper bound,

(6) $$0 \leq M - a_n < \varepsilon, \quad \text{for all } n > m.$$

Then

$$|a_n - M| > \varepsilon, \qquad \text{for all } n > m,$$

so

(7) $$\lim_{n \to \infty} a_n = M.$$

A bounded monotonic increasing sequence converges to its least upper bound.

Theorem 5b may be proved in a similar manner, first showing that a monotonic decreasing sequence must have a greatest lower bound.

If a monotonic increasing sequence $\{a_n\}$ diverges, it must be unbounded by Theorem 5a and since the a_n increase, it follows that $a_n \to \infty$ as $n \to \infty$. Theorem 5b can be extended in the same way; the elements of a divergent monotonic decreasing sequence must $\to -\infty$ as $n \to \infty$.

EXAMPLE (a). Consider the sequence $\{u_n\}$ defined by

(8) $$u_n = \frac{3n}{n+1} - 10^{-n}, \qquad n \geq 0.$$

From (8) we obtain

(9) $$u_n = 3 - \frac{3}{n+1} - 10^{-n}$$

and

$$u_{n+1} = 3 - \frac{3}{n+2} - 10^{-n-1}.$$

Then

$$u_{n+1} - u_n = 3\left(\frac{1}{n+1} - \frac{1}{n+2}\right) + 10^{-n} - 10^{-n-1}$$

$$= \frac{3}{(n+1)(n+2)} + 10^{-n}(1 - 0.1) > 0.$$

Thus $u_{n+1} > u_n$ for all n involved; the sequence is strictly monotonic increasing. By (9), $u_n < 3$. The sequence converges by Theorem 5a.

Of course, each of $(n+1)^{-1}$ and 10^{-n} forms a null sequence; each $\to 0$ as $n \to \infty$. Therefore, by (9),

$$\lim_{n \to \infty} u_n = 3 - 0 - 0 = 3,$$

without any need to investigate the monotonic character of the sequence.

EXAMPLE (b). Show that

$$\lim_{n \to \infty} \left(1 + \frac{1}{n}\right)^n$$

exists.

Let us put

(10) $$v_n = \left(1 + \frac{1}{n}\right)^n, \qquad n > 0.$$

We shall show that the sequence with elements v_n converges.

Application of the binomial theorem to (10) yields

$$v_n = \left(1 + \frac{1}{n}\right)^n = 1 + \sum_{k=1}^{n} \frac{n(n-1)(n-2)\cdots(n-k+1)}{k!}\left(\frac{1}{n}\right)^k$$

$$= 1 + \frac{n}{1}\left(\frac{1}{n}\right) + \sum_{k=2}^{n} \frac{1\cdot\left(1-\frac{1}{n}\right)\left(1-\frac{2}{n}\right)\cdots\left(1-\frac{k-1}{n}\right)}{k!}.$$

Hence, for $n > 2$,

(11) $$v_n = 2 + \sum_{k=2}^{n} \frac{1\cdot\left(1-\frac{1}{n}\right)\left(1-\frac{2}{n}\right)\cdots\left(1-\frac{k-1}{n}\right)}{k!}.$$

From (11) we obtain the next number v_{n+1} in the sequence in the form

(12) $$v_{n+1} = 2 + \sum_{k=2}^{n+1} \frac{1\cdot\left(1-\frac{1}{n+1}\right)\left(1-\frac{2}{n+1}\right)\cdots\left(1-\frac{k-1}{n+1}\right)}{k!}.$$

Since

$$1 - \frac{j}{n+1} > 1 - \frac{j}{n}$$

for each of $j = 1, 2, \ldots, (k-1)$, we may conclude that each term in the summation in (12) is larger than the corresponding term in the summation in (11), and (12) has an extra term, that in which $k = n + 1$. Hence,

(13) $$v_{n+1} > v_n;$$

the v_n increase steadily as n increases.

Furthermore, equation (11) yields

(14) $$v_n < 2 + \sum_{k=2}^{n} \frac{1}{k!}.$$

But $k! = 1 \cdot 2 \cdot 3 \cdots k > 2^{k-1}$, so

$$v_n < 2 + \sum_{k=2}^{n} \frac{1}{2^{k-1}} = 2 + \left(1 - \frac{1}{2^{n-1}}\right).$$

Hence,

(15) $$v_n < 3 - \frac{1}{2^{n-1}}.$$

Therefore $v_n < 3$. We now know that the elements v_n of the sequence (10) steadily increase and are always less than 3. Then the v_n approaches a limit; call that limit e:

(16) $$\lim_{n \to \infty} \left(1 + \frac{1}{n}\right)^n = e.$$

We have shown that $e \leq 3$. Actually $e = 2.718\ \ 281\ \ 828\ \ 5\ldots$.

The sequence treated in this example is the one usually used to define e, the base of the natural logarithms.

12. Subsequences

Consider an infinite sequence A. Any infinite sequence B formed by omitting elements of A without disturbing the order of elements is called a *subsequence* of A. The number of elements omitted may be zero, any positive integer, or infinite. If at least one element of A is omitted, B is a *proper subsequence* of A. If only a finite number of elements of A are omitted in forming B, the sequences A and B are identical from some point on and we are not much interested in distinguishing between them.

We are mainly concerned with infinite subsequences B formed by omitting an infinity of elements of A. In more sophisticated language, we are interested in any subsequence B that is one of a pair of infinite subsequences B and C for which the intersection $B \cap C$ (set of elements belonging to both B and C) is empty and the union $B \cup C$ (set of elements in at least one of B and C) is the original set A. For example, if A denotes the sequence with general element a_n, a pertinent subsequence is the sequence B with elements a_{2^n}. Here B is formed by selecting from

$$a_1, a_2, a_3, a_4, \ldots, a_n, \ldots,$$

the subsequence

$$a_2, a_4, a_8, a_{16}, \ldots, a_{2^n}, \ldots.$$

THEOREM 6. *If a_n approaches a limit as $n \to \infty$ and if $\varphi(n)$ is any strictly monotonic increasing positive integer-valued function of n,*

$$\lim_{n \to \infty} a_{\varphi(n)} = \lim_{n \to \infty} a_n.$$

Any infinite subsequence of a convergent sequence has the same limit as the original sequence. Proof is left as an exercise.

EXAMPLE. Consider the sequence with elements

$$a_n = \frac{3n + 1}{2n - 5}, \qquad n \geq 1.$$

This sequence converges to $\frac{3}{2}$,

$$\lim_{n \to \infty} \frac{3n + 1}{2n - 5} = \frac{3}{2}.$$

The subsequence, with elements

$$b_n = a_{5^n + 4n} = \frac{3(5^n + 4n) + 1}{2(5^n + 4n) - 5}, \qquad n \geq 1,$$

converges to the same limit:

$$\lim_{n \to \infty} \frac{3(5^n + 4n) + 1}{2(5^n + 4n) - 5} = \frac{3}{2}.$$

A divergent sequence can have convergent subsequences. For instance, the sequence formed by using alternately the positive integers and their reciprocals,

$$1, \frac{1}{1}, 2, \frac{1}{2}, 3, \frac{1}{3}, \ldots, k, \frac{1}{k}, k + 1, \frac{1}{k + 1}, \ldots,$$

diverges. Some of the subsequences, such as

$$\frac{1}{1}, \frac{1}{2}, \frac{1}{3}, \ldots, \frac{1}{k}, \ldots,$$

converge, others diverge.

Exercises

1. For a monotonic decreasing sequence, are boundedness and boundedness below (to the left) equivalent?   ANS. Yes.

2. If a sequence is bounded above (to the right) is it necessarily bounded?   ANS. No.

3. Prove Theorem 2, page 13.
4. Prove Theorem 3, page 14.
5. Prove Lemma 2, page 14.
6. Prove Theorem 4, page 14.
7. Prove Theorem 5b, page 16.
8. Prove Theorem 6, page 20.

In Exercises 9–19 determine the limit, if it exists, of the sequence with the given general element for $n > 0$.

9. $4 + \dfrac{(-1)^n}{n^2}$.   ANS.   4.

10. $\dfrac{2n + 1}{n}$.   ANS.   2.

11. $\dfrac{(2n + 1)!}{n!}$.   ANS.   Divergent.

12. $\sin \dfrac{\pi}{n}$.   ANS.   0.

13. $\sin \dfrac{n}{\pi}$.   ANS.   Divergent.

14. $(-1)^n$.   ANS.   Divergent.

15. $e^{-n} \cos (\tfrac{1}{4} n\pi)$.   ANS.   0.

16. $\dfrac{n \cos (\tfrac{1}{4} n\pi)}{n + 1}$.   ANS.   Divergent.

17. $\dfrac{1000 \, n^2}{2^n}$.   ANS.   0.

18. $\dfrac{n!}{10^n}$.   ANS.   Divergent.

19. $\left(1 + \dfrac{3}{n}\right)^n$.   ANS. e^3.

20. Parallel the method used in Example (b), page 18, to show that the sequence in Exercise 19 above is strictly monotonic increasing.

21. For the sequence of Exercise 19, let $a_n = \left(1 + \dfrac{3}{n}\right)^n$. With the method of Example (b), page 18, show that

$$a_n < 4 + \frac{9}{2} + \sum_{k=3}^{n} \frac{3^k}{k!}.$$

Show that $k! \geqq 6 \cdot 4^{k-3}$ for $k \geq 3$, and therefore that $a_n < 26.5$.

22. Which of the sequences in Exercises 9–18 are monotonic decreasing?

         ANS.   Exercise 10, Exercise 12, Exercise 17 for $n > 2$.

23. Which of the sequences in Exercises 9–18 are monotonic increasing?

         ANS.   Exercise 11, Exercise 18 for $n \geq 9$.

24. For the divergent sequence of Exercise 16 exhibit several convergent subsequences and some divergent subsequences. Designate the general element in Exercise 16 by a_n. Consider, for instance, subsequences with n replaced by $4k$, by $8k$, by $8k + 1$, $8k + 2$, etc. Obtain subsequences converging to 0, 1, -1, $\frac{1}{2}\sqrt{2}$, $-\frac{1}{2}\sqrt{2}$.

13. Cluster Points

If the sequence $\{a_n\}$ is such that there exists a subsequence with limit B, then B is called a *cluster point* of the sequence $\{a_n\}$. Thus for B to be a cluster point of the sequence $\{a_n\}$ it is necessary and sufficient that, given any $\varepsilon > 0$, there exists an n_0 such that

$$(1) \qquad\qquad\qquad |a_n - B| < \varepsilon$$

for an infinite sequence of n values $> n_0$, but not necessarily for all $n > n_0$.

EXAMPLE. The sequence $\{a_n\}$ with elements

$$a_{2k+1} = 1, \qquad k \geq 0,$$

$$a_{2k} = 2 - \frac{1}{2k}, \qquad k \geq 1,$$

or

$$1, 2 - \frac{1}{2}, 1, 2 - \frac{1}{4}, 1, 2 - \frac{1}{6}, \ldots, 1, 2 - \frac{1}{2k}, \ldots$$

has $B_1 = 1$ and $B_2 = 2$ as cluster points. The sequence $\{a_n\}$ diverges.

If a sequence converges, the limit of the sequence is a cluster point and the only cluster point of the sequence. A limit must be a cluster point, but a cluster point need not be a limit of the sequence.

The following result, called the Bolzano-Weierstrass theorem* is basic in the theory of sequences.

THEOREM 7. *A bounded sequence has at least one cluster point.*

---

* Discovered by B. Bolzano, 1781–1848; made popular by K. Weierstrass, 1815–1897.

PROOF. Let the bounded sequence be $\{a_n\}$ with its elements lying in a closed interval I. In I designate

(A) As x-numbers those that are exceeded by at most a finite number of elements of $\{a_n\}$

and

(B) As y-numbers those that are exceeded by an infinity of elements of $\{a_n\}$.

The set of x-numbers is not empty because the right endpoint of I is an x-number. If the set of y-numbers were empty, the left endpoint of I would be a cluster point of the sequence. We may therefore assume both sets to be nonempty.

The set of x-numbers and the set of y-numbers have an empty intersection; they have no common elements. Each x-number exceeds every y-number.

This division (called a section) of the interval I defines a number Q, the greatest lower bound of the x-numbers, such that every number $>Q$ in I is an x-number and every number $<Q$ in I is a y-number. For any $\varepsilon > 0$, $(Q + \frac{1}{2}\varepsilon)$ is an x-number and $(Q - \frac{1}{2}\varepsilon)$ is a y-number. That is, there is an infinite subsequence B of the sequence $\{a_n\}$ such that

$$Q - \tfrac{1}{2}\varepsilon < a_n, \qquad \text{for each element in } B.$$

Since $(Q + \frac{1}{2}\varepsilon)$ is an x-number, at most a finite number of elements of B can exceed $(Q + \frac{1}{2}\varepsilon)$. Delete from B those elements that exceed $(Q + \frac{1}{2}\varepsilon)$. The remainder is an infinite subsequence C of $\{a_n\}$ such that

$$Q - \tfrac{1}{2}\varepsilon < a_n \leq Q + \tfrac{1}{2}\varepsilon, \qquad \text{for every } a_n \text{ in } C.$$

It follows that the elements a_n contained in the infinite subsequence C have the property that

$$Q - \varepsilon < a_n < Q + \varepsilon,$$

so

$$|a_n - Q| < \varepsilon, \qquad \text{for all elements } a_n \text{ in } C$$

and Q is a cluster point of the sequence $\{a_n\}$. The proof of Theorem 7 is complete.

The number Q defined in the above proof is called the *upper limit*, the greatest of the cluster points of the sequence $\{a_n\}$. We write

$$Q = \varlimsup_{n \to \infty} a_n.$$

Here Q is a cluster point of $\{a_n\}$ and no cluster point of $\{a_n\}$ exceeds Q. A lower limit, the least of the limits, may be similarly defined.

LEMMA 4. *Each cluster point of a subsequence is a cluster point of the original sequence.*

PROOF. Consider a sequence $\{a_n\}$. Let $\{b_n\}$ be a subsequence with a cluster point T. A subsequence of $\{b_n\}$ converges to T. A subsequence of $\{b_n\}$ is a subsequence of $\{a_n\}$, so a subsequence of $\{a_n\}$ converges to T. Then T is a cluster point of $\{a_n\}$.

THEOREM 8. *If a bounded sequence has only one cluster point L, the sequence converges to L.*

14. Cauchy Criteria

A. L. Cauchy (1789–1857) established a criterion for convergence of a sequence. Two forms of the Cauchy criterion are given in Theorems 9 and 9a. These theorems are particularly useful in the development of a theory of sequences.

THEOREM 9. *A necessary and sufficient condition for the existence of*

$$(1) \qquad\qquad \lim_{n \to \infty} a_n$$

is that, given any positive number ε, there exists an $n_0 = n_0(\varepsilon)$ such that for every pair of indices n, m both greater than n_0,

$$(2) \qquad\qquad |a_n - a_m| < \varepsilon.$$

THEOREM 9a. *A necessary and sufficient condition for the existence of the limit (1) above is that, given any positive number ε, there exists an n_0 such that for all $n > n_0$ and for every positive integer k,*

$$(3) \qquad\qquad |a_{n+k} - a_n| < \varepsilon.$$

PROOF. We first prove the necessity of the condition (2). If the limit (1) exists, call that limit A. By the definition of a limit, page 11, given any $\varepsilon_1 > 0$, there exists an n_0 such that for all $n > n_0$,

$$(4) \qquad\qquad |a_n - A| < \varepsilon_1,$$

and for all $m > n_0$,

(5) $$|a_m - A| < \varepsilon_1.$$

In terms of the ε of (2), choose $\varepsilon_1 = \frac{1}{2}\varepsilon$. Then

$$|a_n - a_m| = |(a_n - A) - (a_m - A)| \leq |a_n - A| + |a_m - A| < \tfrac{1}{2}\varepsilon + \tfrac{1}{2}\varepsilon,$$

which yields the inequality (2). Thus, if the limit (1) exists, (2) must be satisfied.

Now suppose (2) is satisfied. Choose any fixed $m > n_0$ and let $a_m = T$. Then given any $\varepsilon > 0$,

$$|a_n - T| < \varepsilon, \qquad \text{for all } n > n_0,$$

so the a_n form a bounded sequence. By Theorem 7 there is at least one cluster point P and a subsequence $\{p_n\}$ that converges to P. Suppose there is another cluster point $Q \neq P$ with an associated subsequence $\{q_n\}$ that converges to Q. Given $\varepsilon > 0$, n_1 and m_1 exist such that

(6) $$|p_n - P| < \varepsilon, \qquad \text{for all } n > n_1,$$

(7) $$|q_m - Q| < \varepsilon, \qquad \text{for all } m > m_1.$$

By (2), since p_n and q_m are elements of $\{a_n\}$, there exists an n_2 such that

(8) $$|p_n - q_m| < \varepsilon, \qquad \text{for all } n, m > n_2.$$

Now

(9) $$P - Q = (p_n - q_m) - (p_n - P) + (q_m - Q).$$

Choose n_0 larger than the maximum of n_1, m_1, n_2. Then (6), (7), and (8) hold for $n, m > n_0$ and from (9) we obtain

$$|P - Q| \leq |p_n - q_m| + |p_n - P| + |q_m - Q| < 3\varepsilon.$$

Since P and Q are fixed, $|P - Q|$ cannot be arbitrarily small unless it is zero. Thus $P = Q$ and the bounded sequence $\{a_n\}$ has only one cluster point. By Theorem 8, the sequence $\{a_n\}$ converges; the condition (2) is a sufficient condition for convergence of $\{a_n\}$. Thus Theorem 9 is valid. Theorem 9a is another form of Theorem 9.

15. Telescoping Series

The series

(1) $$\sum_{n=1}^{\infty} (b_n - b_{n-1})$$

has the partial sum

(2) $$B_n = \sum_{k=1}^{n} (b_k - b_{k-1}),$$

$$B_n = (b_1 - b_0) + (b_2 - b_1) + (b_3 - b_2) + \cdots + (b_n - b_{n-1}),$$

so

(3) $$B_n = b_n - b_0.$$

Equation (3) is also easily obtained from (2) by using a shift in index. From (2),

$$B_n = \sum_{k=1}^{n} b_k - \sum_{k=1}^{n} b_{k-1} = \sum_{k=1}^{n} b_k - \sum_{k=0}^{n-1} b_k = b_n - b_0.$$

Because of the way in which the partial sum (2) collapses into the form (3), the series (1) is called a *telescoping series*.

When such a series arises naturally, the telescoping of its partial sum can be useful.

EXAMPLE. Sum the series

(4) $$\sum_{n=1}^{\infty} \left[\frac{1}{n^2 + c^2} - \frac{1}{(n-1)^2 + c^2} \right], \qquad c \neq 0.$$

For the series (4), the partial sum is

$$S_n = \frac{1}{n^2 + c^2} - \frac{1}{c^2}.$$

Since

(5) $$\lim_{n \to \infty} \left[\frac{1}{n^2 + c^2} - \frac{1}{c^2} \right] = -\frac{1}{c^2},$$

the series converges to the sum shown in (5).

We must beware of tautologies. For instance, any series may be written in telescopic form. Given

(6) $$\sum_{n=0}^{\infty} a_n$$

with partial sum

$$S_n = \sum_{k=0}^{n} a_k,$$

we see that $a_0 = S_0$ and, for $n \geq 1$, $a_n = S_n - S_{n-1}$. Then we may write (6) in the telescopic form

$$(7) \qquad\qquad S_0 + \sum_{n=1}^{\infty} (S_n - S_{n-1}).$$

Here we are going around in a circle. The desirability of the telescopic form lies in the fact that the partial sum (2) collapses into (3). To get (7) from (6) we needed to have the partial sum at the start. Out of the partial sum we got the partial sum, hardly a cause for celebration.

Exercises

1. Sum the series
$$\sum_{n=1}^{\infty} [\text{Arctan } n - \text{Arctan}(n-1)]. \qquad\qquad \text{ANS.} \quad \tfrac{1}{2}\pi.$$

2. Sum the series
$$\sum_{n=1}^{\infty} [n \exp\{-nx^2\} - (n-1) \exp\{-(n-1)x^2\}].$$
   ANS. 0, for $x \neq 0$; Divergent for $x = 0$.

3. Sum the series
$$\sum_{n=1}^{\infty} [nx \exp\{-nx^2\} - (n-1)x \exp\{-(n-1)x^2\}].$$
   ANS. 0, for all x.

4. Construct an unbounded sequence with one and only one finite cluster point.

5. Show that a convergent sequence cannot have two limits. Let $a_n \to A$ and $a_n \to B$. Consider $A - B = (a_n - B) - (a_n - A)$.

6. Give a constructive proof of the following theorem:

   Given any sequence $\{v_n\}$, there exists a monotonic increasing sequence $\{a_n\}$ and a monotonic decreasing sequence $\{b_n\}$ such that $v_n = a_n + b_n$ for all n.

   Hint: Let $\{c_n\}$ be any sequence of positive elements. Choose a_0 arbitrarily and then choose b_0 to make $v_0 = a_0 + b_0$. For successive n-values,

   (1) If $v_{n+1} \geq v_n$, choose
   $$a_{n+1} = a_n + (1 + c_n)(v_{n+1} - v_n),$$
   $$b_{n+1} = b_n - c_n(v_{n+1} - v_n);$$

   (2) If $v_{n+1} < v_n$, choose
   $$a_{n+1} = a_n + c_n(v_n - v_{n+1}),$$
   $$b_{n+1} = b_n - (1 + c_n)(v_n - v_{n+1}).$$
   Show that from $a_n + b_n = v_n$, it follows that
   $$a_{n+1} + b_{n+1} = v_{n+1},$$
   and show that $a_{n+1} \geq a_n$ and $b_{n+1} \leq b_n$.

7. Prove the following result obtained by A. Pringsheim (1850–1941):

If $c_n > 0$ and $\sum_{n=0}^{\infty} c_n$ converges, there exists a unique unbounded strictly monotonic increasing sequence $\{p_n\}$ such that

(A) $$c_n = \frac{1}{p_n} - \frac{1}{p_{n+1}}, \qquad \text{for } n \geq 0.$$

Hint: By iteration of (A) and addition, show that

$$\frac{1}{p_0} - \frac{1}{p_{n+1}} = S_n,$$

where S_n is the usual partial sum of the original series. Knowing that $\{S_n\}$ is a strictly monotonic increasing sequence that converges to S, obtain p_0, then p_n, and show that the sequence p_n has the stipulated monotonic character.

8. Prove Pringsheim's result: If $d_n > 0$ and $\sum_{n=0}^{\infty} d_n$ diverges, there exists a unique unbounded strictly monotonic increasing sequence $\{p_n\}$ such that $d_0 = p_0$ and

$$d_n = p_n - p_{n-1}, \qquad \text{for } n \geq 1.$$

9. Prove Theorem 8, page 24.

CHAPTER 3

Positive Term Series

16. An Integral Test

Consider a positive term series

$$(1) \qquad \sum_{n=1}^{\infty} a_n$$

whose terms are monotonic decreasing,

$$(2) \qquad 0 < a_{n+1} \leqq a_n.$$

As usual, let the partial sums of (1) be defined by

$$(3) \qquad S_n = \sum_{k=1}^{n} a_k.$$

In an xy-plane, plot the points (n, a_n) for each positive integer n. Let the curve $y = f(x)$ pass through each of the points (n, a_n) and have the property that $f(x)$ is continuous and monotonic decreasing. That is, $f(x)$ is continuous for all $x \geq 1$,

$$(4) \qquad f(x + \delta) \leqq f(x), \qquad \text{for } \delta > 0, \ x \geq 1,$$

and, for each positive integer n,

$$(5) \qquad f(n) = a_n.$$

Such curves exist because one of them may be formed by joining each pair of points $(n-1, a_{n-1})$ and (n, a_n) with a straight-line segment. Other examples are easily constructed. We are most interested in those simple situations in which the desired $f(x)$ can be formed by replacing the running index n by a real variable x in a prescribed formula for a_n.

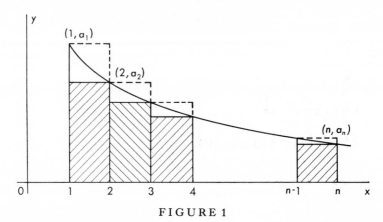

FIGURE 1

Figure 1 shows the points (n, a_n) joined by a curve $y = f(x)$ such that $f(x)$ satisfies (4) and (5). The sum of the areas of the shaded rectangles in Figure 1 is

(6) $$a_2 + a_3 + \cdots + a_n = S_n - a_1.$$

For the taller rectangles, those bounded by the ordinates $x = n - 1$ and $x = n$, the x-axis, and a horizontal line drawn to the right from the point $(n - 1, a_{n-1})$, the sum of the areas is

(7) $$a_1 + a_2 + \cdots + a_{n-1} = S_{n-1}.$$

The area under the curve $y = f(x)$ from $x = 1$ to $x = n$ is

(8) $$\int_1^n f(x) \, dx.$$

Examination of Figure 1 leads us to believe that

(9) $$S_n - a_1 \leq \int_1^n f(x) \, dx \leq S_{n-1}.$$

Our intuitive reaction to a figure does not constitute a proof but it does give us an idea of what to try to prove.

LEMMA 5. *Let $f(x)$ be continuous and monotonic decreasing for $x \geq 1$ and let n be an integer ≥ 2. Then*

(10) $$\sum_{k=2}^{n} f(k) \leq \int_1^n f(x) \, dx \leq \sum_{k=1}^{n-1} f(k).$$

PROOF. Let $k \geq 2$. When x is in the interval $k - 1 \leq x \leq k$, the monotonic decreasing function $f(x)$ satisfies

(11) $$f(k) \leq f(x) \leq f(k-1).$$

Multiply each member of (11) by dx and integrate each from $x = k - 1$ to $x = k$ to get

$$f(k) \int_{k-1}^{k} dx \leq \int_{k-1}^{k} f(x)\, dx \leq f(k-1) \int_{k-1}^{k} dx,$$

or

(12) $$f(k) \leq \int_{k-1}^{k} f(x)\, dx \leq f(k-1).$$

Sum each member of (12) over integral k, from $k = 2$ to $k = n$, and thus obtain

(13) $$\sum_{k=2}^{n} f(k) \leq \sum_{k=2}^{n} \int_{k-1}^{k} f(x)\, dx \leq \sum_{k=2}^{n} f(k-1).$$

Now

$$\sum_{k=2}^{n} \int_{k-1}^{k} f(x)\, dx = \int_{1}^{n} f(x)\, dx$$

and, by a shift in index,

$$\sum_{k=2}^{n} f(k-1) = \sum_{k=1}^{n-1} f(k).$$

Thus the desired inequalities (10) follow from (13).

The functions $f(x)$ in which we are interested satisfy

$$f(n) = a_n.$$

Hence,

$$\sum_{k=2}^{n} f(k) = \sum_{k=2}^{n} a_k = S_n - a_1$$

and

$$\sum_{k=1}^{n-1} f(k) = \sum_{k=1}^{n-1} a_k = S_{n-1}.$$

Therefore we may conclude from (10) the validity of

(9) $$S_n - a_1 \leq \int_{1}^{n} f(x)\, dx \leq S_{n-1}.$$

For a positive term series, the partial sums S_n form a monotonic increasing sequence. By (9), if

(14)
$$\int_1^\infty f(x)\, dx$$

exists, S_n is bounded,

$$S_n \leqq \int_1^\infty f(x)\, dx + a_1,$$

so the series

(1)
$$\sum_{n=1}^\infty a_n = \sum_{n=1}^\infty f(n).$$

converges. Again by (9), if the integral (14) does not exist, S_{n-1} is unbounded and the series (1) diverges.

THEOREM 10 (Integral Test). *If $f(x)$ is positive, continuous and monotonic decreasing for $x \geq 1$, then*

(a) *If $\int_1^\infty f(x)\, dx$ exists, the series $\sum\limits_{n=1}^\infty f(n)$ converges;*

(b) *If $\int_1^\infty f(x)\, dx$ does not exist, the series $\sum\limits_{n=1}^\infty f(n)$ diverges.*

In Theorem 10 above, the lower limit of integration and summation is unessential. By using Lemma 1, page 6, it can be shown that Theorem 10 is still valid if unity is replaced by any other positive integer in all five places that unity occurs in the theorem.

In the application of this integral test, Theorem 10, it is necessary to find an $f(x)$ for which the values $f(n)$, for integral n, coincide with the terms of the series.

EXAMPLE (a). Test the harmonic series

(15)
$$\sum_{n=1}^\infty \frac{1}{n}$$

for convergence.

The terms of the series (15) are positive and monotonic decreasing. This suggests that the integral test is worth trying on (15). We need a pertinent $f(x)$ such that

$$f(n) = \frac{1}{n}.$$

It does not take much brilliance to decide to try

(16) $$f(x) = \frac{1}{x}.$$

For $x \geq 1$, the f of (16) is positive, continuous, and f decreases as x increases. Therefore we are justified in applying the above integral test.

Since

$$\int_1^{\infty} \frac{dx}{x} = [\ln x]_1^{\infty}$$

diverges, the harmonic series diverges, by Theorem 10.

The partial sums of the harmonic series,

(17) $$H_n = \sum_{k=1}^{n} \frac{1}{k} = 1 + \frac{1}{2} + \frac{1}{3} + \cdots + \frac{1}{n},$$

occur frequently in mathematical analysis. By showing that the harmonic series diverges, we have shown that $H_n \to \infty$ as $n \to \infty$. See also Section 52, page 141.

The harmonic series is a classic example of the fact that a series may diverge even if its general term approaches zero as the running index approaches infinity.

EXAMPLE (b). Test the hyperharmonic series

(18) $$\sum_{n=1}^{\infty} \frac{1}{n^p}$$

for convergence.

Again we use the integral test. We are concerned only with p fixed and real. If p is zero or is negative, the terms of the series (18) do not even approach zero, as $n \to \infty$, so (18) diverges for those values of p.

If $p > 0$, consider the function

(19) $$f(x) = \frac{1}{x^p}.$$

The f of (19) coincides with the general term of the series (18) for integral n. For positive p and $x \geq 1$, the function in (19) is continuous and decreases as x increases. Consider the integral

$$(20) \qquad \int_1^\infty \frac{dx}{x^p} = \left[\frac{-1}{(p-1)x^{p-1}} \right]_1^\infty, \qquad p \neq 1.$$

For $0 < p < 1$, the integral in (20) diverges because $x^{1-p} \to \infty$ as $x \to \infty$. For $p = 1$, the series (18) reduces to the harmonic series, which we have already shown is divergent. For $p > 1$, the integral in (20) exists. Indeed,

$$(21) \qquad \int_1^\infty \frac{dx}{x^p} = \frac{1}{p-1}, \qquad p > 1.$$

Hence, the hyperharmonic series (18) converges for $p > 1$.

In summary, the series (18) diverges for $p \leq 1$ and converges for $p > 1$. We may also conclude from (21) that, for $p > 1$,

$$\sum_{n=1}^\infty \frac{1}{n^p} \leq \frac{p}{p-1}.$$

Exercises

In each exercise, use the integral test to determine whether the series is convergent or divergent. The answers are grouped at the end of the set of exercises.

1. $\displaystyle\sum_{n=1}^\infty \frac{1}{n^2 + 1}$.   **2.** $\displaystyle\sum_{n=1}^\infty \frac{n}{1 + n^2}$.

3. $\displaystyle\sum_{n=1}^\infty n \exp(-n^2)$.   **4.** $\displaystyle\sum_{n=1}^\infty \frac{1}{(3n+1)^2}$.

5. $\displaystyle\sum_{k=2}^\infty \frac{\ln k}{k}$.   **6.** $\displaystyle\sum_{k=2}^\infty \frac{1}{k \ln k}$.

7. $\displaystyle\sum_{n=1}^\infty \frac{1}{1 + \sqrt{n}}$.   **8.** $\displaystyle\sum_{n=1}^\infty \frac{1}{(n^2 + 1)^{3/2}}$.

9. $\displaystyle\sum_{n=0}^\infty \frac{1}{(2n+1)^3}$.   **10.** $\displaystyle\sum_{n=1}^\infty \frac{n}{(n^2 + 4)^2}$.

11. $\displaystyle\sum_{n=1}^\infty \frac{n+3}{(n+1)(n+2)}$.

12. $\displaystyle\sum_{n=1}^\infty \frac{1}{(n+1)(n+2)}$.

ANS.   Convergent: Exercises 1, 3, 4, 8, 9, 10, 12.
Divergent: Exercises 2, 5, 6, 7, 11.

17. Direct Comparison Tests

Suppose the positive term series

$$(1) \qquad \sum_{n=1}^{\infty} c_n$$

converges. The partial sums of (1) form a bounded monotonic increasing sequence. Let a second positive term series have partial sums never larger than the corresponding partial sums of (1). Then the second series will converge because its partial sums will also form a bounded monotonic increasing sequence. This leads us to a comparison test for positive term series.

THEOREM 11. *If $a_n > 0$ and $c_n > 0$, if*

$$(2) \qquad a_n \leq c_n,$$

and if

$$(3) \qquad \sum_{n=1}^{\infty} c_n$$

converges, then

$$(4) \qquad \sum_{n=1}^{\infty} a_n$$

converges.

That is, if the positive term series (4) has terms never greater than the corresponding terms of a positive term series (3) that is known to be convergent, then the series (4) also converges.

PROOF. Let the partial sums of (3) and (4) be defined by

$$(5) \qquad T_n = \sum_{k=1}^{n} c_k$$

and

$$(6) \qquad S_n = \sum_{k=1}^{n} a_k.$$

Since c_k and a_k are positive, each of T_n and S_n forms a monotonic increasing sequence. We are given that T_n has a limit as $n \to \infty$. Call that limit T. With the aid of the inequality (2), we may conclude that

$$(7) \qquad 0 < S_n \leq T_n < T.$$

Then S_n is bounded and monotonic increasing, so it has a limit. The series (4) converges. The sum of the series (4) is, by (7), not greater than the sum of the series (3); equality of sums occurs only if (3) and (4) are identical.

THEOREM 12. *If $a_n > 0$ and $d_n > 0$, if*

$$(8) \qquad\qquad a_n \geq d_n,$$

and if

$$(9) \qquad\qquad \sum_{n=1}^{\infty} d_n$$

diverges, then

$$(10) \qquad\qquad \sum_{n=1}^{\infty} a_n$$

diverges.

That is, if the positive term series (10) has terms never less than the corresponding terms of a positive term series that is known to be divergent, then the series (10) also diverges.

PROOF. Let

$$(11) \qquad\qquad U_n = \sum_{k=1}^{n} d_k, \qquad S_n = \sum_{k=1}^{n} a_k.$$

We are given that $d_n > 0$ and $a_n > 0$, so U_n and S_n form monotonic increasing sequences. By (8) and (11),

$$(12) \qquad\qquad S_n \geq U_n.$$

Since (9) diverges, $U_n \to \infty$ as $n \to \infty$. Therefore, by (12) $S_n \to \infty$ as $n \to \infty$ and the series (10) also diverges.

Theorems 11 and 12 are direct comparison tests, one for convergence, one for divergence. These tests are simple ones but in Section 18 we shall obtain other comparison tests which are often easier to use than are Theorems 11 and 12.

The student should keep in mind that to show that a series has its terms less than those of a divergent series (or greater than those of a convergent series) proves nothing.

One immediate application of Theorem 12 is the proof of the following theorem which is called the *Cauchy radical test*.

THEOREM 13. *If $a_n > 0$ and if there exists a constant r such that*

(13) $$\sqrt[n]{a_n} \leqq r < 1,$$

then the series

(14) $$\sum_{n=1}^{\infty} a_n$$

converges; if $a_n > 0$ and if

(15) $$\sqrt[n]{a_n} \geqq 1,$$

then the series (14) *diverges.*

In another form, the theorem states that if the upper limit (page 23) of the sequence $\{\sqrt[n]{a_n}\}$ is r, then (14) converges if $r < 1$, diverges if $r > 1$.

PROOF. Consider the first part of Theorem 13. Since $0 < r < 1$, we know that the geometric series

(16) $$\sum_{n=1}^{\infty} r^n$$

converges. We are given that a_n is positive. By (13),

(17) $$a_n \leqq r^n,$$

and we may therefore apply Theorem 11 with $c_n = r^n$ to conclude that the series (14) converges. On the other hand, if (15) is true, $a_n \geqq 1$ and a_n cannot approach zero as $n \to \infty$, so the series (14) must diverge.

18. Other Comparison Tests

The direct comparison tests of the preceding section are simple in concept, but it is often tedious work to demonstrate the necessary inequality between the general terms of the series being compared. The slightly more sophisticated comparison tests to be developed in this section are easy to use.

THEOREM 14. *If $a_n > 0$ and $b_n > 0$, and if*

(1) $$\lim_{n \to \infty} \frac{a_n}{b_n} = c \neq 0,$$

the series $\sum_{n=1}^{\infty} a_n$ and $\sum_{n=1}^{\infty} b_n$ converge or diverge together.

PROOF. Because of (1), there exists a constant M such that

$$(2) \qquad \left| \frac{a_n}{b_n} - c \right| < M.$$

It is true that M can be made arbitrarily small by taking n sufficiently large in (2), but we have no need of that fact here.

From (2) and the fact that all the quantities involved are positive, it follows that

$$(3) \qquad a_n < (M + c)b_n.$$

If $\sum_{n=1}^{\infty} b_n$ converges, $\sum_{n=1}^{\infty} (M + c)b_n$ converges, by Theorem 2. Then direct comparison, using (3) and Theorem 11, shows that $\sum_{n=1}^{\infty} a_n$ converges. In Theorem 14, a_n and b_n may be interchanged by replacing c by c^{-1}. Therefore, if either series converges, the other converges.

The inequality (3) may be rewritten

$$(4) \qquad b_n > (M + c)^{-1}a_n.$$

Direct comparison, using (4) and Theorem 12, shows that if either series diverges, the other also diverges.

EXAMPLE (a). Test for convergence:

$$(5) \qquad \sum_{n=0}^{\infty} \frac{4n^2 + 1}{n^3 + n^2 + 1}.$$

Here we reason that for large n the general term is well approximated by

$$\frac{4n^2}{n^3} = \frac{4}{n}.$$

We therefore compare the series (5) with the harmonic series

$$(6) \qquad \sum_{n=1}^{\infty} \frac{1}{n}.$$

In Theorem 14, let

$$a_n = \frac{4n^2 + 1}{n^3 + n^2 + 1}, \qquad b_n = \frac{1}{n}.$$

Since

$$\lim_{n \to \infty} \frac{4n^2 + 1}{n^3 + n^2 + 1} \cdot \frac{n}{1} = 4,$$

we conclude that (5) and (6) converge or diverge together. We know that the harmonic series (6) diverges. Then the series (5) diverges.

Theorem 14 can be used to prove the following result, which is known as the polynomial test.

THEOREM 15. *If $P(n)$ is a polynomial in n of degree p and $Q(n)$ is a polynomial in n of degree q, the series*

$$(7) \qquad \sum_{n=1}^{\infty} \frac{P(n)}{Q(n)}$$

converges if $q > p + 1$, diverges if $q \leq p + 1$.

PROOF. It is left as an exercise for the student to prove Theorem 15 by comparison of (7) with the hyperharmonic series treated on page 33.

The following one-sided comparison tests are frequently useful.

THEOREM 16. *If $a_n > 0$ and $c_n > 0$, if*

$$(8) \qquad \lim_{n \to \infty} \frac{a_n}{c_n} = 0,$$

and if $\sum\limits_{n=1}^{\infty} c_n$ converges, then $\sum\limits_{n=1}^{\infty} a_n$ converges.

THEOREM 17. *If $a_n > 0$ and $d_n > 0$, if*

$$(9) \qquad \lim_{n \to \infty} \frac{a_n}{d_n} = \infty,$$

and if $\sum\limits_{n=1}^{\infty} d_n$ diverges, then $\sum\limits_{n=1}^{\infty} a_n$ diverges.

PROOF. Theorems 16 and 17 can be proved by the method we used to prove Theorem 14, page 37, and the proofs are therefore left as exercises.

EXAMPLE (b). Test the series

$$(10) \qquad \sum_{n=0}^{\infty} \frac{1}{n!}.$$

We know that

$$\sum_{n=1}^{\infty} \frac{1}{n^2}$$

converges. Since

$$\lim_{n \to \infty} \frac{1}{n!} \cdot \frac{n^2}{1} = 0,$$

we may use Theorem 16 to conclude that (10) converges.

EXAMPLE (c). Test the series

(11) $$\sum_{k=2}^{\infty} \frac{1}{\ln k}.$$

We shall compare (11) with the harmonic series. In Theorem 17, replace the running index n by k, choose

$$a_k = \frac{1}{\ln k}, \qquad d_k = \frac{1}{k}.$$

Since

$$\lim_{k \to \infty} \frac{1}{\ln k} \cdot \frac{k}{1} = \infty,$$

it follows, from Theorem 17 and the divergence of the harmonic series, that the series (11) diverges.

Exercises

Test each series for convergence. Answers are grouped at the end of the set of exercises.

In Exercises 1–8, use direct comparison, Theorems 11 and 12.

1. $\displaystyle\sum_{n=1}^{\infty} \frac{1}{n^2 + 1}.$

2. $\displaystyle\sum_{n=1}^{\infty} \frac{\sqrt{n}}{n + 1}.$

3. $\displaystyle\sum_{n=1}^{\infty} \frac{2}{3n + 1}.$

4. $\displaystyle\sum_{n=1}^{\infty} \frac{1}{n^n}.$

5. $\displaystyle\sum_{k=1}^{\infty} \frac{4}{(k^2 + 1)^{3/2}}.$

6. $\displaystyle\sum_{k=1}^{\infty} \frac{ke^{-k}}{k^2 + 1}.$

7. $\displaystyle\sum_{n=1}^{\infty} \frac{\sin^2 n}{n^2}.$

8. $\displaystyle\sum_{n=1}^{\infty} \frac{1}{\sqrt{n^2 + 1}}.$

In Exercises 9–14, use the polynomial test, Theorem 15.

9. $\displaystyle\sum_{n=0}^{\infty} \frac{n^2+1}{(n+1)^3}$.

10. $\displaystyle\sum_{n=0}^{\infty} \frac{(n+4)^2}{n^4+1}$.

11. $\displaystyle\sum_{n=1}^{\infty} \frac{6n^3+5}{3n^4+1}$.

12. $\displaystyle\sum_{n=1}^{\infty} \frac{n^2}{(n^2+1)^3}$.

13. Exercise 1.

14. Exercise 3.

In Exercises 15–20, use Theorem 14, page 37.

15. $\displaystyle\sum_{n=1}^{\infty} \frac{n^2 \exp(-2n)}{n^2+1}$.

16. $\displaystyle\sum_{n=1}^{\infty} \frac{1}{(n+1)(2n+1)^{1/2}}$.

17. $\displaystyle\sum_{k=0}^{\infty} \frac{1}{(8k^2+1)^{2/3}}$.

18. $\displaystyle\sum_{k=4}^{\infty} \frac{2k+1}{k(k^2-3)^{3/2}}$.

19. Exercise 5.

20. Exercise 8.

In Exercises 21–32, use any available test.

21. $\displaystyle\sum_{n=1}^{\infty} \frac{1}{n\cdot 2^n}$.

22. $\displaystyle\sum_{k=2}^{\infty} \frac{\ln(k+1)}{k \ln k}$.

23. $\displaystyle\sum_{k=2}^{\infty} \frac{k^3}{k^2+1}$.

24. $\displaystyle\sum_{n=0}^{\infty} \frac{\cos^2 (2n+1)}{(2n+1)^2}$.

25. $\displaystyle\sum_{n=2}^{\infty} n \ln \frac{n}{n+1}$.

26. $\displaystyle\sum_{n=2}^{\infty} \frac{e^n}{(n^2+1)^n}$.

27. $\displaystyle\sum_{n=0}^{\infty} \exp(-n^2)$.

28. $\displaystyle\sum_{n=1}^{\infty} \frac{1}{n}\left(\frac{e+1}{\pi}\right)^n$.

29. $\displaystyle\sum_{n=1}^{\infty} n^3 \exp(-sn)$, $s>0$.

30. $\displaystyle\sum_{n=1}^{\infty} n^3 \exp(-sn)$, $s<0$.

31. $\displaystyle\sum_{k=2}^{\infty} \frac{1}{k^2 \ln k}$.

32. $\displaystyle\sum_{k=2}^{\infty} \frac{1}{(\ln k)^s}$, $s>0$.

33. Prove Theorem 15, page 39.   **34.** Prove Theorem 16, page 39.

35. Prove Theorem 17, page 39.

36. Prove that if γ_n is bounded, $\gamma_n>0$, $c_n>0$, and $\displaystyle\sum_{n=0}^{\infty} c_n$ converges, then $\displaystyle\sum_{n=0}^{\infty} \gamma_n c_n$ converges.

37. Prove that if $\gamma_n \geqq \gamma >0$, $d_n>0$ and $\displaystyle\sum_{n=0}^{\infty} d_n$ diverges, then $\displaystyle\sum_{n=0}^{\infty} \gamma_n d_n$ diverges.

38. Test the series $\displaystyle\sum_{n=1}^{\infty} \frac{7+(-1)^n}{n^2}$.

39. Test the series $\displaystyle\sum_{n=1}^{\infty} \frac{1+(-1)^n e^{-n}}{n}$.

40. Use Exercise 36 to show that if $\displaystyle\sum_{n=0}^{\infty} c_n$ converges, so does $\displaystyle\sum_{n=0}^{\infty} c_n{}^2$.

41. Show that the harmonic series is divergent by grouping the terms :

$$1+\left(\frac{1}{2}\right)+\left(\frac{1}{3}+\frac{1}{4}\right)+\left(\frac{1}{5}+\frac{1}{6}+\frac{1}{7}+\frac{1}{8}\right)+\cdots$$
$$+\left(\frac{1}{2^k+1}+\frac{1}{2^k+2}+\cdots+\frac{1}{2^k+2^k}\right)+\cdots,$$

and proving that the sum of the terms in each group $\geq \frac{1}{2}$.

42. Adapt the suggestion of Exercise 41 to a new proof of the convergence of $\displaystyle\sum_{n=1}^{\infty} \frac{1}{n^p}$ for $p>1$. Group the terms as follows.

$$1+\left(\frac{1}{2^p}+\frac{1}{3^p}\right)+\left(\frac{1}{4^p}+\frac{1}{5^p}+\frac{1}{6^p}+\frac{1}{7^p}\right)+\cdots$$
$$+\left(\frac{1}{2^{np}}+\frac{1}{(2^n+1)^p}+\cdots+\frac{1}{(2^{n+1}-1)^p}\right)+\cdots,$$

and show that the new series has its terms less than the corresponding terms of the convergent geometric series

$$1+\frac{1}{2^{p-1}}+\frac{1}{(2^{p-1})^2}+\cdots+\frac{1}{(2^{p-1})^n}+\cdots.$$

43. Use grouping of terms as in Exercises 41 and 42 to prove the Cauchy therorem :

If $a_n > 0$, if $a_n \geqq a_{n+1}$, and if $a_n \to 0$ as $n \to \infty$, then $\displaystyle\sum_{n=0}^{\infty} a_n$ and $\displaystyle\sum_{n=0}^{\infty} 2^n a_{2^n}$ converge or diverge together.

In Exercises 44–46, use the Cauchy theorem of Exercise 43 to test the series.

44. $\displaystyle\sum_{n=1}^{\infty} \frac{1}{n}$.   **45.** $\displaystyle\sum_{n=1}^{\infty} \frac{1}{n^p}$.   **46.** $\displaystyle\sum_{n=2}^{\infty} \frac{1}{n \ln n}$.

ANS.   Convergent: Exercises 1, 4, 5, 6, 7, 10, 12, 13, 15, 16, 17, 18, 19, 21, 24, 26, 27, 29, 31, 38, 45 for $p>1$.

         Divergent: Exercises 2, 3, 8, 9, 11, 14, 20, 22, 23, 25, 28, 30, 32, 39, 44, 45 for $p \leqq 1$, 46.

19. Ratio Tests

For a positive term series

$$(1) \qquad \sum_{n=0}^{\infty} a_n, \qquad a_n > 0,$$

consider the ratio of consecutive terms

$$(2) \qquad \frac{a_{n+1}}{a_n}.$$

If, for all $n \geq$ some fixed m, the ratio (2) is bounded on the right by a number less than unity,

$$(3) \qquad \frac{a_{n+1}}{a_n} \leq r < 1, \qquad n \geq m,$$

it follows rapidly that the series (1) is convergent.

The inequality (3) yields

$$a_{m+1} \leq a_m r,$$

$$(4) \qquad a_{m+2} \leq a_{m+1} r \leq a_m r^2,$$

$$\vdots$$

$$a_{m+k} \leq a_{m+k-1} r \leq a_m r^k.$$

The series

$$(5) \qquad \sum_{n=m}^{\infty} a_n = \sum_{k=0}^{\infty} a_{m+k}$$

may now be compared with the convergent geometric series

$$(6) \qquad \sum_{k=0}^{\infty} a_m r^k, \qquad 0 < r < 1.$$

By (4), the general term of the series on the right in (5) is never greater than the general term of the series in (6). Hence, the series in (5) is convergent by a comparison test, Theorem 11, page 35. The series in (5) contain all but a finite number of the terms in the series (1). Then by Lemma 1, page 6, the series (1) converges.

On the other hand, if the test ratio is never less than unity for all $n \geq$ some fixed m,

$$(7) \qquad \frac{a_{n+1}}{a_n} \geq 1, \qquad n \geq m,$$

the terms a_n form a monotonic increasing sequence of positive numbers and cannot approach zero as $n \to \infty$. The sequence a_n is not a null sequence, so the infinite series (1) must diverge.

THEOREM 18. *The positive term series*

$$(8) \qquad \sum_{n=0}^{\infty} a_n$$

converges if there exists a fixed m and r such that

$$(9) \qquad \frac{a_{n+1}}{a_n} \leq r < 1, \qquad for\ all\ n \geq m.$$

The series (8) diverges if there exists a fixed m such that

$$(10) \qquad \frac{a_{n+1}}{a_n} \geq 1, \qquad for\ all\ n \geq m.$$

Frequently it is easier to work with the limit, as $n \to \infty$, of the test ratio than it is to establish the inequality in (9) or (10). If it happens that

$$(11) \qquad \lim_{n \to \infty} \frac{a_{n+1}}{a_n} = L,$$

then if $L < 1$, the inequality (9) follows from (11) with r chosen as any number between L and unity, $L < r < 1$. If the limit (11) exists but is greater than unity, the inequality (10) follows at once for some m. If the limit L is unity, no conclusion about the convergence or divergence of the series (8) can be drawn from that fact alone.

We thus obtain from Theorem 18 a weaker result which is valuable because it is often easier to use than is Theorem 18.

THEOREM 19. *For the positive term series* $\sum_{n=0}^{\infty} a_n$,

(a) *If* $\lim_{n \to \infty} \dfrac{a_{n+1}}{a_n} = L < 1$, *the series converges*;

(b) *If* $\lim_{n \to \infty} \dfrac{a_{n+1}}{a_n} = L > 1$, *or if* $\dfrac{a_{n+1}}{a_n} \to \infty$, *the series diverges*;

(c) *If* $\lim_{n \to \infty} \dfrac{a_{n+1}}{a_n} = 1$, *or if the ratio does not approach a limit, finite or infinite, the test fails and no conclusion may be drawn without additional information.*

Theorem 19 is called D'Alembert's ratio test (J. d'Alembert, 1717–1783).

When we are confronted with the situation in (c), we try more delicate tests, such as that in Theorem 18 or those in Chapter 4.

EXAMPLE (a). Test the series $\sum\limits_{n=1}^{\infty} \dfrac{n^2+1}{3^n}$.

Here

$$\frac{a_{n+1}}{a_n} = \frac{(n+1)^2+1}{3^{n+1}} \cdot \frac{3^n}{n^2+1} = \frac{n^2+2n+2}{3(n^2+1)}.$$

Then

$$\lim_{n\to\infty} \frac{a_{n+1}}{a_n} = \frac{1}{3}$$

so the series converges by Theorem 19.

EXAMPLE (b). Test the series $\sum\limits_{n=0}^{\infty} \dfrac{1}{(2n)!}$.

At once

$$\lim_{n\to\infty} \frac{a_{n+1}}{a_n} = \lim_{n\to\infty} \frac{(2n)!}{(2n+2)!} = \lim_{n\to\infty} \frac{1}{(2n+1)(2n+2)} = 0.$$

Since $0 < 1$, the series converges by Theorem 19.

EXAMPLE (c). Test the series $\sum\limits_{n=1}^{\infty} \dfrac{1\cdot3\cdot5\cdots(2n-1)}{n^4}$.

We find that

$$\lim_{n\to\infty} \frac{a_{n+1}}{a_n} = \lim_{n\to\infty} \frac{1\cdot3\cdot5\cdots(2n-1)(2n+1)}{(n+1)^4} \cdot \frac{n^4}{1\cdot3\cdot5\cdots(2n-1)}$$

$$= \lim_{n\to\infty} \frac{(2n+1)n^4}{(n+1)^4} = \infty.$$

Therefore the series is divergent by Theorem 19.

EXAMPLE (d). Test the series $\sum\limits_{n=0}^{\infty} a_n$, in which

$$\text{for even } n=2k, \qquad a_n = a_{2k} = \frac{1}{3^k}$$

and

$$\text{for odd } n = 2k+1, \qquad a_n = a_{2k+1} = \frac{2}{3^{k+1}}.$$

In this series the test ratio takes on different forms according to whether n is even or odd. Indeed,

$$\frac{a_{2k+1}}{a_{2k}} = \frac{2}{3^{k+1}} \cdot \frac{3^k}{1} = \frac{2}{3}$$

and

$$\frac{a_{2k+2}}{a_{2k+1}} = \frac{1}{3^{k+1}} \cdot \frac{3^{k+1}}{2} = \frac{1}{2}.$$

The elements of the sequence $\left\{ \dfrac{a_{n+1}}{a_n} \right\}$ are alternately $\dfrac{2}{3}$ (for n even) and $\dfrac{1}{2}$ (for n odd). The limit of the ratio does not exist, so Theorem 19 tells us nothing. But, for any n,

$$\frac{a_{n+1}}{a_n} \leqq \frac{2}{3} < 1,$$

so the series converges by the stronger test, Theorem 18, page 44.

EXAMPLE (e). Test the series $\displaystyle\sum_{n=0}^{\infty} b_n$, in which $b_n = \left(\dfrac{1}{2}\right)^n$ for even n, and $b_n = \left(\dfrac{1}{3}\right)^n$ for odd n.

Here we have

$$b_{2k} = \frac{1}{2^{2k}}, \qquad b_{2k+1} = \frac{1}{3^{2k+1}}.$$

Therefore

$$\frac{b_{2k+1}}{b_{2k}} = \frac{2^{2k}}{3^{2k+1}} = \frac{1}{3}\left(\frac{4}{9}\right)^k$$

and

$$\frac{b_{2k+2}}{b_{2k+1}} = \frac{3^{2k+1}}{2^{2k+2}} = \frac{3}{4}\left(\frac{9}{4}\right)^k.$$

The even numbered elements of the sequence $\left\{ \dfrac{b_{n+1}}{b_n} \right\}$ approach 0 as $n \to \infty$, and the odd numbered elements of the same sequence $\to \infty$ as $n \to \infty$. Neither of our ratio tests, Theorems 18 and 19, yields an answer.

The series is, however, convergent because

$$0 < b_n \leqq (\tfrac{1}{2})^n$$

and comparison with a simple geometric series gives the desired result.

20. Rearrangement of Terms

Rearrangement of a finite number of terms does not alter the convergence or divergence of a series, as is easily proved using Lemma 1, page 6. If the original series converges, the sum is preserved when only a finite number of terms are reordered.

We shall now prove that for convergent positive term series an infinite rearrangement of terms also leaves untouched both the property of convergence and the sum of the series. A technical definition of a rearrangement is contained in (4) and (5), page 48.

THEOREM 20. *If $c_n > 0$ and $\sum\limits_{n=0}^{\infty} c_n$ converges to the sum S, and if the sequence $\{b_n\}$ contains exactly the same elements as the sequence $\{c_n\}$, then the series $\sum\limits_{n=0}^{\infty} b_n$ also converges to the sum S.*

PROOF. In proving this theorem we wish to avoid subscripts on subscripts and therefore introduce a notation we shall use frequently later. We define

$$(1) \qquad c(n) = c_n, \qquad b(n) = b_n.$$

Let the partial sums of the series

$$(2) \qquad \sum_{n=0}^{\infty} c(n) \quad \text{and} \quad \sum_{n=0}^{\infty} b(n)$$

be

$$(3) \qquad S_n = \sum_{k=0}^{n} c(k) \quad \text{and} \quad T_n = \sum_{k=0}^{n} b(k),$$

respectively. From the fact that the sequence $\{S_n\}$ is a strictly monotonic increasing sequence of positive elements converging to S, we wish to show that the sequence $\{T_n\}$ also converges to S.

We are given that the sequence $\{b(n)\}$ is a reordering of the sequence $\{c(n)\}$ and, therefore, also that $\{c(n)\}$ is a reordering of $\{b(n)\}$. That is, there exists a sequence $\{\gamma_k\}$, whose elements are the non-negative integers in some order, such that

(4) $$b(k) = c(\gamma_k), \qquad \text{for each } k \geq 0.$$

There must also exist a sequence $\{\delta_k\}$, whose elements are the non-negative integers in some order, such that

(5) $$c(k) = b(\delta_k), \qquad \text{for each } k \geq 0.$$

For each n, define m as the maximum of the set of $(n + 1)$ integers $\gamma_0, \gamma_1, \ldots, \gamma_n$, and define r as the maximum of the set of $(n + 1)$ integers $\delta_0, \delta_1, \ldots, \delta_n$. Then every term of the partial sum T_n is included in the partial sum S_m and every term in the partial sum S_n is included in the partial sum T_r. That is,

$$T_n = \sum_{k=0}^{n} b(k) = \sum_{k=0}^{n} c(\gamma_k) \leq \sum_{k=0}^{m} c(k) = S_m,$$

$$S_n = \sum_{k=0}^{n} c(k) = \sum_{k=0}^{n} b(\delta_k) \leq \sum_{k=0}^{r} b(k) = T_r.$$

We have thus shown that

(6) $$0 < T_n \leq S_m$$

and

(7) $$0 < S_n \leq T_r.$$

The sequences $\{T_n\}$ and $\{S_n\}$ are each strictly monotonic increasing and $\{S_n\}$ converges to S. Then $\{S_n\}$ is bounded and (6) tells us that T_n is bounded and, being monotonic increasing, must converge to some limit T. Also, by (6),

(8) $$0 < T \leq S.$$

In the same way, now that we know $\{T_n\}$ converges to T, (7) yields

(9) $$0 < S \leq T.$$

The inequalities (8) and (9) together force $T = S$,

(10) $$\lim_{n \to \infty} T_n = \lim_{n \to \infty} S_n = S,$$

which concludes the proof.

Theorem 20 will prove useful in the multiplication of series.

Exercises

In Exercises 1–22, test the series by using Theorem 19, page 44.

1. $\displaystyle\sum_{n=1}^{\infty} \frac{1000\, n^3}{\pi^n}.$

2. $\displaystyle\sum_{n=0}^{\infty} \frac{e^n}{n!}.$

3. $\displaystyle\sum_{n=0}^{\infty} \frac{(n+1)}{(2n+1)!}.$

4. $\displaystyle\sum_{n=1}^{\infty} n\left(\frac{\pi}{3}\right)^{n+1}.$

5. $\displaystyle\sum_{n=1}^{\infty} \frac{1\cdot 4\cdot 7\cdots (3n+1)}{n^5}.$

6. $\displaystyle\sum_{n=1}^{\infty} \frac{(n+3)(n+4)}{2\cdot 4\cdot 6\cdots (2n)}.$

7. $\displaystyle\sum_{n=0}^{\infty} \frac{3n+1}{2^n n!(2n+1)}.$

8. $\displaystyle\sum_{n=1}^{\infty} n^{1000}\, e^{-n}.$

9. $\displaystyle\sum_{n=4}^{\infty} \frac{3\cdot 6\cdot 9\cdots (3n)}{1\cdot 3\cdot 5\cdot 7\cdots (2n-1)}.$

10. $\displaystyle\sum_{n=0}^{\infty} \frac{(2n+1)!}{n!}.$

11. $\displaystyle\sum_{k=1}^{\infty} \frac{3\cdot 6\cdot 9\cdots (3k)}{1\cdot 5\cdot 9\cdots (4k+1)}.$

12. $\displaystyle\sum_{k=0}^{\infty} \frac{1}{(2k+1)3^{2k}}.$

13. $\displaystyle\sum_{k=0}^{\infty} \frac{k^3 3^k}{(k^2+1)2^{2k}}.$

14. $\displaystyle\sum_{n=1}^{\infty} \frac{n^n}{n!}.$

15. $\displaystyle\sum_{n=1}^{\infty} \frac{n!}{n^n}.$

16. Exercise 4, page 40.

17. Exercise 15, page 41.

18. Exercise 21, page 41.

19. Exercise 27, page 41.

20. Exercise 28, page 41.

21. Exercise 29, page 41.

22. Exercise 30, page 41.

23. Use Theorem 18, page 44, to test the series $\sum\limits_{n=0}^{\infty} a_n$ in which $a_{2k} = \dfrac{1}{2^k}$,

$a_{2k+1} = \dfrac{3}{2^{k+2}}$.

In Exercises 24–27, show that the ratio tests fail. Test by an appropriate theorem.

24. $\sum\limits_{n=1}^{\infty} a_n$, in which $a_{2k} = \dfrac{1}{2^{2k}}$, $a_{2k+1} = \dfrac{3}{2^{2k}}$.

25. $\sum\limits_{n=1}^{\infty} a_n$, in which $a_{2k} = \dfrac{k}{9^k}$, $a_{2k+1} = \dfrac{k+1}{4^{k+1}}$.

26. $\sum\limits_{n=1}^{\infty} a_n$, in which $a_{2k} = \dfrac{1}{2k}$, $a_{2k+1} = \dfrac{1}{4^{k+1}}$.

27. $\sum\limits_{n=1}^{\infty} a_n$, in which $a_{2k} = \dfrac{2}{3^k}$, $a_{2k+1} = \dfrac{3}{2^k}$.

ANS.   Convergent: Exercises 1, 2, 3, 6, 7, 8, 11, 12, 13, 15, 16, 17, 18, 19, 21, 23, 24, 25, 27.
Divergent: Exercises 4, 5, 9, 10, 14, 20, 22, 26.

CHAPTER 4

Tests of Kummer, Raabe, and Gauss

21. Ratio-Comparison Tests

We have already developed some comparison tests and some ratio tests for positive term series. We now obtain two theorems on the comparison of ratios.

THEOREM 21. *If $a_n > 0$, if $c_n > 0$, if $\sum\limits_{n=0}^{\infty} c_n$ converges, and if*

$$(1) \qquad \frac{a_{n+1}}{a_n} \leqq \frac{c_{n+1}}{c_n},$$

then $\sum\limits_{n=0}^{\infty} a_n$ converges.

PROOF. Define γ_n by

$$(2) \qquad \gamma_n = \frac{a_n}{c_n}.$$

Then

$$\frac{\gamma_{n+1}}{\gamma_n} = \frac{a_{n+1}}{c_{n+1}} \cdot \frac{c_n}{a_n} = \frac{a_{n+1}}{a_n} \cdot \frac{c_n}{c_{n+1}} \leqq \frac{c_{n+1}}{c_n} \cdot \frac{c_n}{c_{n+1}} = 1.$$

Hence $\gamma_{n+1} \leqq \gamma_n$, so $\{\gamma_n\}$ is a monotonic decreasing sequence of positive elements. Then γ_n is bounded and we use a comparison test or Exercise 36, page 41, to conclude that $\sum\limits_{n=0}^{\infty} \gamma_n c_n$ converges. But, by (2), $\gamma_n c_n = a_n$, so $\sum\limits_{n=0}^{\infty} a_n$ converges.

THEOREM 22. *If $a_n > 0$, if $d_n > 0$, if $\sum\limits_{n=0}^{\infty} d_n$ diverges, and if*

$$(3) \qquad\qquad \frac{a_{n+1}}{a_n} \geq \frac{d_{n+1}}{d_n},$$

then $\sum\limits_{n=0}^{\infty} a_n$ diverges.

PROOF. From (3) we obtain

$$\frac{a_{n+1}}{d_{n+1}} \geq \frac{a_n}{d_n},$$

so $\left\{\dfrac{a_n}{d_n}\right\}$ is a monotonic increasing sequence of positive elements and it therefore has a lower bound $T > 0$. Then

$$(4) \qquad\qquad a_n \geq T d_n.$$

Since $\sum\limits_{n=0}^{\infty} T d_n$ diverges, it follows from (4) that $\sum\limits_{n=0}^{\infty} a_n$ diverges by a direct comparison test, Theorem 12, page 36.

The critical inequalities, (1) in Theorem 21 and (3) in Theorem 22, need be established only for n greater than some fixed m, because of Lemma 1, page 6.

EXAMPLE. Test the series

$$(5) \qquad\qquad \sum\limits_{n=1}^{\infty} \frac{1 \cdot 3 \cdot 5 \cdots (2n-1)}{2^n(n+1)!}.$$

Using a_n for the general term in (5), we obtain

$$\frac{a_{n+1}}{a_n} = \frac{1 \cdot 3 \cdot 5 \cdots (2n-1)(2n+1)}{2^{n+1}(n+2)!} \cdot \frac{2^n(n+1)!}{1 \cdot 3 \cdot 5 \cdots (2n-1)},$$

from which it follows that

$$(6) \qquad\qquad \frac{a_{n+1}}{a_n} = \frac{2n+1}{2(n+2)}.$$

The test ratio in (6) is < 1 and the ratio $\to 1$ as $n \to \infty$, so the ratio tests do not yield any conclusion.

We know by Exercise 16, page 41, or by comparison with $\sum\limits_{n=1}^{\infty} \dfrac{1}{n^{3/2}}$, that

(7)
$$\sum_{n=1}^{\infty} \frac{1}{(n+1)(2n+1)^{1/2}}$$

converges. Let c_n denote the general term in (7). Then

(8)
$$\frac{c_{n+1}}{c_n} = \frac{(n+1)(2n+1)^{1/2}}{(n+2)(2n+3)^{1/2}}.$$

From the ratios (6) and (8) we have

$$\frac{a_{n+1}}{a_n} \cdot \frac{c_n}{c_{n+1}} = \frac{2n+1}{2(n+2)} \cdot \frac{(n+2)(2n+3)^{1/2}}{(n+1)(2n+1)^{1/2}} = \frac{(2n+1)^{1/2}(2n+3)^{1/2}}{2(n+1)}.$$

Therefore,

$$\frac{a_{n+1}}{a_n} \cdot \frac{c_n}{c_{n+1}} = \frac{(4n^2+8n+3)^{1/2}}{(4n^2+8n+4)^{1/2}} < 1.$$

Hence,

$$\frac{a_{n+1}}{a_n} < \frac{c_{n+1}}{c_n},$$

and Theorem 21 shows that the series (5) converges.

22. Kummer's Criteria

O. Stolz (1842–1905) gave a neat proof of a theorem due to E. E. Kummer (1810–1893).

THEOREM 23. *If $a_n > 0$, if $\gamma_n > 0$, and if*

(1)
$$\gamma_n - \frac{a_{n+1}\,\gamma_{n+1}}{a_n} \geq \sigma > 0, \qquad \text{for all } n > m,$$

where σ is independent of n, then $\sum\limits_{n=0}^{\infty} a_n$ converges.

PROOF. Since $a_n > 0$, (1) yields

(2)
$$a_n\gamma_n - a_{n+1}\,\gamma_{n+1} \geq a_n\sigma > 0.$$

From (2) we obtain $a_{n+1}\gamma_{n+1} \leq a_n\gamma_n$, so $\{a_n\gamma_n\}$ is a monotonic decreasing sequence and is bounded below because $a_n\gamma_n > 0$. Then the sequence $\{a_n\gamma_n\}$ converges.

Consider the telescoping series

(3)
$$\sum_{n=0}^{\infty} \frac{1}{\sigma}(a_n\gamma_n - a_{n+1}\gamma_{n+1})$$

with partial sum

(4)
$$T_n = \sum_{k=0}^{n} \frac{1}{\sigma}(a_k\gamma_k - a_{k+1}\gamma_{k+1}) = \frac{1}{\sigma}(a_0\gamma_0 - a_{n+1}\gamma_{n+1}).$$

Since $\{a_n\gamma_n\}$ converges, the sequence $\{T_n\}$ converges, so the series (3) converges. By (2),

(5)
$$a_n \leqq \frac{1}{\sigma}(a_n\gamma_n - a_{n+1}\gamma_{n+1}),$$

so $\sum_{n=0}^{\infty} a_n$ converges by comparison with the series (3), which concludes the proof.

In using Theorem 23 as a convergence test, note that the only restrictions on the sequence $\{\gamma_n\}$ are that its elements be positive and that we be able to select γ_n so that the condition (1) will be satisfied. Suppose, now, we add the restriction that

$$\sum_{n=0}^{\infty} \frac{1}{\gamma_n}$$

diverge. We put $\frac{1}{\gamma_n} = d_n$, require that $\sum_{n=0}^{\infty} d_n$ diverge and are thus led to what may be called Kummer's criteria, a combination of Theorems 22 and 23.

THEOREM 24. *If $a_n > 0$, if $d_n > 0$, and if $\sum_{n=0}^{\infty} d_r$ diverges, then*

(A)
$$\textit{If } \frac{1}{d_n} - \frac{a_{n+1}}{a_n} \cdot \frac{1}{d_{n+1}} \geqq \sigma > 0, \sum_{n=0}^{\infty} a_n \textit{ converges},$$

and

(B)
$$\textit{If } \frac{1}{d_n} - \frac{a_{n+1}}{a_n} \cdot \frac{1}{d_{n+1}} \leqq 0, \sum_{n=0}^{\infty} a_n \textit{ diverges}.$$

PROOF. Part (A) of Theorem 24 follows at once from Theorem 23 with $\gamma_n = \frac{1}{d_n}$. Part (B) of Theorem 24 is a rewording of Theorem 22, since

$$\frac{a_{n+1}}{a_n} \geqq \frac{d_{n+1}}{d_n}$$

is equivalent to

$$\frac{a_{n+1}}{a_n} \cdot \frac{1}{d_{n+1}} \geqq \frac{1}{d_n}$$

or

$$\frac{1}{d_n} - \frac{a_{n+1}}{a_n} \cdot \frac{1}{d_n} \leqq 0.$$

The advantage of Theorem 24 over the combined Theorems 22 and 23 lies in the fact that the left members of the test inequalities in (A) and (B) of Theorem 24 are identical.

The greater generality of Theorem 23 over part (A) of Theorem 24 is, in a sense, illusory. Suppose in Theorem 23 we are able to find a sequence $\{\gamma_n\}$ for which the inequality (1) holds true and $\sum\limits_{n=0}^{\infty} \frac{1}{\gamma_n}$ converges instead of diverging. Put $\frac{1}{\gamma_n} = c_n$. Then the inequality (1) yields

(6)
$$\frac{1}{c_n} - \frac{a_{n+1}}{a_n} \cdot \frac{1}{c_{n+1}} \geqq \sigma > 0,$$

so

$$\frac{a_{n+1}}{a_n} \leqq \frac{c_{n+1}}{c_n}$$

and the ratio-comparison test of Theorem 21 could have been used instead of the more delicate Theorem 23.

It is often convenient to employ a weaker form of the Kummer criteria, Theorem 25, which is sometimes called *Kummer's test*.

THEOREM 25. *If $a_n > 0$, if $d_n > 0$, if $\sum\limits_{n=0}^{\infty} d_n$ diverges, and if*

(7)
$$\lim_{n \to \infty} \left(\frac{1}{d_n} - \frac{a_{n+1}}{a_n} \cdot \frac{1}{d_{n+1}} \right) = h,$$

then $\sum\limits_{n=0}^{\infty} a_n$ converges if $h > 0$, diverges if $h < 0$.

Proof of Theorem 25 follows so easily from Theorem 24 that it is left as an exercise.

The proofs of Theorems 26 and 27 in the next two sections furnish examples of the use of Kummer's test.

23. Raabe's Test

J. L. Raabe (1801–1859) gave a test which disposes of some situations in which the test ratio in Theorem 19, page 44, approaches unity.

THEOREM 26. *If $a_n > 0$, if $\varepsilon_n \to 0$ as $n \to \infty$, and if*

$$(1) \qquad \frac{a_{n+1}}{a_n} = 1 - \frac{\beta}{n} + \frac{\varepsilon_n}{n},$$

where β is independent of n, then $\sum\limits_{n=0}^{\infty} a_n$ converges if $\beta > 1$ and diverges if $\beta < 1$.

PROOF. To prove Theorem 26, turn to Kummer's test, Theorem 25, page 55, and choose $d_n = 1/n$, for $n \geq 1$. Then $\sum\limits_{n=0}^{\infty} d_n$ diverges, no matter what d_0 is, and if (1) is satisfied,

$$\lim_{n \to \infty} \left(\frac{1}{d_n} - \frac{a_{n+1}}{a_n} \cdot \frac{1}{d_{n+1}} \right) = \lim_{n \to \infty} \left[n - (n+1)\left(1 - \frac{\beta}{n} + \frac{\varepsilon_n}{n} \right) \right]$$

$$= \lim_{n \to \infty} \left[-1 + \frac{\beta(n+1)}{n} - \frac{\varepsilon_n(n+1)}{n} \right]$$

$$= \beta - 1,$$

because $\dfrac{(n+1)}{n} \to 1$ and $\varepsilon_n \to 0$ as $n \to \infty$. Then $(\beta - 1)$ plays the role of the h in Theorem 25 and $h > 0$ means $\beta > 1$, $h < 0$ means $\beta < 1$, so Theorem 26 follows from Theorem 25.

EXAMPLE. Test the series

$$(2) \qquad \sum_{n=1}^{\infty} \frac{1 \cdot 3 \cdot 5 \cdots (2n-1)}{2 \cdot 4 \cdot 6 \cdots (2n)}.$$

Denote the general term in (2) by a_n. Then

$$\frac{a_{n+1}}{a_n} = \frac{1 \cdot 3 \cdot 5 \cdots (2n-1)(2n+1)}{2 \cdot 4 \cdot 6 \cdots (2n)(2n+2)} \cdot \frac{2 \cdot 4 \cdot 6 \cdots (2n)}{1 \cdot 3 \cdot 5 \cdots (2n-1)},$$

so

$$(3) \qquad \frac{a_{n+1}}{a_n} = \frac{2n+1}{2n+2} = 1 - \frac{1}{2n+2}.$$

We can write equation (3) in the form

$$\frac{a_{n+1}}{a_n} = 1 - \frac{1}{2n} + \left(\frac{1}{2n} - \frac{1}{2n+2}\right),$$

or

(4)
$$\frac{a_{n+1}}{a_n} = 1 - \frac{\frac{1}{2}}{n} + \frac{1}{n(2n+2)}.$$

Equation (4) fits the equation (1) of Raabe's test, Theorem 26, with the choices

$$\varepsilon_n = \frac{1}{2n+2}, \qquad \beta = \tfrac{1}{2}.$$

Since $\varepsilon_n \to 0$ as $n \to \infty$, and $\beta < 1$, we conclude that the series (2) diverges.

A shift of index often simplifies the algebra involved in using a test. In the series (2) replace n by $(n-1)$. The series becomes

(5)
$$\sum_{n=2}^{\infty} \frac{1 \cdot 3 \cdot 5 \cdots (2n-3)}{2 \cdot 4 \cdot 6 \cdots (2n-2)},$$

and with b_n denoting the general term in (5) we have

(6)
$$\frac{b_{n+1}}{b_n} = \frac{2n-1}{2n} = 1 - \frac{\frac{1}{2}}{n}.$$

The ratio (6) fits into Raabe's test with $\varepsilon_n \equiv 0$ and $\beta = \tfrac{1}{2}$, thus eliminating some of the work done earlier in this example. It is, of course, not necessary to perform the shift of index in the series being tested; the shift can be used on the ratio itself, thus moving from (3) to (6).

24. Gauss' Test

Some situations not covered by Raabe's test, Theorem 26, can be handled by a test due to C. F. Gauss (1777–1855).

THEOREM 27. *If $a_n > 0$, if θ_n is bounded, and if*

(1)
$$\frac{a_{n+1}}{a_n} = 1 - \frac{\beta}{n} + \frac{\theta_n}{n^{1+\lambda}}, \qquad \lambda > 0,$$

then $\sum\limits_{n=0}^{\infty} a_n$ converges if $\beta > 1$, diverges if $\beta \leq 1$.

PROOF. For $\beta \neq 1$, Theorem 27 follows from Raabe's test, Theorem 26, by employing $\varepsilon_n = \dfrac{\theta_n}{n^\lambda}$. Since $\lambda > 0$ and θ_n is bounded, $\varepsilon_n \to 0$ as required in Theorem 26.

Now consider $\beta = 1$. In Theorem 25, page 55, choose $d_n = \dfrac{1}{n \ln n}$, for $n \geq 1$. Then $\sum\limits_{n=0}^{\infty} d_n$ diverges. Using $\beta = 1$ and the assumed relation (1) of Theorem 27, we get

$$\lim_{n \to \infty} \left(\frac{1}{d_n} - \frac{a_{n+1}}{a_n} \cdot \frac{1}{d_{n+1}} \right) = \lim_{n \to \infty} \left[n \ln n - (n+1)\ln(n+1)\left\{ 1 - \frac{1}{n} + \frac{\theta_n}{n^{1+\lambda}} \right\} \right]$$

$$= \lim_{n \to \infty} \left[n \ln n - \frac{n^2 - 1}{n} \ln(n+1) - \frac{(n+1)}{n} \cdot \frac{\theta_n \ln(n+1)}{n^\lambda} \right]$$

$$= \lim_{n \to \infty} \left[n \ln \frac{n}{n+1} + \frac{\ln(n+1)}{n} - \frac{n+1}{n} \cdot \frac{\theta_n \ln(n+1)}{n^\lambda} \right]$$

$$= -1 + 0 - 0 = -1.$$

Thus, for $\beta = 1$, Theorem 27 follows from Theorem 25, page 55, with $h = -1$.

In evaluating the above limit we have used two elementary results from calculus,

$$\lim_{n \to \infty} \frac{\ln(n+1)}{n} = 0, \qquad \lim_{n \to \infty} \left[n \ln \frac{n}{n+1} \right] = -1.$$

Gauss' test was devised for application to the hypergeometric series (Chapter 9) with unit argument,

(2)
$$1 + \sum_{n=1}^{\infty} \frac{[\alpha(\alpha+1)(\alpha+2) \cdots (\alpha+n-1)][\beta(\beta+1)(\beta+2) \cdots (\beta+n-1)]}{n!\, \gamma(\gamma+1)(\gamma+2) \cdots (\gamma+n-1)}.$$

At present we must assume that α, β, γ are positive numbers.

Let a_n denote the general term of the series (2). Then

(3)
$$\frac{a_{n+1}}{a_n} = \frac{(\alpha+n)(\beta+n)}{(1+n)(\gamma+n)}.$$

Division of $(\alpha+n)(\beta+n)$ by $(\gamma+n)$ yields

(4)
$$\frac{(\alpha+n)(\beta+n)}{\gamma+n} = n + \alpha + \beta - \gamma + \frac{(\alpha-\gamma)(\beta-\gamma)}{n+\gamma}.$$

Because of (4), the ratio in (3) may be written in the form

$$(5) \qquad \frac{a_{n+1}}{a_n} = \frac{1}{n+1}\left[n+1-(1+\gamma-\alpha-\beta)+\frac{(\alpha-\gamma)(\beta-\gamma)}{n+1+(\gamma-1)}\right]$$

and a shift of index gives us

$$(6) \qquad \frac{a_n}{a_{n-1}} = 1-\frac{1+\gamma-\alpha-\beta}{n}+\frac{(\alpha-\gamma)(\beta-\gamma)}{n(n+\gamma-1)}.$$

We may, of course, apply Gauss' test with this ratio replacing that of (5).

To use Gauss' test, Theorem 27, here, we choose for λ any number in $0<\lambda<1$, say $\lambda=\frac{1}{2}$, and we set

$$(7) \qquad \theta_n = \frac{(\alpha-\gamma)(\beta-\gamma)n^{1/2}}{n+\gamma-1}.$$

As $n\to\infty$, the θ_n of (7) is not only bounded, it $\to 0$. We may thus write (6) in the form

$$(8) \qquad \frac{a_n}{a_{n-1}} = 1-\frac{1+\gamma-\alpha-\beta}{n}+\frac{\theta_n}{n^{1+(1/2)}}$$

and conclude that the series (2) converges if $(\gamma-\alpha-\beta)>0$ and diverges if $(\gamma-\alpha-\beta)\leq 0$.

Exercises

1. Use Raabe's test, Theorem 26, page 56, on the series (5) page 52.

2. Use Gauss' test, Theorem 27, page 57, on the series

$$1+\sum_{n=1}^{\infty}\frac{\alpha(\alpha+1)(\alpha+2)\cdots(\alpha+n-1)}{n!}, \qquad \alpha>0.$$

ANS.   Divergent.

3. Use Gauss' test, Theorem 27, page 57, on the series

$$1+\sum_{n=1}^{\infty}\frac{\alpha(\alpha+1)(\alpha+2)\cdots(\alpha+n-1)}{\gamma(\gamma+1)(\gamma+2)\cdots(\gamma+n-1)}, \qquad \alpha>0, \quad \gamma>0.$$

ANS.   Convergent if $\gamma-\alpha>1$;
Divergent if $\gamma-\alpha\leq 1$.

4. Prove Theorem 25.

CHAPTER 5

Series of Constants

25. Series of Absolute Values

We have concerned ourselves, up to this point, with infinite series of positive terms. Now, we turn to series of real terms and later to series of complex terms. At present we think of the terms involved as constants. This means only that we are not yet studying the properties of series as functions of parameters involved in the series.

Fortunately, it is possible to make extensive use of the results on series of positive terms in our study of other series because of the following result.

THEOREM 28. *If $\sum\limits_{n=1}^{\infty} |u_n|$ converges, $\sum\limits_{n=1}^{\infty} u_n$ converges.*

PROOF. Consider the partial sums

$$(1) \qquad\qquad S_n = \sum_{k=1}^{n} |u_k|$$

and

$$(2) \qquad\qquad s_n = \sum_{k=1}^{n} u_k.$$

Each of S_n and s_n is the general element of a sequence. We are given that the sequence $\{S_n\}$ converges; we wish to prove that $\{s_n\}$ converges.

By a Cauchy criterion, Theorem 9, page 24, we know that given any $\varepsilon > 0$, there exists an n_0 such that for all n and m each greater than n_0,

(3) $$|S_n - S_m| < \varepsilon.$$

Simply as a matter of notation, let $n > m > n_0$. Then, by (1),

(4) $$S_n - S_m = \sum_{k=m+1}^{n} |u_k|$$

and, by (2),

(5) $$s_n - s_m = \sum_{k=m+1}^{n} u_k.$$

Since the absolute value of a sum never exceeds the sum of the absolute values,

$$|s_n - s_m| \leq |S_n - S_m| < \varepsilon,$$

so the convergence of $\{S_n\}$ implies the convergence of $\{s_n\}$, as stated.

26. Absolute Convergence

DEFINITION. A series is said to be *absolutely convergent* if the series formed from it by replacing each term by its absolute value is convergent.

Theorem 28 may now be reworded as follows.

THEOREM 28 a. *If a series is absolutely convergent, it is convergent.*

If a series is convergent but is not absolutely convergent, we say that the series is *simply convergent*. Examples of simply convergent series appear in Section 32, page 73.

Theorem 28a is useful in testing series for convergence. This theorem permits us to employ the tests for positive term series to the series of absolute values; if absolute convergence is demonstrated, convergence follows. Other important applications of absolute convergence will appear soon.

It is possible to write theorems that are tests for absolute convergence by translating our tests for positive term series. From Theorem 11 on page 35, for example, we have the result:

If $c_n > 0$, if $\sum_{n=0}^{\infty} c_n$ converges, and if $|u_n| \leq c_n$, then $\sum_{n=0}^{\infty} u_n$ is absolutely convergent.

Without additional argument, comparison of $\sum\limits_{n=0}^{\infty} |u_n|$ with divergent series tells us little because all that follows from the divergence of $\sum\limits_{n=0}^{\infty} |u_n|$ is that $\sum\limits_{n=0}^{\infty} u_n$ is not absolutely convergent. The latter series may still be simply convergent or it may itself diverge.

With additional argument, the ratio tests of Section 19 do go over into forms fully as useful as the original ones. Theorem 18, page 44, leads us to the following form.

THEOREM 29. *The series*

(1)
$$\sum_{n=0}^{\infty} u_n$$

is absolutely convergent if there exist a fixed m and r such that

(2)
$$\left| \frac{u_{n+1}}{u_n} \right| \leqq r < 1, \quad \text{for all } n > m.$$

The series (1) *is divergent if there exists a fixed m such that*

(3)
$$\left| \frac{u_{n+1}}{u_n} \right| \geqq 1, \quad \text{for all } n > m.$$

PROOF. The first part of Theorem 29 follows from Theorem 18. The second part of Theorem 29 is true because if (3) holds, $|u_n|$ cannot approach zero as $n \to \infty$ and therefore u_n cannot approach zero as $n \to \infty$, so the series diverges by Theorem 1a, page 7.

In a similar manner, additional argument permits us to convert D'Alembert's ratio test, Theorem 19, page 44, into the form below.

THEOREM 30. *For the series* $\sum\limits_{n=0}^{\infty} u_n$,

(a) *If* $\lim\limits_{n\to\infty} \left| \dfrac{u_{n+1}}{u_n} \right| = L < 1$, *the series is absolutely convergent;*

(b) *If* $\lim\limits_{n\to\infty} \left| \dfrac{u_{n+1}}{u_n} \right| = L > 1$, *or if* $\left| \dfrac{u_{n+1}}{u_n} \right| \to \infty$, *the series diverges;*

(c) *otherwise the rest fails.*

PROOF. The conclusion in (a) follows from Theorem 19, the conclusion in (b) results from separate argument of the type used in proving the second part of Theorem 29.

As a rule, it seems simplest to retain the tests for positive term series in the forms given in Chapters 3 and 4. In treating

$$(4) \qquad \sum_{n=0}^{\infty} u_n,$$

we may use the methods of Chapters 3 and 4 on the corresponding series of absolute values,

$$(5) \qquad \sum_{n=0}^{\infty} |u_n|.$$

If (5) converges, (4) is absolutely convergent and so also convergent. If (5) diverges, (4) may or may not converge, but at least is not absolutely convergent.

EXAMPLE (a). Test the series $\displaystyle\sum_{n=1}^{\infty} \frac{\cos \frac{1}{3} n\pi}{n^2 + 1}$.

The terms of this series are not all of the same sign. We therefore consider the series of absolute values,

$$(6) \qquad \sum_{u=1}^{\infty} \frac{|\cos \frac{1}{3} n\pi|}{n^2 + 1}.$$

For real x, $|\cos x| \leq 1$. Therefore

$$\frac{|\cos \frac{1}{3} n\pi|}{n^2 + 1} \leq \frac{1}{n^2 + 1}.$$

We know by the polynomial test, Theorem 15, page 39, that

$$\sum_{n=1}^{\infty} \frac{1}{n^2 + 1}$$

converges. Then, by a comparison test, the series (6) converges. Hence, the series being tested is absolutely convergent.

EXAMPLE (b). Test the series $\displaystyle\sum_{n=1}^{\infty} \frac{(-1)^n n(n+1)}{2^n}$.

Denote the general term by u_n. Let us use a ratio test on the corresponding series of absolute values. We obtain

$$\left|\frac{u_{n+1}}{u_n}\right| = \frac{(n+1)(n+2)}{2^{n+1}} \cdot \frac{2^n}{n(n+1)} = \frac{n+2}{2n}.$$

Then

$$\lim_{n\to\infty}\left|\frac{u_{n+1}}{u_n}\right| = \frac{1}{2}.$$

Since $\frac{1}{2} < 1$, we conclude from Theorem 30, page 62, that the series being tested is absolutely convergent.

EXAMPLE (c). Test the series

$$(7) \qquad \sum_{n=0}^{\infty} \frac{1 + 7(-1)^n\sqrt{n}}{2 + 3n^2}.$$

Here the numerator takes on alternately positive and negative values. But

$$\left|\frac{1 + 7(-1)^n\sqrt{n}}{2 + 3n^2}\right| \leq \frac{1 + 7\sqrt{n}}{2 + 3n^2}$$

and the series

$$(8) \qquad \sum_{n=0}^{\infty} \frac{1 + 7\sqrt{n}}{2 + 3n^2}$$

can be compared with the known convergent series

$$\sum_{n=1}^{\infty} \frac{1}{n^{3/2}}.$$

Since

$$\lim_{n\to\infty} \frac{1 + 7\sqrt{n}}{2 + 3n^2} \cdot \frac{n^{3/2}}{1} = \frac{7}{3},$$

we may use Theorem 14, page 37, to conclude that the series (8) is also convergent. Then the series (7) is absolutely convergent by comparison with (8).

EXAMPLE (d). Test the series

$$(9) \qquad \sum_{n=0}^{\infty} \frac{(-1)^n x^{2n}}{(2n)!}.$$

Here the terms depend not only upon the dummy index n, but also on a parameter x. For the present purpose we consider the x arbitrary but fixed.

Now,

$$\lim_{n\to\infty} \left| \frac{u_{n+1}}{u_n} \right| = \lim_{n\to\infty} \left| \frac{(-1)^{n+1}x^{2n+2}}{(2n+2)!} \cdot \frac{(2n)!}{(-1)^n x^{2n}} \right|$$

$$= \lim_{n\to\infty} \frac{x^2}{(2n+1)(2n+2)} = 0, \qquad \text{for } x \neq 0.$$

Then the series (9) is absolutely convergent at least for all finite nonzero x. Division by x in the application of the ratio test does not permit us to use that test for $x = 0$. However, for $x = 0$, the given infinite series becomes

$$1 + 0 + 0 + \cdots + 0 + \cdots = 1 + \sum_{n=1}^{\infty} 0,$$

so $S_n = 1$ for all n. The series converges to unity for $x = 0$. In summary, the series (9) converges for all finite x.

EXAMPLE (e). Test the series

(10)
$$\sum_{n=1}^{\infty} \frac{(-1)^{n+1}}{n}.$$

Let u_n denote the general term. Then $|u_n| = \dfrac{1}{n}$, but

$$\sum_{n=1}^{\infty} \frac{1}{n},$$

the harmonic series, is divergent. We have shown that the series (10) is not absolutely convergent and this is the most we can say at present. Later we shall find that the series (10) is convergent and, indeed, has the sum $\ln 2$.

Exercises

In Exercises 1–16, test the series for absolute convergence.

1. $\displaystyle\sum_{n=0}^{\infty} \frac{3 + 4(-1)^n}{n^3 + 8}.$

2. $\displaystyle\sum_{n=1}^{\infty} \frac{(-1)^n(n^2 + 1)}{4n^4 + 1}.$

3. $\displaystyle\sum_{n=0}^{\infty} \frac{(-1)^n(n + 2)}{3n^2 + 5}.$

4. $\displaystyle\sum_{n=1}^{\infty} \frac{\sin(\frac{1}{4}n\pi)}{n^3 + 6}.$

5. $\displaystyle\sum_{n=0}^{\infty} \frac{(-1)^n x^{2n+1}}{(2n + 1)!}.$

6. $\displaystyle\sum_{n=2}^{\infty} n^2 y^{n-1}.$

7. $\displaystyle\sum_{n=0}^{\infty} x^n.$

8. $\displaystyle\sum_{n=0}^{\infty} (-1)^n \exp(-3n).$

9. $\displaystyle\sum_{k=2}^{\infty} \frac{(-1)^{k+1}}{k \ln k}.$

10. $\displaystyle\sum_{k=2}^{\infty} \frac{(-1)^k \ln k}{k}.$

11. $\displaystyle\sum_{k=0}^{\infty} \frac{(-1)^k}{(3k+1)^2}.$

12. $\displaystyle\sum_{k=1}^{\infty} \frac{(-1)^{k+1}}{k(k+1)}.$

13. $\displaystyle\sum_{n=1}^{\infty} \frac{(-1)^n n! w^n}{n^n}.$

14. $\displaystyle\sum_{n=0}^{\infty} \frac{(-1)^n 2^n n!}{1 \cdot 5 \cdot 9 \cdots (4n+1)}.$

15. $\displaystyle\sum_{n=1}^{\infty} \frac{(-1)^n (n+2)^4 x^n}{3^n n^2}.$

16. $\displaystyle\sum_{n=0}^{\infty} \frac{(-1)^n (2n+3) 3^{2n}}{(n+1)!}.$

17. Prove that if $\displaystyle\sum_{n=0}^{\infty} a_n$ is absolutely convergent and if γ_n is a bounded

sequence, $\displaystyle\sum_{n=1}^{\infty} \gamma_n a_n$ is absolutely convergent.

ANS. Absolutely Convergent: Exercises 1, 2, 4, Exercise 5 for all x, Exercise 6 for $|y| < 1$, Exercise 7 for $|x| < 1$, Exercises 8, 11, 12, Exercise 13 for $|w| < e$, Exercise 14, Exercise 15 for $|x| < 3$, Exercise 16. Not Absolutely Convergent: Exercise 3, Exercise 6 for $|y| \geq 1$, Exercise 7 for $|x| \geq 1$, Exercises 9, 10, Exercise 13 for $|w| \geq e$, Exercise 15 for $|x| \geq 3$.

27. Insertion of Parentheses

Given a convergent series we can introduce parentheses as desired, thus grouping terms without disturbing their order, and the resultant series is convergent to the same sum as was the original series. This is true because the partial sums of the new series form a subsequence of the sequence of partial sums of the original series.

Parentheses may not be removed from the terms of a series unless the resultant series converges. The sequence of partial sums of the resultant series contains as a subsequence the partial sums of the original series. Convergence of a subsequence does not force convergence of the whole sequence. The removal of parentheses may convert a convergent series into a divergent one. A classic example is furnished by the convergent series

$$(1-1) + (1-1) + \cdots + (1-1) + \cdots = \sum_{n=0}^{\infty} (1-1),$$

for which $s_n = 0$ for every n, so the series converges to the sum zero.

Removal of parentheses from the terms of this series yields the divergent series

$$1 - 1 + 1 - 1 + \cdots + (-1)^n + \cdots = \sum_{n=0}^{\infty} (-1)^n,$$

a series for which the general term does not even approach zero.

28. Addition of Series

Convergent series may be added (or subtracted) term by term and the resulting series will converge to the sum (or difference) of the original series. This follows at once from the relation among the partial sums involved. Absolute convergence is not needed for addition or subtraction.

Multiplication of series will be treated in Section 30. Division of series will be avoided except in the discussion of power series.

29. Rearrangement of Absolutely Convergent Series

We know by Theorem 20, page 47, that any rearrangement of terms of a convergent positive term series leaves untouched the property of convergence and the sum of the series. We shall prove that absolutely convergent series have the same property of insensitivity to rearrangement of terms.

Let the partial sums of the series

(1)
$$\sum_{n=0}^{\infty} u_n \quad \text{and} \quad \sum_{n=0}^{\infty} |u_n|$$

be

(2)
$$S_n = \sum_{k=0}^{n} u_k \quad \text{and} \quad S_n^* = \sum_{k=0}^{n} |u_k|,$$

respectively. Assume that the first series in (1) is absolutely convergent. Then the sequence $\{S_n\}$ has a limit S, the sum of the first infinite series in (1) and the sequence $\{S_n^*\}$ converges. The sequence $\{S_n^*\}$ is a monotonic increasing one and, since it converges, it must be bounded.

Let $\{a_k\}$ be the subsequence of all the positive elements in the sequence $\{u_n\}$ and let $\{-b_k\}$ be the subsequence of all the zero and negative elements in the sequence $\{u_n\}$. The sequences $\{a_k\}$ and $\{-b_k\}$ must be infinite sequences, or Theorem 20 is applicable and there is nothing to be proved.

Let the partial sums of the infinite series

(3)
$$\sum_{k=0}^{\infty} a_k \quad \text{and} \quad \sum_{k=0}^{\infty} b_k$$

be

(4)
$$A_k = \sum_{t=0}^{k} a_t \quad \text{and} \quad B_k = \sum_{t=0}^{k} b_t,$$

respectively. Then we have

(5)
$$S_n = A_m - B_j, \qquad m + j = n,$$

and

(6)
$$S_n^* = A_m + B_j, \qquad m + j = n.$$

Each of the sequences $\{A_m\}$ and $\{B_j\}$ is a monotonic increasing sequence because $a_k > 0$ and $b_k \geq 0$. The sequence $\{S_n^*\}$ is bounded so, by (6), the sequences $\{A_m\}$ and $\{B_j\}$ are each bounded. Every bounded monotonic increasing sequence converges. Then $\{A_m\}$ converges to some limit A and $\{B_j\}$ converges to some limit B. The two series in (3), one of positive terms, the other of zero and positive terms, are both convergent and therefore both absolutely convergent. Since $\{S_n\}$ converges to S, it follows from (5) that $S = A - B$, which concludes the proof of the following result.

THEOREM 31. *If $\sum_{n=0}^{\infty} u_n$ is absolutely convergent to the sum S, if $\{a_k\}$ is the subsequence of all positive elements of the sequence $\{u_n\}$ and if $\{-b_k\}$ is the subsequence of all zero and negative elements of u_n, then $\sum_{k=0}^{\infty} a_k$ and $\sum_{k=0}^{\infty} b_k$ are absolutely convergent to sums A and B, respectively, and*

(7)
$$S = A - B.$$

Now let the sequence $\{v_n\}$ contain precisely the same elements as the sequence $\{u_n\}$ but with a different ordering of elements. Let $\{c_k\}$ be the infinite subsequence of all positive elements of $\{v_n\}$ and $\{-d_k\}$ be the infinite subsequence of all zero and negative elements of $\{v_n\}$. Then $\{c_k\}$ and $\{-d_k\}$ are reorderings of the sequences $\{a_k\}$ and $\{-b_k\}$ of Theorem 31.

Let the partial sums of the series

(8)
$$\sum_{n=0}^{\infty} v_n, \quad \sum_{k=0}^{\infty} c_k, \quad \text{and} \quad \sum_{k=0}^{\infty} d_k$$

be

(9)
$$T_n = \sum_{k=0}^{n} v_k, \quad C_k = \sum_{t=0}^{k} c_t, \quad \text{and} \quad D_k = \sum_{t=0}^{k} d_t,$$

respectively. Then

(10)
$$T_n = C_m - D_j, \qquad m + j = n.$$

It follows from Theorem 20, page 47, that the sequences $\{C_m\}$ and $\{D_j\}$ are convergent monotonic increasing sequences with limits A and B in the notation of Theorem 31. Then

(11)
$$\sum_{k=0}^{n} |v_k| = C_m + D_j, \qquad m + j = n,$$

and (10) and (7) combine to yield

(12)
$$\lim_{n \to \infty} T_n = A - B = S.$$

The first series in (8) is absolutely convergent because of (11) and converges to S by (12).

THEOREM 32. *If $\sum_{n=0}^{\infty} u_n$ is absolutely convergent to the sum S and if the sequence $\{v_n\}$ contains precisely the same elements as the sequence $\{u_n\}$, but with different ordering, then $\sum_{n=0}^{\infty} v_n$ is also absolutely convergent to the sum S.*

It is not difficult to see that if $\sum_{n=0}^{\infty} u_n$ is only simply convergent (convergent, but not absolutely convergent), then a reordering $\{v_n\}$ of the sequence $\{u_n\}$ can be found to make $\sum_{n=0}^{\infty} v_n$ converge to any desired sum. This follows from the fact that the partial sums A_m and B_j used in the proof of Theorem 31 form divergent monotonic increasing sequences but the sequences $\{a_k\}$ and $\{-b_k\}$ are still null sequences. If the sum Q is desired, we add positive terms until the sum $> Q$, then add negative terms until the sum $< Q$, then more positive terms until the sum $> Q$, more negative terms until the sum $< Q$, and continue in that manner. A formal proof can be constructed but is omitted here.

30. Multiplication of Series

Let the partial sums of the series

$$\text{(1)} \qquad \sum_{n=0}^{\infty} a_n \quad \text{and} \quad \sum_{n=0}^{\infty} b_n$$

be

$$\text{(2)} \qquad A_n = \sum_{k=0}^{n} a_k \quad \text{and} \quad B_n = \sum_{k=0}^{n} b_k,$$

respectively. The sum of the products of each term of one series in (1) and every term of the other series in (1) may be arranged in the two way array shown below:

$$
\begin{aligned}
\text{(3)} \qquad & a_0b_0 + a_0b_1 + a_0b_2 + \cdots + a_0b_n + \cdots \\
&+ a_1b_0 + a_1b_1 + a_1b_2 + \cdots + a_1b_n + \cdots \\
&+ a_2b_0 + a_2b_1 + a_2b_2 + \cdots + a_2b_n + \cdots \\
&+ \cdots \\
&+ a_nb_0 + a_nb_1 + a_nb_2 + \cdots + a_nb_n + \cdots \\
&+ \cdots .
\end{aligned}
$$

We shall show that if the series in (1) are both absolutely convergent, then any grouping of the above array into an infinite series of finite sums is absolutely convergent to the product of the sums of the series in (1).

Form the sequence $\{A_nB_n\}$. The elements are the sums of all terms enclosed in successive squares, starting at the upper left corner, of the array (3) and are exhibited in the array (4):

$$
\begin{array}{lllll}
\text{(4)} \qquad a_0b_0 & + a_0b_1 & + a_0b_2 & + \cdots & + a_0b_n & + \cdots \\
+ a_1b_0 & + a_1b_1 & + a_1b_2 & + \cdots & + a_1b_n & + \cdots \\
+ a_2b_0 & + a_2b_1 & + a_2b_2 & + \cdots & + a_2b_n & + \cdots \\
+ \cdots \\
+ a_nb_0 & + a_nb_1 & + a_nb_2 & + \cdots & + a_nb_n & + \cdots \\
+ \cdots .
\end{array}
$$

Next form the infinite series

(5) $$A_0B_0 + \sum_{n=1}^{\infty} (A_nB_n - A_{n-1}B_{n-1}).$$

The series (5) has its terms equal to the sum of the terms enclosed between successive solid lines in the array (4). The series (5) telescopes with partial sum A_nB_n.

If we assume convergence of the series in (1) to the sums A and B, respectively, then the sequence $\{A_n\}$ converges to A and the sequence $\{B_n\}$ converges to B. Since

$$\lim_{n \to \infty} (A_nB_n) = AB,$$

the series in (5) converges to the sum AB.

If we further assume that the convergence of the series in (1) is absolute convergence, it follows that the series (5) is also absolutely convergent. In the proof of this statement we make use of the following simple result.

LEMMA 6. *From*

(6) $$A_n = \sum_{k=0}^{n} a_k \quad and \quad B_n = \sum_{k=0}^{n} b_k,$$

it follows that

(7) $$A_nB_n - A_{n-1}B_{n-1} = a_nB_n + b_nA_{n-1}, \qquad n \geq 1.$$

The truth of (7) may be seen by examining the array (4). Formally,

$$A_nB_n - A_{n-1}B_{n-1} = (a_nB_n + A_{n-1}B_n) - A_{n-1}B_{n-1}$$

$$= a_nB_n + (B_n - B_{n-1})A_{n-1}$$

$$= a_nB_n + b_nA_{n-1}.$$

Let us now introduce the series

(8) $$\sum_{n=0}^{\infty} |a_n| \quad and \quad \sum_{n=0}^{\infty} |b_n|$$

with partial sums

(9) $$A_n^* = \sum_{k=0}^{n} |a_k| \quad and \quad B_n^* = \sum_{k=0}^{n} |b_k|$$

respectively. The infinite series

(10)
$$A_0^* B_0^* + \sum_{n=1}^{\infty} (A_n^* B_n^* - A_{n-1}^* B_{n-1}^*)$$

is formed from the sums (9) as the series (5) was formed from the sums (2). By Lemma 6,

(11)
$$A_n^* B_n^* - A_{n-1}^* B_{n-1}^* = |a_n| B_n^* + |b_n| A_{n-1}^*.$$

We compare the series (5) with the series (10) and find that

$$|A_n B_n - A_{n-1} B_{n-1}| = |a_n B_n + b_n A_{n-1}| \leq |a_n| B_n^* + |b_n| A_{n-1}^*,$$

so, with the aid of (11), we obtain

(12)
$$|A_n B_n - A_{n-1} B_{n-1}| \leq |A_n^* B_n^* - A_{n-1}^* B_{n-1}^*|.$$

Absolute convergence of the series in (1) means convergence of the series in (8), from which convergence of the positive term series (10) follows. Then by (12), the series (5), namely

$$A_0 B_0 + \sum_{n=1}^{\infty} (A_n B_n - A_{n-1} B_{n-1})$$

is absolutely convergent. We already know the sum of the series is AB.

We have proved that absolute convergence of the series in (1) to the respective sums A and B yields absolute convergence of the series (5) to the sum AB. Any grouping of the terms of the array (3), page 70, into an infinite series of finite sums is a rearrangement of the terms of the absolutely convergent series (5) and is therefore also absolutely convergent to the same sum AB.

THEOREM 33. *If the series*

(13)
$$\sum_{n=0}^{\infty} a_n \quad \text{and} \quad \sum_{n=0}^{\infty} b_n$$

are both absolutely convergent and have the sums A and B, respectively, then any grouping into an infinite series of finite sums of the terms in the formal product of the series in (13) is absolutely convergent to the sum AB.

31. Cauchy Products

In the array (3), page 70, let us group the terms in diagonals such that the term with index n is the sum of all products $a_k b_j$ for which $k + j = n$. This grouping of terms yields what is called the *Cauchy product* of the two series, the right member of equation (2) below.

THEOREM 34. *If the series*

(1) $$\sum_{n=0}^{\infty} a_n \quad \text{and} \quad \sum_{n=0}^{\infty} b_n$$

are both absolutely convergent and have the sums A and B, respectively, then

(2) $$\left(\sum_{n=0}^{\infty} a_n\right)\left(\sum_{n=0}^{\infty} b_n\right) = \sum_{n=0}^{\infty}\left(\sum_{k=0}^{n} a_k b_{n-k}\right)$$

in the sense that the series on the right in (2) is also absolutely convergent and has the sum AB.

PROOF. Theorem 34 is a special case of Theorem 33 at the end of the preceding section. The parentheses on the right in (2) are not needed but are included to emphasize that the finite sum is the general term of the product series.

The Cauchy product was devised for convenience in multiplying power series (Chapters 7 and 8) because the Cauchy product of two power series is also a power series. To save space we shall not introduce examples or exercises on multiplication of series until the pertinent material on power series has been developed.

32. Alternating Series Test

Consider a series in which the terms alternate in sign,

(1) $$\sum_{n=0}^{\infty} (-1)^n a_n, \qquad a_n > 0.$$

If $a_n \to 0$, as $n \to \infty$, and if a_n is a monotonic decreasing sequence,

(2) $$0 < a_{n+1} \leqq a_n,$$

the series must converge.

To demonstrate the convergence, let the partial sum be

(3) $$S_n = \sum_{j=0}^{n} (-1)^j a_j.$$

Then, for any positive integer k,

(4) $$S_{n+k} - S_n = \sum_{j=n+1}^{n+k} (-1)^j a_j.$$

If k is odd, there are an even number of terms after the first term on the right in (4). We may therefore, for k odd, group the terms in (4) as follows:

(5) $\quad S_{n+k} - S_n = (-1)^{n+1}[a_{n+1} - (a_{n+2} - a_{n+3}) - (a_{n+4} - a_{n+5})$

$$- \cdots - (a_{n+k-1} - a_{n+k})].$$

If k is even, we may group the terms in (4) as follows:

(6) $\quad S_{n+k} - S_n = (-1)^{n+1}[a_{n+1} - (a_{n+2} - a_{n+3})$

$$\cdots - \cdots - (a_{n+k-2} - a_{n+k-1}) - a_{n+k}].$$

Because of the condition (2),

$$(a_{n+j} - a_{n+j+1}) \geq 0, \qquad \text{for each } j.$$

Hence, it follows that the quantity inside the square brackets in each of (5) and (6) is never larger than a_{n+1}. Therefore,

(7) $$\qquad\qquad |S_{n+k} - S_n| \leq a_{n+1}.$$

We assumed that $a_n \to 0$, as $n \to \infty$, so by (7) and a Cauchy criteria for convergence of sequences, Theorem 9a, page 24, we may conclude that $\{S_n\}$ converges. Then the series (1) converges.

The convergence or divergence of a series is not affected by the behavior of a fixed finite number of terms by Lemma 1, page 6. Hence, the proof above also yields convergence when the alternation in sign and the monotonic decreasing character of the a_n take effect only from some fixed n-value onward. What we have proved is the validity of the following test.

THEOREM 35 (The Alternating Series Test). *If the series* $\sum\limits_{n=0}^{\infty} u_n$ *has the three properties:*

(A) *The signs alternate for all* $n >$ *some fixed* n_0,
(B) *The terms are monotonic decreasing in magnitude,*

$$|u_{n+1}| \leq |u_n|, \qquad \text{for } n > n_0,$$

and

(C) $\lim\limits_{n \to \infty} u_n = 0$,

the series is convergent.

If all three conditions are satisfied, the series is said to be "convergent by the alternating series test." If (C) does not hold, the series diverges by Theorem 1a, page 7. If (C) is satisfied but (A) or (B), or both (A) and (B) are not true, the series may converge or may diverge, but the alternating series test does not yield any conclusion.

The importance of Theorem 35 lies largely in the fact that from it we get Theorem 36 below that gives a bound on the error made by using a partial sum S_n to approximate the actual sum S. Theorem 35 is also our first test, other than the definition of convergence, that is capable of demonstrating convergence of some series that are not absolutely convergent.

THEOREM 36. *If a series $\sum\limits_{n=0}^{\infty} u_n$ with partial sum*

$$(8) \qquad\qquad S_n = \sum_{k=0}^{n} u_k$$

has been shown to converge by the alternating series test, and if we call the sum of the series S, then

$$(9) \qquad\qquad |S - S_n| < |u_{n+1}|, \qquad for \ n > n_0 .$$

Theorem 36 states that when the series has been shown to be convergent by the alternating series test, the magnitude of the error made by stopping at any term in the series is less than the magnitude of the first term omitted.

PROOF. To prove Theorem 36, let us revert to the notation used in the proof of Theorem 35. We put

$$(10) \qquad\qquad u_n = (-1)^n a_n$$

and have, for all $n > n_0$, $|u_n| = a_n$ and $0 < a_{n+1} \leq a_n$. We write

$$(11) \qquad\qquad S = \sum_{n=0}^{\infty} (-1)^n a_n , \qquad S_n = \sum_{k=0}^{n} (-1)^k a_k ,$$

and conclude that

$$(12) \qquad\qquad S - S_n = \sum_{k=n+1}^{\infty} (-1)^k a_k .$$

We may group terms in a convergent series (Section 27) and thus conclude from (12) that

$$(13) \qquad S - S_n = (-1)^{n+1} \left[a_{n+1} - \sum_{j=0}^{\infty} (a_{n+2+2j} - a_{n+3+2j}) \right].$$

For $n > n_0$, each term $(a_{n+2+2j} - a_{n+3+2j})$ on the right in (13) must be positive or zero and some of these terms must be nonzero or the sum S

would be known exactly. Hence the quantity inside the square brackets in (13) is less than a_{n+1}. Thus

$$(14) \qquad |S - S_n| < a_{n+1}, \qquad n > n_0,$$

which means

$$(15) \qquad |S - S_n| < |u_{n+1}|, \qquad n > n_0,$$

as stated in Theorem 36.

It is easy to double the efficiency of Theorem 36. Let P_n denote the sum of the convergent series on the right in (13). We already know that

$$(16) \qquad 0 < P_n < a_{n+1}.$$

Then also

$$(17) \qquad |\tfrac{1}{2}a_{n+1} - P_n| < \tfrac{1}{2}a_{n+1}.$$

We write (13) in the form

$$(18) \qquad S - S_n - \tfrac{1}{2}(-1)^{n+1}a_{n+1} = (-1)^{n+1}(\tfrac{1}{2}a_{n+1} - P_n)$$

and conclude, because of (17), that

$$(19) \qquad |S - S_n - \tfrac{1}{2}(-1)^{n+1}a_{n+1}| < \tfrac{1}{2}a_{n+1}.$$

That is, if we approximate S by using the partial sum S_n plus one-half of the first term omitted, the error made is less in magnitude than one-half the first term omitted.

THEOREM 37. *If a series $\sum\limits_{n=0}^{\infty} u_n$ with partial sum*

$$(20) \qquad S_n = \sum_{k=0}^{n} u_k$$

has been shown to be convergent by the alternating series test, and if we call the sum of the series S, then

$$(21) \qquad |S - S_n - \tfrac{1}{2}u_{n+1}| < \tfrac{1}{2}|u_{n+1}|, \qquad for\ n > n_0.$$

The examples below include series to which the test and theorems of this section are applicable and also alternating series not covered by the alternating series test.

EXAMPLE (a). Test the series

$$(22) \qquad \sum_{n=0}^{\infty} \frac{(-1)^n}{n+1}.$$

We already know that this series is not absolutely convergent. The terms of (22) satisfy the conditions of the alternating series test:

(A) The signs alternate;

(B) $\dfrac{1}{n+2} < \dfrac{1}{n+1}$;

(C) $\lim\limits_{n\to\infty} \dfrac{1}{n+1} = 0$.

Hence, the series is simply convergent.

EXAMPLE (b). Compute to three decimal places the sum of the series

(23)
$$\sum_{n=1}^{\infty} \frac{(-1)^{n+1}}{n^4}.$$

The series (23) is absolutely convergent but that fact alone does not yield any indication of the accuracy of computations based on partial sums. We wish to use Theorem 37, page 76, so we need to apply the alternating series test to (23).

The signs of the terms in (23) alternate,

$$\frac{1}{(n+1)^4} < \frac{1}{n^4}$$

and

$$\lim_{n\to\infty} \frac{1}{n^4} = 0.$$

Therefore the series (23) is known to be convergent by the alternating series test and Theorem 37 may be used on it.

In performing computations we can shift index to make (23) fit the notation of Theorem 37, or we can stipulate that $u_0 = 0$ and $u_n = \dfrac{(-1)^{n+1}}{n^4}$.

Let us define S and S_n by

(24)
$$S = \sum_{n=1}^{\infty} \frac{(-1)^{n+1}}{n^4}, \qquad S_n = \sum_{k=1}^{n} \frac{(-1)^{k+1}}{k^4}.$$

We know, by Theorem 37, that

$$\left| S - S_n - \frac{(-1)^n}{2(n+1)^4} \right| < \frac{1}{2(n+1)^4}.$$

To obtain three decimal place accuracy, we need to use an n such that

$$\frac{1}{2(n+1)^4} \leq 0.0005.$$

Then $(n+1)^4 \geq 1000$, so $n \geq 4.6$. We use $n = 5$ and compute as follows:

$$
\begin{aligned}
&+1.000\ 000 \\
&-0.062\ 500 \\
&+0.012\ 346 \\
&-0.003\ 906 \\
&+0.001\ 600 \\
\hline
\end{aligned}
$$

$$
\begin{aligned}
S_5 &= +0.947\ 540 \\
\tfrac{1}{2}u_6 &= -0.000\ 386 \\
\hline
&+0.947\ 154.
\end{aligned}
$$

We may thus conclude that $S = 0.947$, correct to three decimal places. In the chapter on Fourier series we shall find the exact sum to be

$$S = \frac{7\pi^4}{720}.$$

Simple computation yields $\dfrac{7\pi^4}{720} = 0.947\ 03$, giving us a check.

EXAMPLE (c). Study the series

(25) $$\sum_{n=0}^{\infty} u_n$$

in which

(26) $$u_{2k} = \frac{1}{3^{2k}}, \qquad u_{2k+1} = \frac{-1}{2^{2k+1}}.$$

The series (25) may also be written in the form

(27) $$1 - \frac{1}{2} + \frac{1}{3^2} - \frac{1}{2^3} + \frac{1}{3^4} - \frac{1}{2^5} + \cdots + \frac{1}{3^{2k}} - \frac{1}{2^{2k+1}} + \cdots.$$

In the series (25), the signs alternate and $u_n \to 0$, as $n \to \infty$. Also

$$\left| \frac{u_{2k+2}}{u_{2k+1}} \right| = \frac{2^{2k+1}}{3^{2k+2}} < 1,$$

but

$$\left|\frac{u_{2k+1}}{u_{2k}}\right| = \frac{3^{2k}}{2^{2k+1}} = \frac{1}{2}\left(\frac{9}{4}\right)^k > 1, \qquad \text{for } k \geq 1.$$

Hence, $|u_{n+1}| < |u_n|$ is not true for all sufficiently large n; it fails to be true for even n. The alternating series test will not work on this series.

Since $|u_n| \leq \frac{1}{2^n}$, the series (25) is absolutely convergent. Let us put

$$S = \sum_{n=0}^{\infty} u_n, \qquad S_n = \sum_{k=0}^{n} u_k.$$

We can apply Theorem 31, page 68, find that (25) is the difference of two geometric series and thus compute its sum, $S = \frac{11}{24}$. We can also show (see Exercise 22, page 82) that

(28) $$|S - S_{2k}| > |u_{2k+1}|$$

and

(29) $$|S - S_{2k+1}| > |u_{2k+2}|.$$

That is, the error made by replacing the sum S by the partial sum S_n is always greater than the absolute value of the first term omitted. Contrast this with Theorem 36, page 75.

Example (c) is included to emphasize that the inequalities in Theorems 36 and 37 do not apply to "convergent alternating series"; they apply to series shown to converge by the alternating series test.

33. Series of Complex Terms

Let i denote $\sqrt{-1}$. Consider a series of complex terms

(1) $$\sum_{n=0}^{\infty} (x_n + iy_n),$$

with x_n and y_n real. Let the series (1) have partial sums

(2) $$S_n = \sum_{k=0}^{n} (x_k + iy_k) = \sum_{k=0}^{n} x_k + i\sum_{k=0}^{n} y_k = A_n + iB_n.$$

Then $\lim_{n\to\infty} S_n$ exists if and only if $\lim_{n\to\infty} A_n$ and $\lim_{n\to\infty} B_n$ exist. The A_n and B_n are partial sums of two series of real terms,

(3)
$$\sum_{n=0}^{\infty} x_n \quad \text{and} \quad \sum_{n=0}^{\infty} y_n.$$

In essence the study of (1) is the study of the two series in (3).

One theorem on series of complex terms is vital in our work.

THEOREM 38. *If x_n and y_n are real and if $\sum_{n=0}^{\infty} |x_n + iy_n|$ converges, then $\sum_{n=0}^{\infty} (x_n + iy_n)$ converges.*

That is, absolute convergence implies convergence for a series of complex terms as well as for series of real terms.

PROOF. We know that $|x_n + iy_n| = \sqrt{x_n^2 + y_n^2}$. It follows that

(4)
$$|x_n| \leq |x_n + iy_n| \leq |x_n| + |y_n|$$

and

(5)
$$|y_n| \leq |x_n + iy_n| \leq |x_n| + |y_n|.$$

The proof of Theorem 38 follows quickly by using comparison tests based on (4) and (5). If

(6)
$$\sum_{n=0}^{\infty} |x_n + iy_n|$$

converges, it follows from the left-hand inequalities in (4) and (5) that

(7)
$$\sum_{n=0}^{\infty} |x_n| \quad \text{and} \quad \sum_{n=0}^{\infty} |y_n|$$

converge. Then the series

(8)
$$\sum_{n=0}^{\infty} x_n \quad \text{and} \quad \sum_{n=0}^{\infty} y_n$$

converge, so

(9)
$$\sum_{n=0}^{\infty} (x_n + iy_n)$$

converges.

From the right-hand inequalities in (4) and (5) it follows that if the two series in (7) converge, the series (6) converges.

Reordering of the sequence $\{x_n + iy_n\}$ means reordering of the sequences $\{x_n\}$ and $\{y_n\}$. It follows that the theorems on rearrangement of terms of absolutely convergent series are also valid for series of complex terms.

By this time the student should be able to convert into theorems on series of complex terms whatever he needs from the previous work on positive term series. As an example, D'Alembert's ratio test, Theorem 30, page 62, goes over unchanged.

Exercises

In Exercises 1–21, test the series (a) for absolute convergence and (b) for convergence. Answers are at the end of the set of exercises.

1. $\displaystyle\sum_{n=0}^{\infty} \frac{(-1)^n}{2n+1}$.

2. $\displaystyle\sum_{n=0}^{\infty} \frac{(-1)^n}{(2n+1)^2}$.

3. $\displaystyle\sum_{n=0}^{\infty} \frac{(-1)^n(2n-1)}{3n+1}$.

4. $\displaystyle\sum_{n=1}^{\infty} \frac{(-1)^{n+1}(10n)^{10}}{\pi^n}$.

5. $\displaystyle\sum_{n=0}^{\infty} \frac{(-1)^n 10^{3n}}{n!}$.

6. $\displaystyle\sum_{n=0}^{\infty} \frac{(-1)^n n!}{1000^n}$.

7. $\displaystyle\sum_{n=0}^{\infty} \frac{(-1)^n}{n^3+1}$.

8. $\displaystyle\sum_{n=0}^{\infty} \frac{(-1)^n(n+1)}{n^2+4n+5}$.

9. $\displaystyle\sum_{k=1}^{\infty} \frac{(-1)^{k+1}}{\sqrt{k}}$.

10. $\displaystyle\sum_{k=2}^{\infty} \frac{(-1)^{k-1}}{k\sqrt{k-1}}$.

11. $\displaystyle\sum_{n=1}^{\infty} \frac{(-1)^n n \pi^n}{e^{2n}+1}$.

12. $\displaystyle\sum_{n=1}^{\infty} \frac{\sin n}{n^2}$.

13. $\displaystyle\sum_{n=1}^{\infty} \frac{n \cos\left(\frac{1}{4}n\pi\right)}{n+2}$.

14. $\displaystyle\sum_{n=0}^{\infty} \frac{(-1)^n}{n + 5^n}$.

15. $\displaystyle\sum_{n=0}^{\infty} \frac{(-1)^n}{n + (\frac{1}{2})^n}$.

16. Exercise 3, page 65.

17. Exercise 9, page 66.

18. Exercise 10, page 66.

19. $\displaystyle\sum_{n=0}^{\infty} u_n$, in which $u_{2k} = \dfrac{1}{2^{4k}}$, $\qquad u_{2k+1} = \dfrac{-1}{2^{2k+1}}$.

20. $\displaystyle\sum_{n=1}^{\infty} a_n$, in which $a_n = \dfrac{1}{n}$ for n even, $\qquad a_n = \dfrac{-1}{n\sqrt{n}}$ for n odd.

21. $\displaystyle\sum_{n=1}^{\infty} v_n$, in which $v_{2k+1} = \dfrac{1}{a^{2k+1}}$, $\qquad v_{2k} = \dfrac{-1}{b^{2k}}$, $\quad a > 1, \quad b > 1$.

22. For the series in Example (c), page 78, show that $S = \dfrac{11}{24}$ and

$$|S - S_{2k}| = \frac{2}{3}\left(\frac{1}{4}\right)^k - \frac{1}{8}\left(\frac{1}{9}\right)^k > |u_{2k+1}|$$

and

$$|S - S_{2k+1}| = \frac{1}{6}\left(\frac{1}{4}\right)^k - \frac{1}{8}\left(\frac{1}{9}\right)^k > |u_{2k+2}|.$$

23. For the series of Exercise 19, show that $|S - S_n|$ is never less than $|u_{n+1}|$.

24. Write a formal proof that if $\displaystyle\sum_{n=0}^{\infty} a_n$ and $\displaystyle\sum_{n=0}^{\infty} b_n$ converge,

$$\sum_{n=0}^{\infty} a_n + \sum_{n=0}^{\infty} b_n = \sum_{n=0}^{\infty} (a_n + b_n).$$

ANS.   Absolutely Convergent: Exercises 2, 4, 5, 7, 10, 11, 12, 14, 19, 21;
Simply Convergent: Exercises 1, 8, 9, 15, 16, 17, 18;
Divergent: Exercises 3, 6, 13, 20.

CHAPTER 6

Uniform Convergence

34. Series of Functions

Consider a series

$$(1) \qquad \sum_{n=0}^{\infty} u_n(x)$$

whose terms depend upon a parameter x, other than the running index n. The series (1) may converge for some values of x and diverge for others. For real x the series often converges for all x in an interval, or intervals; for complex x there may be a region of convergence, or more than one region.

Suppose x is real and the series (1) converges for all x in some closed interval $a \leq x \leq b$. The sum of the series will be, in general, a function of x,

$$(2) \qquad s(x) = \sum_{n=0}^{\infty} u_n(x), \qquad a \leq x \leq b.$$

It is natural to expect properties of the series, of its general term $u_n(x)$, or of its partial sums

$$(3) \qquad s_n(x) = \sum_{k=0}^{n} u_k(x),$$

to be reflected in properties of its sum-function $s(x)$, and vice-versa. Sometimes, as happens in solving linear differential equations by power series, we encounter a series and wish to study the function defined by that series. At other times, we have a function and wish to expand it into a series of stipulated type, as we shall in our study of Fourier series in Chapter 11.

If the general term $u_n(x)$ is a continuous function of x on the interval (a, b), it is reasonable to ask whether $s(x)$ is continuous and whether integration of the series term-by-term yields a series whose sum is the corresponding integral of $s(x)$. A similar question arises for term-by-term differentiation of the series. Sufficient conditions for a series to have the desired properties may be expressed simply in terms of uniform convergence, a concept to be defined in the next section.

35. Uniformly Convergent Series

Let the series

(1)
$$\sum_{n=0}^{\infty} u_n(x)$$

with partial sums

(2)
$$s_n(x) = \sum_{k=0}^{n} u_k(x)$$

converge to $s(x)$ on the closed interval $a \leq x \leq b$. For each x on the interval and for arbitrary positive ε, there exists an n_0, usually dependent upon both x and ε, such that

(3)
$$|s(x) - s_n(x)| < \varepsilon, \qquad \text{for all } n > n_0(\varepsilon, x).$$

If it is possible to replace the $n_0(\varepsilon, x)$ of (3) by an $n_1(\varepsilon)$, independent of x for all x on the closed interval, we call the convergence *uniform*. We now state a formal definition of uniform convergence both for sequences and for series.

DEFINITION. A sequence of functions $\{s_n(x)\}$ is *uniformly convergent* to the function $s(x)$ over the closed interval $a \leq x \leq b$ if, and only if, for arbitrary positive ε there exists an $n_1(\varepsilon)$, independent of x, such that

(4) $|s(x) - s_n(x)| < \varepsilon$,   for all $n > n_1(\varepsilon)$ and for all x on $a \leq x \leq b$.

A series is uniformly convergent over a closed interval if and only if the sequence of its partial sums is uniformly convergent over the interval.

Uniform convergence is equally well described by paralleling the Cauchy criteria, Theorems 9 and 9a, page 24, for convergence.

THEOREM 39. *A necessary and sufficient condition that the sequence $\{s_n(x)\}$ converge uniformly over the closed interval $a \leq x \leq b$ is that, for every positive ε, there exists an $n_1(\varepsilon)$, independent of x, such that*

(5) $$|s_n(x) - s_m(x)| < \varepsilon, \quad \text{for all } n > n_1(\varepsilon), \quad \text{and } m > n_1(\varepsilon),$$

and for all x on $a \leq x \leq b$.

We shall examine the concept of uniform convergence in detail. In constructing examples to illustrate the ideas involved, we stipulate the partial sums $s_n(x)$. The terms of the corresponding infinite series may be obtained from $u_0(x) = s_0(x)$,

(6) $$u_n(x) = s_n(x) - s_{n-1}(x), \qquad n \geq 1.$$

EXAMPLE (a). Consider, on the interval $0 \leq x \leq 1$, the series with partial sums

(7) $$s_n(x) = \frac{x}{nx + 1}.$$

It follows from (7) that

(8) $$s(x) = \lim_{n \to \infty} s_n(x) = 0, \qquad \text{for } 0 \leq x \leq 1.$$

Using $u_0(x) = s_0(x)$, and obtaining $u_n(x)$, $n \geq 1$, from (6), we find that the series being studied in this example is

(9) $$x - \sum_{n=1}^{\infty} \frac{x^2}{(nx + 1)(nx - x + 1)}.$$

Let us analyze the problem of choosing the n_1 of (4). We seek an n to lead us to the inequality

(10) $$\left| 0 - \frac{x}{nx + 1} \right| < \varepsilon, \qquad \text{for } 0 \leq x \leq 1.$$

For $x = 0$, (10) is satisfied for all non-negative n. For $x > 0$, (10) yields

$$x < \varepsilon(nx + 1),$$

or

$$n\varepsilon x > x - \varepsilon,$$

(11) $$n > \frac{1}{\varepsilon} - \frac{1}{x}, \qquad \varepsilon > 0, \quad 0 < x \leq 1.$$

From (11) we see that a natural choice for the $n_0(\varepsilon, x)$ of (3) would be

(12) $$n_0(\varepsilon, x) = \frac{1}{\varepsilon} - \frac{1}{x}, \qquad \varepsilon > 0, \quad 0 < x \leq 1,$$

$$n_0(\varepsilon, 0) = \frac{1}{\varepsilon}, \qquad \varepsilon > 0.$$

For $x = 0$, the choice is quite arbitrary, since $|0 - 0| < \varepsilon$, for any n. For all n greater than the n_0 of (12), reversal of the steps leading to (12) would yield (10) and thus demonstrate convergence of the series to the sum zero over the interval $0 \leq x \leq 1$.

To demonstrate uniform convergence we seek an n_1 independent of x and greater than, or equal to, the n_0 of (12) for all x on the interval $0 \leq x \leq 1$. We therefore choose

(13) $$n_1(\varepsilon) = \frac{1}{\varepsilon}$$

and proceed to prove the uniform convergence of the series on the interval $0 \leq x \leq 1$.

PROOF. For the series (9),

$$s_n(x) = \frac{x}{nx + 1} \quad \text{and} \quad s(x) = 0, \qquad \text{for } 0 \leq x \leq 1.$$

Given any $\varepsilon > 0$, then for all $n > \dfrac{1}{\varepsilon}$, it follows that

$$|s(0) - s_n(0)| = |0 - 0| < \varepsilon, \qquad \text{for } x = 0,$$

and, for $0 < x \leq 1$,

$$n > \frac{1}{\varepsilon}$$

yields

$$n > \frac{1}{\varepsilon} - \frac{1}{x},$$

from which

$$n\varepsilon x > x - \varepsilon,$$

or

$$x < \varepsilon nx + \varepsilon,$$

so

$$\frac{x}{nx+1} < \varepsilon.$$

Therefore

$$\left| 0 - \frac{x}{nx+1} \right| < \varepsilon.$$

We have shown that, given any $\varepsilon > 0$,

$$|s(x) - s_n(x)| < \varepsilon, \quad \text{for all } n > \frac{1}{\varepsilon} \quad \text{and all } x \text{ on } 0 \le x \le 1.$$

Since $\frac{1}{\varepsilon}$ is independent of x, we have proved that the series (9) is uniformly convergent over the closed interval $0 \le x \le 1$.

EXAMPLE (b). Consider, on the interval $0 \le x \le 1$, the series with partial sums

$$(14) \qquad\qquad s_n(x) = \frac{1}{nx+1},$$

the series

$$(15) \qquad\qquad 1 - \sum_{n=1}^{\infty} \frac{x}{(nx+1)(nx-x+1)}.$$

Here

$$\lim_{n \to \infty} s_n(x) = 1, \qquad \text{for } x = 0,$$

$$= 0, \qquad \text{for } 0 < x \le 1.$$

The sum function is the discontinuous one,

$$s(x) = 1, \qquad \text{for } x = 0,$$

$$= 0, \qquad \text{for } 0 < x \le 1.$$

Here the inequality implied by the existence of the limit of $s_n(x)$ as $n \to \infty$ is

$$(16) \qquad\qquad |1 - 1| < \varepsilon, \qquad \text{for } x = 0,$$

and

(17)
$$\left| 0 - \frac{1}{nx+1} \right| < \varepsilon, \qquad \text{for } 0 < x \leq 1.$$

The inequality in (16) holds for all non-negative n. The first inequality in (17) requires that

$$\frac{1}{nx+1} < \varepsilon,$$

or

$$1 < n\varepsilon x + \varepsilon,$$

from which we get

(18)
$$n > \frac{1-\varepsilon}{\varepsilon x}.$$

For convergence we may choose as our n_0 the right member of (18). For uniform convergence we would need an n_1 independent of x and such that $n > n_1$ would imply (18) for all x in $0 < x \leq 1$. But, for $\varepsilon < 1$, the right member of (19) $\to \infty$ as $x \to 0^+$, so the n_1 described does not exist. The series (15) is not uniformly convergent on the interval $0 \leq x \leq 1$.

The nonuniform convergence in this example is also easily demonstrated in the following way. Examine the inequality (17). No matter how large n may be, the choice $x = \dfrac{1}{n}$, an x in the range $0 < x \leq 1$, yields

$$\left| 0 - \frac{1}{nx+1} \right| = \left| 0 - \frac{1}{1+1} \right| = \frac{1}{2}.$$

But $\frac{1}{2}$ is not less than ε for all positive ε, although $\frac{1}{2}$ is less than ε for some positive ε. Thus no n_1 independent of x can be chosen to yield the desired inequality.

In Example (a), the difference between $s_n(x)$ and the sum function $s(x)$ can be made as small as we wish by choosing n sufficiently large for all x at once in the closed interval. In Example (b), x must be fixed first, then n can be chosen to make $s_n(x)$ as close as desired to $s(x)$; the nearer the positive x is to zero, the larger n must be to make $|s_n - s|$ arbitrarily small.

The series (15), of Example (b), is uniformly convergent in the closed interval $a \leq x \leq b$, if a is positive. See Exercise 1 on page 89.

It is particularly important to notice that uniform convergence is defined only for a closed interval in real variables, only for a closed region in complex variables. The theorems which make uniform convergence useful, Theorems 41–43 of Sections 38–40, would simply not be true if we permitted other than closed intervals.

Exercises

1. Show that the series of Example (b), with

$$s_n(x) = \frac{1}{nx + 1}$$

is uniformly convergent on the interval $a \leq x \leq b$, with $a > 0$. Hint: Choose

$$n_1 = \frac{|1 - \varepsilon|}{a\varepsilon}.$$

2. Show that the series with partial sums

$$s_n(x) = \frac{1}{n + x}$$

is uniformly convergent on the interval $0 \leq x \leq c$, c arbitrary positive.

3. Show that the series with partial sums

$$s_n(x) = \frac{\sin nx}{n}$$

is uniformly convergent on any closed interval, $a \leq x \leq b$.

4. Recall from calculus that $\lim\limits_{y \to \infty} [y \exp(-y)] = 0$. Show that the series

$$x + \sum_{n=1}^{\infty} x[n - (n - 1)e^x] \exp(-nx)$$

with partial sums

$$s_n(x) = x + nx \exp(-nx)$$

is convergent, but not uniformly convergent, on the interval

$$0 \leq x \leq c,$$

for arbitrary positive c.

5. Show that for $b > 0$, the series of Exercise 4 is uniformly convergent on the interval $b \leq x \leq c$.

6. Show that if

$$S_n(x) = nx \exp(-nx^2),$$

the series is not uniformly convergent on the interval $0 \leq x \leq 1$.

36. Graphical Interpretation

To understand more fully the distinction between uniform and nonuniform convergence, let us examine the graphical meaning involved. For simplicity, we focus our attention on the closed interval $0 \leq x \leq 1$. If a series with sum $s(x)$ and partial sums $s_n(x)$ is uniformly convergent on this interval, then

(1) $|s - s_n| < \varepsilon$,   for all $n > n_0(\varepsilon)$,   and all x on $0 \leq x \leq 1$.

Draw the curves

(2) $y = s(x)$, $y = s(x) - \varepsilon$, $y = s(x) + \varepsilon$,

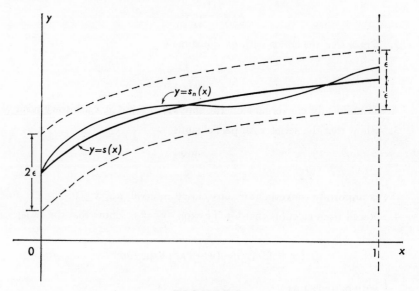

FIGURE 2

and thus get a band of vertical width (2ε) about the curve $y = s(x)$. No matter how small the positive number ε is made, the curves

(3) $y = s_n(x)$,   for all $n > n_0$,

lie within this band throughout the entire interval. See Figure 2.

For a series not uniformly convergent on the interval, no matter how large an n_0 is chosen, some curve (3) will go outside this band.

EXAMPLE (a). Consider a series for which

(4) $S_n(x) = nx \exp(-nx^2)$, $s(x) = 0$,   for $0 \leq x \leq 1$.

For this series the curves (3) become

(5) $$y = nx \exp(-nx^2).$$

Then

(6) $$y' = n(1 - 2nx^2) \exp(-nx^2).$$

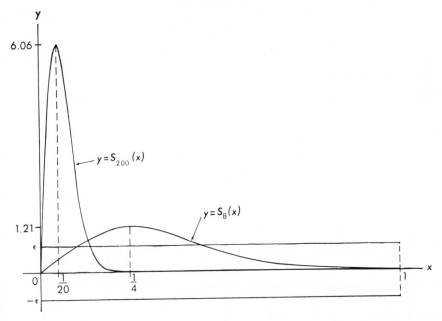

FIGURE 3

On the interval $0 \leq x \leq 1$, each curve (5) has one critical point, the point with coordinates

(7) $$x_c = \sqrt{\frac{1}{2n}}, \qquad y_c = \sqrt{\frac{n}{2}} \exp\left(-\frac{1}{2}\right).$$

Always $0 < x_c < 1$ and, as $n \to \infty$, $y_c \to \infty$. The curves (5) go outside the prescribed band, as shown in Figure 3.

Of course, the series still converges to zero on the interval, although the convergence is not uniform. For each fixed x,

$$\lim_{n \to \infty} [nx \exp(-nx^2)] = 0.$$

Hence, there is an n_1, dependent upon both ε and x, such that the curves (5) lie within the band of vertical width (2ε) for all $n > n_1$. But, the closer x is to zero, the greater the n_1 must be.

EXAMPLE (b). Consider a series for which

(8) $s_n(x) = nx \exp(-nx),$ $s(x) = 0,$ for $0 \leq x \leq 1.$

Again the series is not uniformly convergent on the stipulated interval. For the curves

(9)
$$y = nx \exp(-nx),$$
$$y' = n(1 - nx) \exp(-nx),$$
$$y'' = n^2(nx - 2) \exp(-nx).$$

Then (9) has a critical point at

$$x_c = \frac{1}{n}, \qquad y_c = \frac{1}{e} = 0.37,$$

and an inflection point at

$$x_i = \frac{2}{n}, \qquad y_i = \frac{2}{e^2} = 0.27.$$

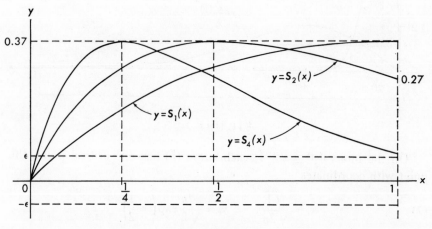

FIGURE 4

In spite of the fact that the curves (9) approach zero for each x on the interval $0 \leq x \leq 1$, each of the curves rises to the height $e^{-1} = 0.37$ as a maximum. That maximum occurs at $x_c = \frac{1}{n}$ and, as $n \to \infty$, $x_c \to 0$. The approximation curves (9) cannot be restricted to the band of width (2ε) for all x at once by choosing n sufficiently large. The nearer x is to zero, the larger n must be to bring the curve within the band.

37. The Weierstrass M-test

A simple and frequently useful sufficient condition for uniform convergence was given by Weierstrass nearly a century ago.

THEOREM 40 (Weierstrass M-test). *If there exists a convergent series* $\sum_{n=0}^{\infty} M_n$, *with* M_n *independent of* x, *such that* $|u_n(x)| \leq M_n$ *for all* x *on the closed interval* $a \leq x \leq b$, *then the series* $\sum_{n=0}^{\infty} u_n(x)$ *is absolutely and uniformly convergent on that interval.*

PROOF. Since $\sum_{n=0}^{\infty} M_n$ is a convergent series of positive terms and

$$(1) \qquad |u_n(x)| \leq M_n, \qquad \text{for } a \leq x \leq b,$$

$$(2) \qquad \sum_{n=0}^{\infty} u_n(x)$$

is absolutely convergent for all x on $a \leq x \leq b$ by a comparison test.

Let the partial sums of the series

$$(3) \qquad s(x) = \sum_{n=0}^{\infty} u_n(x) \quad \text{and} \quad T = \sum_{n=0}^{\infty} M_n$$

be

$$(4) \qquad s_n(x) = \sum_{k=0}^{n} u_k(x) \quad \text{and} \quad T_n = \sum_{k=0}^{n} M_k,$$

respectively. Since M_n is independent of x and the second series in (3) is convergent, we know that for any $\varepsilon > 0$, there exists an n_1, independent of x, such that

$$(5) \qquad |T - T_n| < \varepsilon, \qquad \text{for } n > n_1(\varepsilon).$$

Now for all x on $a \leq x \leq b$, we conclude from (1) and the convergence of the series involved, that

$$(6) \quad |s(x) - s_n(x)| = \left| \sum_{k=n+1}^{\infty} u_k(x) \right| \leq \sum_{k=n+1}^{\infty} |u_k(x)| \leq \sum_{k=n+1}^{\infty} M_k = |T - T_n|.$$

The inequalities (5) and (6) yield, for all x on $a \leq x \leq b$,

$$(7) \qquad |s(x) - s_n(x)| < \varepsilon, \qquad \text{for } n > n_1(\varepsilon).$$

Therefore, the series (2) is also uniformly convergent on the closed interval $a \leq x \leq b$.

Exercises

Use the Weierstrass M-test to demonstrate uniform convergence in each exercise. If the interval is not stipulated, it is to be an arbitrary closed interval, $a \leq x \leq b$.

1. $\displaystyle\sum_{n=1}^{\infty} \frac{1}{n^2 + x^2}$.

2. $\displaystyle\sum_{n=0}^{\infty} \frac{(-1)^n x^{2n}}{(2n)!}$.

3. $\displaystyle\sum_{n=0}^{\infty} \frac{x^n}{n!}$.

4. $\displaystyle\sum_{n=0}^{\infty} \frac{(-1)^n x^{2n+1}}{(2n+1)!}$.

5. $\displaystyle\sum_{n=0}^{\infty} (-1)^n x^{2n}, \quad -b \leq x \leq b < 1$.

6. $\displaystyle\frac{\pi^2}{3} + 4 \sum_{n=1}^{\infty} \frac{(-1)^n \cos nx}{n^2}$.

7. $\displaystyle\frac{c^4}{5} + 8c^4 \sum_{n=1}^{\infty} (-1)^n \frac{n^2 \pi^2 - 6}{n^4 \pi^4} \cos \frac{n\pi x}{c}$.

8. $\displaystyle\frac{8c^2}{\pi^3} \sum_{k=0}^{\infty} \frac{\sin[(2k+1)nx/c]}{(2k+1)^3}$.

9. $\displaystyle\frac{1}{2} + \frac{4}{\pi^2} \sum_{n=1}^{\infty} \frac{1}{n^2}\left[2 \cos \frac{n\pi}{2} - 1 - (-1)^n\right] \cos \frac{n\pi x}{2}$.

10. $\displaystyle\frac{8}{\pi} \sum_{k=0}^{\infty} \frac{\cos[(2k+1)x]}{(2k-1)(2k+3)}$.

38. Continuity

Uniform convergence of a series of continuous functions on a closed interval is sufficient to make the sum of the series also a continuous function on that interval.

THEOREM 41. *If the functions $u_n(x)$ are continuous on the closed interval $a \leq x \leq b$, and if the series*

$$(1) \qquad\qquad\qquad \sum_{n=0}^{\infty} u_n(x)$$

converges uniformly on that interval to a sum function $s(x)$, then $s(x)$ is continuous on $a \leq x \leq b$.

PROOF. Let the partial sum of the series (1) be

$$(2) \qquad s_n(x) = \sum_{k=0}^{n} u_k(x).$$

From the uniform convergence of the series (1) to the sum $s(x)$ it follows that given any $\varepsilon_1 > 0$, there exists an $n_1 = n_1(\varepsilon_1)$ such that

$(3) \quad |s_n(x) - s(x)| < \varepsilon_1$, for all $n > n_1(\varepsilon_1)$ and all x on $a \leq x \leq b$,

and, of course

$(4) \quad |s_n(y) - s(y)| < \varepsilon_1$, for all $n > n_1(\varepsilon_1)$ and all y on $a \leq y \leq b$.

From the continuity of the $u_k(x)$ on $a \leq x \leq b$, the continuity of the finite sum $s_n(x)$ of (2) follows at once. That is, given any $\varepsilon_2 > 0$, there exists a $\delta_2 = \delta_2(\varepsilon_2)$ such that

$(5) \quad |s_n(x) - s_n(y)| < \varepsilon_2$, for all x, y in $0 < |x - y| < \delta_2$,

$$a \leq x \leq b, \quad a \leq y \leq b.$$

Now, given any $\varepsilon > 0$, choose $\varepsilon_1 = \dfrac{\varepsilon}{3}$ in (3) and (4) and $\varepsilon_2 = \dfrac{\varepsilon}{3}$ in (5).

Then for any $\varepsilon > 0$, there exists an $n_0 = n_1\left(\dfrac{\varepsilon}{3}\right)$ and a $\delta = \delta_2\left(\dfrac{\varepsilon}{3}\right)$ such that

$(6) \qquad |s_n(x) - s(x)| < \dfrac{\varepsilon}{3}$, for all $n > n_0$ and all x on $a \leq x \leq b$,

and

$(7) \qquad |s_n(y) - s(y)| < \dfrac{\varepsilon}{3}$, for all $n > n_0$ and all y on $a \leq y \leq b$,

$(8) \quad |s_n(x) - s_n(y)| < \dfrac{\varepsilon}{3}$, for all $n > n_0$, $0 < |x - y| < \delta$,

$$a \leq x \leq b, \quad a \leq y \leq b.$$

From (6), (7), and (8) we get

$$|s(x) - s(y)| = |\{s_n(y) - s(y)\} - \{s_n(x) - s(x)\} + \{s_n(x) - s_n(y)\}|$$

$$< \frac{\varepsilon}{3} + \frac{\varepsilon}{3} + \frac{\varepsilon}{3},$$

so

$(9) \quad |s(x) - s(y)| < \varepsilon$, for $0 < |x - y| < \delta$, $a \leq x \leq b$, $a \leq y \leq b$.

The inequality (9) means that

(10) $$\lim_{x \to y} s(x) = s(y), \qquad \text{for all } a \leq y \leq b.$$

It is necessary to restrict x to the closed interval; that is, for y at either endpoint, $y = a$ or $y = b$, the approach must be the one-sided approach from inside the closed interval. A purist would write (10) in three parts:

(10′) $$\lim_{x \to y} s(x) = s(y), \qquad \text{for } a < y < b,$$

$$\lim_{x \to a^+} s(x) = s(a),$$

$$\lim_{x \to b^-} s(x) = s(b).$$

Equation (10) is the result stated in Theorem 41; the sum of the limits $s(y)$ exists, the limit of the sum $s(x)$ exists, and the two are equal. Thus $s(x)$ is continuous on $a \leq x \leq b$.

The theorem may be reworded thus: If

(11) $$\sum_{n=0}^{\infty} u_n(x)$$

converges uniformly to the sum $s(x)$ on the interval $a \leq x \leq b$, and if each $u_n(x)$ is continuous on the interval, then $s(x)$ is continuous on the same interval.

We thus obtain, under the conditions of Theorem 41,

(12) $$\lim_{x \to y} \sum_{n=0}^{\infty} u_n(x) = \sum_{n=0}^{\infty} \lim_{x \to y} u_n(x), \qquad \text{for } a \leq x \leq b, \quad a \leq y \leq b.$$

Equation (12) may also be written in the form

(13) $$\lim_{x \to y} \lim_{n \to \infty} s_n(x) = \lim_{n \to \infty} \lim_{x \to y} s_n(x), \qquad \text{for } a \leq y \leq b,$$

the equation being valid if the $u_n(x)$ are continuous on $a \leq x \leq b$ and $\sum_{n=0}^{\infty} u_n(x)$ is uniformly convergent on $a \leq x \leq b$.

We shall consider three examples related to Theorem 41. Example (a) exhibits a series to which the theorem is applicable. Example (b) shows that the theorem is not trivial; there exist nonuniformly convergent series of continuous functions with discontinuous sum functions. Example (c) shows that the conditions in the theorem, although sufficient, are not necessary; there exist nonuniformly convergent series of continuous functions with continuous sum functions.

EXAMPLE (a). Consider the series

(14) $$x - \sum_{n=1}^{\infty} \frac{x^2}{(nx+1)(nx-x+1)}$$

of Example (a), page 85. The series (14) is a telescoping series with

$$s_n(x) = \frac{x}{nx+1}.$$

We showed that (14) is uniformly convergent on $0 \leq x \leq 1$. The general term is continuous over that same interval. By Theorem 41, the sum function must also be continuous on the interval. We found that (14) has the sum $s(x) = 0$, thus yielding an illustration of the theorem of this section.

EXAMPLE (b). Consider, on the interval $0 \leq x \leq 1$, the series with partial sum

(15) $$s_n(x) = \frac{nx-1}{nx+1}.$$

The terms of the series, namely $s_0(x)$ and $[s_n(x) - s_{n-1}(x)]$ for $n \geq 1$, are all continuous on the interval $0 \leq x \leq 1$. From (15) we find the sum of the series to be

$$s(x) = -1, \qquad \text{for } x = 0,$$
$$= +1, \qquad \text{for } 0 < x \leq 1.$$

The sum function is discontinuous at $x = 0$. The series, of course, is not uniformly convergent. Note that

$$s(x) - s_n(x) = 0, \qquad\qquad \text{for } x = 0$$
$$= \frac{2}{nx+1}, \qquad \text{for } 0 < x \leq 1.$$

We cannot make $|s - s_n| < \varepsilon$ for $n > n_0(\varepsilon)$, independent of x on the whole closed interval, because the choice $x = \frac{1}{n}$ gives

$$s\left(\frac{1}{n}\right) - s_n\left(\frac{1}{n}\right) = \frac{2}{1+1} = 1,$$

which cannot be made arbitrarily small.

EXAMPLE (c). Consider the series with partial sum

(16) $$s_n(x) = nx \exp(-nx), \qquad 0 \leq x \leq b, \quad b > 0.$$

Here it follows rapidly from (16) that

(17) $s(x) = 0,$ for all x on $0 \leq x \leq b.$

The sum function is continuous on the closed interval. But the series with partial sum (16) is not uniformly convergent on that interval because the choice $x = \dfrac{1}{n}$ yields

$$\left| s\left(\frac{1}{n}\right) - s_n\left(\frac{1}{n}\right) \right| = 1 \cdot e^{-1}$$

which cannot be made arbitrarily small by choosing n large. Therefore, nonuniformity of convergence of a series of continuous functions does not necessarily force discontinuity of the sum function.

39. Term-by-Term Integration

Uniform convergence of a series of continuous functions on a closed interval is sufficient to guarantee that term-by-term integration within that interval is legitimate; the series of integrals will converge to the corresponding integral of the sum function.

THEOREM 42. *If the functions $u_n(x)$ are continuous over the closed interval $a \leq x \leq b$, and if the series*

(1) $$\sum_{n=0}^{\infty} u_n(x)$$

converges uniformly on that interval to a sum function $s(x)$, then

(2) $$\int_a^x s(\beta)\, d\beta = \sum_{n=0}^{\infty} \int_a^x u_n(\beta)\, d\beta, \qquad for\ a \leq x \leq b.$$

Once the theorem has been established, it follows at once that (2) is valid with the limits of integration replaced by any two x-values on the interval (a, b):

(3) $$\int_{x_1}^{x_2} s(\beta)\, d\beta = \sum_{n=0}^{\infty} \int_{x_1}^{x_2} u_n(\beta)\, d\beta, \qquad for\ a \leq x_1 \leq b, \quad a \leq x_2 \leq b.$$

As usual, let the partial sum of the series (1) be

(4) $$s_n(x) = \sum_{k=0}^{n} u_k(x).$$

Because (1) is uniformly convergent on $a \leq x \leq b$, we know that given any $\varepsilon_0 > 0$, there exists an $n_0 = n_0(\varepsilon_0)$, independent of x, such that

(5) $\quad |s(x) - s_n(x)| < \varepsilon_0$,	for all $n > n_0(\varepsilon_0)$,	and all x on $a \leq x \leq b$.

Since $u_k(x)$ is continuous on the interval, $s(x)$ is continuous on the interval, by Theorem 41, and $s_n(x)$ is continuous on the interval because it is a finite sum. Then both $s(x)$ and $s_n(x)$ are integrable over the interval.

Given any $\varepsilon > 0$, choose $\varepsilon_0 = \dfrac{\varepsilon}{x - a}$ for any fixed x on $a < x \leq b$. Then

$$n_0(\varepsilon_0) = n_1(\varepsilon_0, x)$$

and, by (5), for all $n > n_1(\varepsilon_0, x)$.

(6) $\quad |s(\beta) - s_n(\beta)| < \dfrac{\varepsilon}{x - a}$,	for all β on $a \leq \beta \leq b$, and all x on $a < x \leq b$.

Therefore, by (6), for all $n > n_1$, and for fixed x on $a < x \leq b$,

(7) $\quad \left| \displaystyle\int_a^x s(\beta)\, d\beta - \sum_{k=0}^{n} \int_a^x u_k(\beta)\, d\beta \right| = \left| \displaystyle\int_a^x s(\beta)\, d\beta - \int_a^x s_n(\beta)\, d\beta \right|$

$$\leq \int_a^x |s(\beta) - s_n(\beta)|\, d\beta$$

$$< \int_a^x \frac{\varepsilon}{x - a}\, d\beta = \varepsilon.$$

At $x = a$ the left member of (7) is zero, so $x = a$ also fits into the inequality. Thus, for fixed x on $a \leq x \leq b$ and for all $n > n_1$,

(8) $\quad \left| \displaystyle\int_a^x s(\beta)\, d\beta - \sum_{k=0}^{n} \int_a^x u_k(\beta)\, d\beta \right| < \varepsilon.$

Therefore

$$\lim_{n \to \infty} \sum_{k=0}^{n} \int_a^x u_k(\beta)\, d\beta = \int_a^x s(\beta)\, d\beta,$$

which means

(9) $\quad \displaystyle\sum_{n=0}^{\infty} \int_a^x u_n(\beta)\, d\beta = \int_a^x s(\beta)\, d\beta,$	for $a \leq x \leq b$.

That is, a series of continuous functions uniformly convergent on a closed interval may be integrated term-by-term and the sum of the resulting series is the corresponding integral of the sum function.

Note that (9) is equivalent to

(10) $$\lim_{n\to\infty} \int_a^x s_n(\beta)\, d\beta = \int_a^x \lim_{n\to\infty} s_n(\beta)\, d\beta, \qquad a \leq x \leq b.$$

Equation (10) is a convenient form for testing whether a given series is term-by-term integrable on the specified interval.

EXAMPLE (a). Consider the series of Example (a), page 85, for which

(11) $$s_n(x) = \frac{x}{nx+1}, \qquad s(x) = 0, \qquad \text{on } 0 \leq x \leq 1.$$

On the interval $0 \leq x \leq 1$,

(12) $$\int_0^x s(\beta)\, d\beta = 0,$$

$$\int_0^x s_n(\beta)\, d\beta = \int_0^x \frac{\beta\, d\beta}{n\beta+1} = \frac{1}{n}\int_0^x \left[1 - \frac{1}{n\beta+1}\right] d\beta$$

$$= \frac{1}{n}\left[\beta - \frac{1}{n}\ln(n\beta+1)\right]_0^x = \frac{1}{n}\left[x - \frac{1}{n}\ln(nx+1)\right].$$

Then

$$\lim_{n\to\infty} \int_0^x s_n(\beta)\, d\beta = 0 = \int_0^x s(\beta)\, d\beta;$$

an illustration of Theorem 42.

EXAMPLE (b). Consider, on the interval $0 \leq x \leq b$, $b > 0$, the series with partial sum

(13) $$s_n(x) = nx \exp(-nx^2).$$

At once we get

(14) $$s(x) = 0, \qquad \text{on } 0 \leq x \leq b,$$

(15) $$|s(x) - s_n(x)| = nx \exp(-nx^2), \qquad \text{on } 0 \leq x \leq b.$$

Choose $x = \dfrac{1}{\sqrt{n}}$ to see that

(16) $$\left| s\left(\frac{1}{\sqrt{n}}\right) - s_n\left(\frac{1}{\sqrt{n}}\right) \right| = \sqrt{n}\, \exp(-1)$$

which cannot be made arbitrarily small by choosing n large. The series is not uniformly convergent on $0 \leq x \leq b$.

Next note that

$$\int_0^x \lim_{n \to \infty} s_n(\beta)\, d\beta = \int_0^x s(\beta)\, d\beta = \int_0^x 0 \cdot d\beta = 0, \qquad \text{for } 0 \leq x \leq b,$$

but that

$$\lim_{n \to \infty} \int_0^x s_n(\beta)\, d\beta = \lim_{n \to \infty} \int_0^x n\beta \exp(-n\beta^2)\, d\beta = \lim_{n \to \infty} \left[-\tfrac{1}{2} \exp(-n\beta^2) \right]_0^x$$

$$= \lim_{n \to \infty} [\tfrac{1}{2} - \tfrac{1}{2} \exp(-nx^2)] = \tfrac{1}{2}, \qquad \text{for } 0 < x \leq b.$$

Therefore, the series is not "term-by-term integrable"; that is, the sum of the integrals is not the integral of the sum. Theorem 42 is not trivial.

EXAMPLE (c). Consider, on $0 \leq x \leq 1$, the series with partial sum

$$(17) \qquad\qquad s_n(x) = \frac{nx - 1}{nx + 1},$$

the series of Example (b), page 97.

We know the series is not uniformly convergent on the interval stipulated. We also know the sum function,

$$(18) \qquad\qquad s(x) = -1, \qquad \text{for } x = 0,$$

$$= +1, \qquad \text{for } 0 < x \leq 1.$$

Now

$$\int_0^x s(\beta)\, d\beta = \int_0^x 1 \cdot d\beta = x, \qquad \text{on } 0 \leq x \leq 1.$$

Also

$$\lim_{n \to \infty} \int_0^x s_n(\beta)\, d\beta = \lim_{n \to \infty} \int_0^x \frac{n\beta - 1}{n\beta + 1}\, d\beta$$

$$= \lim_{n \to \infty} \int_0^x \left[1 - \frac{2}{n\beta + 1} \right] d\beta$$

$$= \lim_{n \to \infty} \left[\beta - \frac{2}{n} \ln(n\beta + 1) \right]_0^x$$

$$= \lim_{n \to \infty} \left[x - \frac{2}{n} \ln(nx + 1) \right] = x, \qquad \text{on } 0 \leq x \leq 1.$$

Hence, although this series of continuous functions is not uniformly convergent on the interval specified, it is term-by-term integrable on that interval. Theorem 42 furnishes sufficient, but not necessary, conditions for term-by-term integration.

40. Term-by-Term Differentiation

Uniform convergence of a series has no bearing on its term-by-term differentiability, but differentiation is the inverse of integration, so we naturally try inverting our conditions. That is, we impose uniformity of convergence on the series of derivatives. But the sum of the series of derivatives must be integrated if we are to return to the original series. If we add the condition that the derivatives of the terms be continuous, the sum function will be continuous and therefore integrable.

THEOREM 43. *If $u_n(x)$ is such that $u_n'(x)$ is continuous on the interval $a \leq x \leq b$, if $\sum\limits_{n=0}^{\infty} u_n'(x)$ is uniformly convergent on the interval $a \leq x \leq b$, and if $\sum\limits_{n=0}^{\infty} u_n(x)$ converges to $s(x)$, then $\sum\limits_{n=0}^{\infty} u_n'(x)$ converges to $s'(x)$ for all x on $a \leq x \leq b$.*

Let us restate Theorem 43 in the following form: If

$$(1) \qquad \sum_{n=0}^{\infty} u_n(x) \text{ converges on } a \leq x \leq b,$$

and if

$$(2) \qquad u_n'(x) \text{ is continuous on } a \leq x \leq b \quad \text{(for all } n\text{)},$$

and if

$$(3) \qquad \sum_{n=0}^{\infty} u_n'(x) \text{ is uniformly convergent on } a \leq x \leq b,$$

then

$$(4) \qquad \sum_{n=0}^{\infty} u_n'(x) = \left(\sum_{n=0}^{\infty} u_n(x) \right)', \qquad \text{on } a \leq x \leq b.$$

PROOF. We are given that the series

$$(5) \qquad \sum_{n=0}^{\infty} u_n(x)$$

with partial sum

$$s_n(x) = \sum_{k=0}^{n} u_k(x)$$

converges to $s(x)$. We are also given that

(6)
$$\sum_{n=0}^{\infty} u_n'(x)$$

converges uniformly on $a \leq x \leq b$. The sum of the series (6) is continuous on the interval $a \leq x \leq b$ by Theorem 41. Hence the sum of (6) may be integrated on the interval, so the sum is the derivative of some function $g(x)$. We may therefore call the sum of the series (6) $g'(x)$ for ease in indicating its indefinite integral,

(7)
$$g'(x) = \sum_{n=0}^{\infty} u_n'(x), \qquad a \leq x \leq b.$$

We wish to prove that $g'(x) = s'(x)$. Because each of the $u_n'(x)$ in (7) is continuous on $a \leq x \leq b$, we may use Theorem 42 to conclude that

(8)
$$\sum_{n=0}^{\infty} \int_{a}^{x} u_n'(\beta) \, d\beta = \int_{a}^{x} g'(\beta) \, d\beta.$$

From (8) we get

(9)
$$\sum_{n=0}^{\infty} [u_n(x) - u_n(a)] = g(x) - g(a).$$

For x on the interval $a \leq x \leq b$, the convergence of (5) to $s(x)$ permits us to write from (9), the identity

(10)
$$s(x) - s(a) = g(x) - g(a).$$

From (10) it follows that $g'(x) = s'(x)$, so the proof is complete.

41. Hardy's Test

In our study of power series, we shall make use of a special case of a test for uniform convergence devised by Hardy.* The following lemma, due to N. H. Abel (1802–1829), will facilitate our proof of the validity of Hardy's test.

* G. H. Hardy, 1877–1947. For the more general test given by Hardy, see E. T. Whittaker and G. N. Watson, *Modern Analysis*, 4th ed., Cambridge, Cambridge University Press, 1927, p. 50.

LEMMA 7. *If $0 \leq v_{k+1} \leq v_k$, if $B_t = \sum\limits_{k=0}^{t} b_k$, and if B is the maximum of $|B_k|$ for $k = 0, 1, 2, \ldots, t$, then*

(1)
$$\left| \sum_{k=0}^{t} b_k v_k \right| \leq B v_0 .$$

PROOF. Since $b_0 = B_0$ and $b_k = B_k - B_{k-1}$ for $k \geq 1$, we may write

$$\sum_{k=0}^{t} b_k v_k = B_0 v_0 + \sum_{k=1}^{t} (B_k - B_{k-1}) v_k$$

$$= \sum_{k=0}^{t} B_k v_k - \sum_{k=1}^{t} B_{k-1} v_k$$

$$= \sum_{k=0}^{t} B_k v_k - \sum_{k=0}^{t-1} B_k v_{k+1}$$

$$= B_t v_t + \sum_{k=0}^{t-1} B_k (v_k - v_{k+1}).$$

Now $v_t \geq 0$, $(v_k - v_{k+1}) \geq 0$, and B is the maximum of all $|B_k|$ involved. Hence,

(2)
$$\left| \sum_{k=0}^{t} b_k v_k \right| \leq B v_t + \sum_{k=0}^{t-1} B(v_k - v_{k+1}).$$

The series on the right in (2) telescopes,

$$B v_t + \sum_{k=0}^{t-1} B(v_k - v_{k+1}) = B v_0 ,$$

so, by (2),

$$\left| \sum_{k=0}^{t} b_k v_k \right| \leq B v_0.$$

THEOREM 44 (Hardy's test). *If the series of constants*

(3)
$$\sum_{n=0}^{\infty} c_n$$

converges, and if

(4) $0 \leq u_{n+1}(x) \leq u_n(x) \leq M,$ *for all x on $a \leq x \leq b$,*

with M independent of n and x, then

(5)
$$\sum_{n=0}^{\infty} c_n u_n(x)$$

converges uniformly on $a \leq x \leq b$.

PROOF. Let

(6)
$$s_n(x) = \sum_{k=0}^{n} c_k u_k(x)$$

and

(7)
$$A_n = \sum_{k=0}^{n} c_k.$$

Given any $\varepsilon_1 > 0$, the convergence of (3) implies that there exists an n_0, necessarily independent of x because the c_n are constants, such that

(8) $|A_n - A_m| < \varepsilon_1,$ for all $n > n_0(\varepsilon_1)$ and $m > n_0(\varepsilon_1).$

Let $n > m$ for convenience. From (6) we obtain

$$s_n(x) - s_m(x) = \sum_{k=m+1}^{n} c_k u_k(x) = \sum_{k=0}^{n-m-1} c_{k+m+1} u_{k+m+1}(x).$$

In Lemma 7, choose $b_k = c_{k+m+1}$, $v_k = u_{k+m+1}(x)$, and $t = n - m - 1$. Because of (4), the conditions of the lemma are satisfied and it follows that, for $n > m > n_0(\varepsilon_1)$,

$$|s_n(x) - s_m(x)| = \left| \sum_{k=0}^{n-m-1} c_{k+m+1} u_{k+m+1}(x) \right| \leq u_{m+1}(x) \cdot \text{Max}|A_n - A_m|,$$

so

$$|s_n(x) - s_m(x)| < M\varepsilon_1.$$

Now choose $\varepsilon_1 = \dfrac{\varepsilon}{M}$ and note that $n_1(\varepsilon) = n_0\left(\dfrac{\varepsilon}{M}\right)$ is independent of x. We find that

(9) $|s_n(x) - s_m(x)| < \varepsilon,$ for $n > m > n_1(\varepsilon),$ and for all x on $a \leq x \leq b.$

Thus the series (5) converges uniformly on $a \leq x \leq b.$

Exercises

In Exercises 1–3, show that term-by-term integration and differentiation are legitimate on any closed x-interval.

1. $\displaystyle\sum_{n=0}^{\infty} \frac{x^n}{n!}.$

2. $\displaystyle\sum_{n=0}^{\infty} \frac{(-1)^n x^{2n}}{(2n)!}.$

3. $\displaystyle\sum_{n=0}^{\infty} \frac{(-1)^n x^{2n+1}}{(2n+1)!}$.

4. A series has the partial sums

$$s_n(x) = e^{-nx} \sin nx.$$

Show that this series is not uniformly convergent on $0 \leq x \leq 1$, but that term-by-term integration of the series is legitimate.

5. On the interval $0 \leq x \leq 1$, define $\varphi(x)$ by

$$\varphi(x) = \sum_{n=1}^{\infty} \frac{x^n}{n(n^2+4)}.$$

Show that, on $0 \leq x \leq 1$,

$$x\varphi'(x) = \sum_{n=1}^{\infty} \frac{x^n}{n^2+4}.$$

6. For the series of Exercise 8, page 94, show that term-by-term differentiation is legitimate. See also Exercise 7, page 199.

In Exercises 7–9 show that the given series is term-by-term integrable over any closed interval.

7. $\displaystyle\frac{8}{\pi^2} \sum_{k=0}^{\infty} \frac{(-1)^k}{(2k+1)^2} \sin \frac{(2k+1)\pi x}{2}$.

See Exercise 8, page 199.

8. $\displaystyle\frac{1-e^{-c}}{c} + 2c \sum_{n=1}^{\infty} \frac{1-(-1)^n e^{-c}}{c^2+n^2\pi^2} \cos \frac{n\pi x}{c}$.

See Exercise 12, page 204.

9. $\displaystyle\frac{c^3}{4} + \frac{6c^3}{\pi^2} \sum_{n=1}^{\infty} \left[\frac{(-1)^n}{n^2} + \frac{2}{\pi^2} \cdot \frac{1-(-1)^n}{n^4} \right] \cos \frac{n\pi x}{c}$.

See Exercise 15, page 204.

In Exercises 10–12 test each series for uniform convergence on the interval $0 \leq x \leq 1$.

10. $\displaystyle\sum_{n=0}^{\infty} \frac{x^2}{(x^2+1)^n}$.

11. $\displaystyle\sum_{n=0}^{\infty} \frac{1}{(n+x)^2}$.

12. $\displaystyle\sum_{n=0}^{\infty} [x^n(1-x)]$.

13. Use your knowledge of geometric series to find the sum of

$$\sum_{n=0}^{\infty} (-1)^n x^{2n}, \qquad \text{for } 0 \leq x \leq c < 1.$$

Show that term-by-term integration of the series is legitimate and thus arrive at

$$\text{Arctan } x = \sum_{n=0}^{\infty} \frac{(-1)^n x^{2n+1}}{2n+1}, \qquad 0 \leq x \leq c < 1.$$

14. Suppose the power series $\sum_{n=0}^{\infty} a_n x^n$ is known to be absolutely convergent for $x = R$. Show that a function $f(x)$ is defined by

$$f(x) = \sum_{n=0}^{\infty} a_n x^n, \qquad -R \leq x \leq R,$$

that $f(x)$ is continuous on the interval, that

$$f(R) = \sum_{n=0}^{\infty} a_n R^n,$$

and obtain a series that converges to $\int_0^x f(\beta) \, d\beta$.

CHAPTER **7**

Power Series

42. Two Fundamental Problems

A *power series* is a series of the form

(1)
$$\sum_{n=0}^{\infty} a_n x^n$$

or

(2)
$$\sum_{n=0}^{\infty} b_n (x - a)^n,$$

in which $\{a_n\}$ and $\{b_n\}$ may, of course, have subsequences with all elements zero. At times, the term power series is extended to include series similar to (1) and (2) but with the range of the index of summation extended to include some or all negative integers.

Two problems appear at once. If a specific power series converges for some set of x-values, the series may be used to define a function, the sum of the series. Then we are confronted with the problem of obtaining properties of the function from properties of the series. On the other hand, we may have a function given, with some of its properties already known, and wish to expand the function into a power series, to find a power series that converges to the function for some set of x-values. Much of our work in this and the next two chapters is concerned with these two problems.

We shall use power series to define certain nonelementary functions. On page 156 we define the hypergeometric function by its power series and, on page 163, a Bessel function in a similar manner.

43. Convergence of Power Series

A power series

$$(1) \qquad \sum_{n=0}^{\infty} b_n(x-a)^n$$

may converge only at $x = a$, or for all finite x, or in an interval symmetric about $x = a$ (for complex x, within a circle centered at $x = a$) as we shall prove in this section.

THEOREM 45. *If the power series* (1) *converges at* $x - a = x_0$, $x_0 \neq 0$, *the series is absolutely convergent for all x in* $|x - a| < |x_0|$ *and uniformly convergent in* $|x - a| \leq r|x_0|$ *for every r in* $0 < r < 1$.

If (1) converges at $(x - a) = x_0$, then $b_n x_0^n \to 0$, as $n \to \infty$. A null sequence is bounded, so a constant M exists such that

$$(2) \qquad |b_n x_0^n| \leq M.$$

For any fixed x in the interval (circular region for complex x)

$$(3) \qquad |x - a| < |x_0|,$$

there exists an r such that

$$(4) \qquad \left| \frac{x-a}{x_0} \right| \leq r < 1.$$

We now compare the series

$$(5) \qquad \sum_{n=0}^{\infty} |b_n(x-a)^n|$$

with the series

$$(6) \qquad \sum_{n=0}^{\infty} M r^n.$$

The geometric series (6) is a series of positive terms independent of x and the series converges because $r < 1$.

In the entire closed interval (or region)

$$(7) \qquad |x - a| \leq r|x_0|$$

we have, by (2) and (4),

$$|b_n(x-a)^n| = |b_n x_0^n| \cdot \left| \frac{x-a}{x_0} \right|^n \leq M r^n,$$

so the series (1) is absolutely and uniformly convergent in the closed interval (region) (7) by the Weierstrass M-test, page 93. This completes the proof of Theorem 45.

Suppose the series

$$(8) \qquad \sum_{n=0}^{\infty} b_n(x-a)^n$$

converges for at least one $x \neq a$, that it converges for $x - a = x_0$. By Theorem 45, there exists an open interval (or region)

$$|x - a| < |x_0|$$

in which (8) is absolutely convergent. If (8) is absolutely convergent for any value of $|x - a|$, it is absolutely convergent for all smaller values of $|x - a|$ by a comparison test. Therefore, unless (8) is absolutely convergent for all finite x, we have a sectioning of the positive numbers $|x - a|$ into a left class for which (8) is absolutely convergent and a right class for which (8) is not absolutely convergent. Thus a number R is defined such that (8) is absolutely convergent for all $|x - a| < R$ and not absolutely convergent, for all $|x - a| > R$. It follows quickly that (8) diverges for $|x - a| > R$, because if (8) converges for some x for which $|x - a| = R + \delta$, $\delta > 0$, then (8) would be absolutely convergent for $|x - a| = R + \frac{1}{2}\delta$, contrary to the definition of R. The number R is called the *radius of convergence* of the power series.

THEOREM 46. *The power series*

$$(8) \qquad \sum_{n=0}^{\infty} b_n(x-a)^n$$

either

(A) *Converges only at $x = a$,*

or

(B) *Converges absolutely and uniformly in every finite closed interval (or region),*

or

(C) *There exists a positive number R such that (8) is absolutely convergent for all $|x - a| < R$, and divergent for all $|x - a| > R$, and is uniformly convergent in the closed interval (or region) $|x - a| \leq r < R$.*

The statements about uniform convergence in Theorem 46 follow directly from Theorem 45. Note that Theorem 46 says nothing about convergence behavior on $|x - a| = R$, the circumference of the circle of convergence if x is complex, the endpoints of the interval of convergence if x is real. On the boundary $|x - a| = R$, the series may diverge, may converge for some x and diverge for others, or may be absolutely convergent for all $|x - a| = R$.

We must exhibit examples to show that parts (A) and (B) of Theorem 46 are not concerned with empty sets. Examples (a) and (b) of this section show just that, as do several of the exercises at the end of the section.

Another method for defining the radius of convergence R is to use the concept of upper limit of a bounded sequence, page 23. If the sequence $\{\sqrt[n]{|b_n|}\}$ is unbounded, the series diverges for all $x \neq a$. If the sequence is bounded, it has an upper limit and we define R by

$$(9) \qquad\qquad \frac{1}{R} = \varlimsup_{n \to \infty} \sqrt[n]{|b_n|}.$$

From (9) we get

$$(10) \qquad\qquad \lim_{n \to \infty} \sqrt[n]{|b_n(x - a)^n|} = \frac{|x - a|}{R}$$

and Theorem 46 follows with a little argument.

In Chapters 8 and 9, we shall make extensive use of the fact that power series are absolutely and uniformly convergent in any closed interval within the interval of convergence, the result stated in Theorem 46.

In determining where specific power series converge the most commonly useful test is D'Alembert's ratio test, Theorem 30, page 62.

EXAMPLE (a). Test the series

$$(11) \qquad\qquad \sum_{n=0}^{\infty} n!(x - a)^n.$$

For $x \neq a$, we set up the test ratio and find that

$$\lim_{n \to \infty} \left| \frac{(n + 1)!(x - a)^{n+1}}{n!(x - a)^n} \right| = \lim_{n \to \infty} (n + 1)|x - a| = \infty, \qquad x \neq a.$$

Then (11) diverges for $x \neq a$. At $x = a$, the series contains only one nonzero term, the $n = 0$ term, so (11) converges at $x = a$.

EXAMPLE (b). Test the series

$$(12) \qquad\qquad \sum_{n=0}^{\infty} \frac{(x - a)^n}{n!}.$$

Here, for $x \neq a$, we obtain

$$\lim_{n\to\infty} \left| \frac{(x-a)^{n+1}}{(n+1)!} \cdot \frac{n!}{(x-a)^n} \right| = \lim_{n\to\infty} \frac{|x-a|}{n+1} = 0.$$

Then (12) converges for all finite x and therefore converges absolutely and uniformly in every closed region or interval.

EXAMPLE (c). Test the series

(13)
$$\sum_{n=0}^{\infty} \frac{(-1)^n 2^n x^n}{3n+1}.$$

Since, for $x \neq 0$,

$$\lim_{n\to\infty} \left| \frac{(-1)^{n+1} 2^{n+1} x^{n+1}}{3n+4} \cdot \frac{3n+1}{(-1)^n 2^n x^n} \right| = 2|x|,$$

it follows that (13) is absolutely convergent for $|x| < \frac{1}{2}$ and is divergent for $|x| > \frac{1}{2}$.

Let us restrict x to real values. Then the endpoints of the interval of convergence, $x = \pm\frac{1}{2}$, still need to be considered. At $x = -\frac{1}{2}$, (13) becomes

$$\sum_{n=0}^{\infty} \frac{1}{3n+1},$$

which we know diverges by the polynomial test or by a comparison test. At $x = \frac{1}{2}$, (13) becomes

$$\sum_{n=0}^{\infty} \frac{(-1)^n}{3n+1},$$

which can be shown to be convergent by the alternating series test.

Exercises

In Exercises 1–28, find the interval of convergence and test the series at the endpoints of the interval.

1. $\sum_{n=0}^{\infty} (-1)^n x^n.$ ANS. $-1 < x < 1.$

2. $\sum_{n=1}^{\infty} \frac{x^n}{2n-1}.$ ANS. $-1 \leq x < 1.$

3. $\sum_{n=0}^{\infty} \frac{(-1)^n y^n}{(2n+1)^2 3^{n+1}}.$ ANS. $-3 \leq y \leq 3.$

4. $\displaystyle\sum_{n=1}^{\infty} \frac{(n+1)y^{2n}}{5^n}$.   ANS. $-\sqrt{5} < y < \sqrt{5}$.

5. $\displaystyle\sum_{n=0}^{\infty} (-1)^n n! x^n$.   ANS. $x = 0$.

6. $\displaystyle\sum_{n=1}^{\infty} \frac{n! x^n}{2n-1}$.   ANS. $x = 0$.

7. $\displaystyle\sum_{n=0}^{\infty} \frac{n^2(x+2)^n}{n+1}$.   ANS. $-3 < x < -1$.

8. $\displaystyle\sum_{n=0}^{\infty} \frac{(x-x_0)^{2n}}{(2n)!}$.   ANS.   All values of x.

9. $\displaystyle\sum_{n=0}^{\infty} \frac{(x-x_0)^{2n+1}}{(2n+1)!}$.   ANS.   All values of x.

10. $\displaystyle\sum_{n=1}^{\infty} \frac{(y-4)^n}{2^{2n}(n+1)^3}$.   ANS. $0 \leqq y \leqq 8$.

11. $\dfrac{x}{2 \cdot 3 \cdot 4} - \dfrac{x^2}{5 \cdot 6 \cdot 7} + \dfrac{x^3}{8 \cdot 9 \cdot 10} - \cdots + \dfrac{(-1)^{n-1}x^n}{(3n-1)(3n)(3n+1)} + \cdots$.

12. $\dfrac{1}{1 \cdot 2} - \dfrac{x^2}{2 \cdot 3} + \dfrac{x^4}{3 \cdot 4} - \dfrac{x^6}{4 \cdot 5} + \cdots + \dfrac{(-1)^n x^{2n}}{(n+1)(n+2)} + \cdots$.

13. $\displaystyle\sum_{n=0}^{\infty} \frac{(-1)^n x^{n+2}}{(n+1)^2 2^{2n}}$.   ANS. $-4 \leqq x \leqq 4$.

14. $\displaystyle\sum_{n=1}^{\infty} \frac{n x^{2n+3}}{(n+1)^2}$.   ANS. $-1 < x < 1$.

15. $\displaystyle\sum_{n=0}^{\infty} \frac{(-1)^n x^{2n+1}}{(2n+1)!}$.   ANS.   All values of x.

16. $\displaystyle\sum_{n=0}^{\infty} \frac{n! x^n}{(2n+1)!}$.   ANS.   All values of x.

17. $\displaystyle\sum_{k=1}^{\infty} (-1)^{k-1}(3k+1)y^{2k}$.

18. $\displaystyle\sum_{k=0}^{\infty} \frac{(-1)^k(3k+1)y^{2k}}{2^k}$.

19. $\displaystyle\sum_{n=1}^{\infty} n^2(x+1)^n$.   ANS. $-2 < x < 0$.

20. $\displaystyle\sum_{n=0}^{\infty} \frac{(-1)^n(x-4)^{n+1}}{(n+1)^3}$.   ANS. $3 \leqq x \leqq 5$.

21. $\displaystyle\sum_{n=1}^{\infty} n(x-2)^n.$

22. $\displaystyle\sum_{n=1}^{\infty} \frac{n(x+3)^n}{(2n-1)^3}.$

23. $\displaystyle\sum_{n=0}^{\infty} \frac{(n+2)(x-1)^n}{n!}.$

24. $\displaystyle\sum_{n=1}^{\infty} \frac{(-1)^n(2n-1)x^{2n-1}}{(2n)!}.$

25. $\displaystyle\sum_{n=1}^{\infty} \frac{(-1)^n}{nx^n}.$ ANS. $x \geq 1$, and $x < -1.$

26. $\displaystyle\sum_{n=0}^{\infty} \frac{n+1}{2^{n+2}x^n}.$ ANS. $x > \frac{1}{2}$, and $x < -\frac{1}{2}.$

27. $\displaystyle\sum_{n=0}^{\infty} \frac{(-1)^n 5^n}{(3n+1)x^n}.$

28. $\displaystyle\sum_{n=2}^{\infty} \frac{(-1)^n 2^{n+1}}{n^2 x^{n+2}}.$

In Exercises 29–33, find the interval of convergence, but do not test the series at the endpoints of the interval.

29. $\displaystyle\sum_{n=1}^{\infty} \frac{1 \cdot 3 \cdot 5 \cdot 7 \cdots (2n-1)x^{2n}}{2^n n!}.$

30. $\displaystyle\sum_{n=1}^{\infty} \frac{n^n x^n}{n!}.$ ANS. $|x| < \dfrac{1}{e}.$

31. $\displaystyle\sum_{n=1}^{\infty} \frac{n! x^n}{n^n}.$

32. $\displaystyle\sum_{n=1}^{\infty} \frac{1 \cdot 3 \cdot 5 \cdot 7 \cdots (2n-1)x^{2n}}{2 \cdot 4 \cdot 6 \cdot 8 \cdots (2n+2)}.$

33. $\displaystyle 1 + \sum_{n=1}^{\infty} \frac{m(m-1)\cdots(m-n+1)x^n}{n!}.$ ANS. $|x| < 1.$

44. Taylor and Maclaurin Series

We now seek, for sufficiently well-behaved $f(x)$, a power series that will converge to $f(x)$ on some interval. First, we get a finite series expansion by repeated integration by parts and then move from the finite series to an infinite series representation for $f(x)$.

Suppose there is an interval $c_1 \leq x \leq c_2$ in which $f(x)$ and its derivative $f'(x)$ are continuous.* For any x in the closed interval and any a in the open interval,

(1)
$$\int_a^x f'(y)\, dy = f(x) - f(a).$$

Let us rewrite (1) as

(2)
$$f(x) = f(a) + \int_a^x f'(y)\, dy.$$

We shall use integration by parts on the integral in (2), differentiating $f'(y)$ to get $f''(y)\, dy$ and integrating dy to get $(y - x)$. The choice $(y - x)$ rather than y as an integral of dy is made to simplify the integrated portion at the upper limit of integration.

$$\frac{f'(y)}{f''(y)\, dy}\,\bigg|\,\frac{dy}{-(x - y)}$$

If we assume the existence of $f''(y)$, the above integration by parts performed on equation (2) leads us to

$$f(x) = f(a) - \left[(x - y)f'(y)\right]_a^x + \int_a^x (x - y)f''(y)\, dy,$$

or

(3)
$$f(x) = f(a) + (x - a)f'(a) + \int_a^x (x - y)f''(y)\, dy.$$

Let us now apply integration by parts again.

$$\frac{f''(y)}{f'''(y)\, dy}\,\bigg|\,\frac{(x - y)\, dy}{-\tfrac{1}{2}(x - y)^2}$$

The choice indicated in the table leads us from equation (3) to the form shown below:

$$f(x) = f(a) + (x - a)f'(a) - \tfrac{1}{2}\left[(x - y)^2 f''(y)\right]_a^x + \tfrac{1}{2}\int_a^x (x - y)^2 f'''(y)\, dy,$$

and thus to the equation

(4) $f(x) = f(a) + (x - a)f'(a) + \tfrac{1}{2}(x - a)^2 f''(a) + \tfrac{1}{2}\int_a^x (x - y)^2 f'''(y)\, dy.$

* The mere existence of $f'(x)$ implies the continuity of $f(x)$. We shall continue to favor simplicity of wording over removal of such minor redundancies.

The above process may be iterated and, if all the derivatives involved are continuous, all the integrals exist. We are thus led in n steps to the following result.

THEOREM 47. *If $f(x)$ and its first $(n+1)$ derivatives are continuous in the interval $c_1 \leq x \leq c_2$, and if $c_1 < a < c_2$, then for x in the stipulated interval,*

$$(5) \qquad f(x) = f(a) + \sum_{k=1}^{n} \frac{f^{(k)}(a)(x-a)^k}{k!} + R_n(x, a)$$

in which

$$(6) \qquad R_n(x, a) = \frac{1}{n!} \int_a^x (x-y)^n f^{(n+1)}(y)\, dy.$$

The term $R_n(x, a)$ in (5) and (6) is called the *remainder*; Theorem 47 is a remainder theorem. Equation (5) is a finite form of a Taylor* series. The problem of showing that $f(x)$ is represented by its *Taylor series*

$$(7) \qquad f(x) = f(a) + \sum_{n=1}^{\infty} \frac{f^{(n)}(a)(x-a)^n}{n!},$$

in some interval about $x = a$, is precisely the problem of showing that, in the interval,

$$\lim_{n \to \infty} R_n(x, a) = 0.$$

Before proceeding to obtain Taylor series for specific functions, we shall develop another form for the remainder term in equation (5). It is convenient to use the following theorem taken from calculus.

LEMMA 8 (Rolle's theorem). *If $f(x)$ is continuous over the closed interval $c_1 \leq x \leq c_2$, if the derivative $f'(x)$ exists throughout the open interval $c_1 < x < c_2$, if $f(c_1) = 0$ and $f(c_2) = 0$, then there exists an x_1 in the open interval, $c_1 < x_1 < c_2$ such that $f'(x_1) = 0$.*

Suppose $f(x)$ and its first n derivatives are continuous in the closed interval $c_1 \leq x \leq c_2$ and that $f^{(n+1)}(x)$ exists throughout the open interval $c_1 < x < c_2$. Let a be in the open interval $c_1 < a < c_2$. Then for all x in the open interval we define $R_n(x, a)$ by

$$(8) \qquad f(x) = f(a) + \sum_{k=1}^{n} \frac{f^{(k)}(a)(x-a)^k}{k!} + R_n(x, a).$$

* Brooks Taylor, 1685–1731.

Now consider the function

$$(9) \quad \varphi(y) = f(x) - f(y) - \sum_{k=1}^{n} \frac{f^{(k)}(y)(x-y)^k}{k!} - \frac{(x-y)^{n+1}r_n(x, a)}{(n+1)!}.$$

We wish to make $\varphi(y)$ satisfy the conditions of Rolle's theorem, Lemma 8, on the interval $a \leq y \leq x$ with $c_1 < a < c_2$ and $c_1 < x < c_2$. By (9), $\varphi(x) = 0$, and

$$(10) \quad \varphi(a) = f(x) - f(a) - \sum_{k=1}^{n} \frac{f^{(k)}(a)(x-a)^k}{k!} - \frac{(x-a)^{n+1}r_n(x, a)}{(n+1)!}.$$

Because of (8) the $\varphi(a)$ of (10) will be zero if we choose $r_n(x, a)$ to satisfy the relation

$$R_n(x, a) = \frac{(x-a)^{n+1}r_n(x, a)}{(n+1)!}.$$

From equation (9) it follows that

$$\varphi'(y) = -f'(y) - \sum_{k=1}^{n} \frac{f^{(k+1)}(y)(x-y)^k}{k!}$$
$$+ \sum_{k=1}^{n} \frac{f^{(k)}(y)(x-y)^{k-1}}{(k-1)!} + \frac{(x-y)^n r_n(x, a)}{n!}.$$

A shift of index from k to $(k+1)$ in the last summation above permits us to write

$$\varphi'(y) = -f'(y) - \sum_{k=1}^{n} \frac{f^{(k+1)}(y)(x-y)^k}{k!}$$
$$+ \sum_{k=0}^{n-1} \frac{f^{(k+1)}(y)(x-y)^k}{k!} + \frac{(x-y)^n r_n(x, a)}{n!},$$

or

$$(11) \quad \varphi'(y) = -\frac{f^{(n+1)}(y)(x-y)^n}{n!} + \frac{(x-y)^n r_n(x, a)}{n!},$$

since all the other terms drop out. We now see that $\varphi'(y)$ exists in the interval $a \leq y \leq x$. Therefore Rolle's theorem may be applied to $\varphi(y)$. Hence there exists an x_1 in the open interval $a < x_1 < x$ such that $\varphi'(x_1) = 0$. Since $(x - x_1) \neq 0$, we may conclude from $\varphi'(x_1) = 0$ and equation (11) that

$$(12) \quad r_n(x, a) = f^{(n+1)}(x_1), \qquad a < x_1 < x.$$

We have thus proved the following result.

THEOREM 48. *If $f(x)$ and its first n derivatives are continuous in $c_1 \leq x \leq c_2$, if $f^{(n+1)}(x)$ exists throughout the open interval $c_1 < x < c_2$, and if $c_1 < a < c_2$, then*

$$(13) \qquad f(x) = f(a) + \sum_{k=1}^{n} \frac{f^{(k)}(a)(x-a)^k}{k!} + R_n(x, a)$$

in which

$$(14) \qquad R_n(x, a) = \frac{(x-a)^{n+1} f^{(n+1)}(x_1)}{(n+1)!}$$

for some x_1 in the open interval $a < x_1 < x$.

Again we have a finite form of Taylor series, with the remainder term this time given by (14) corresponding to the earlier form (6), page 116. Since differentiation is frequently a more elementary process than is integration, we make more use of (14) than we do of (6).

If we show for the R_n of (14) that

$$\lim_{n \to \infty} R_n(x, a) = 0$$

throughout an interval, then the function is represented by its Taylor series

$$(15) \qquad f(x) = f(a) + \sum_{n=1}^{\infty} \frac{f^{(n)}(a)(x-a)^n}{n!}$$

throughout the interval because the right member of (13) will converge to $f(x)$.

The special Taylor series in which $a = 0$ is called a *Maclaurin* series*,

$$(16) \qquad f(x) = f(0) + \sum_{n=1}^{\infty} \frac{f^{(n)}(0)x^n}{n!}.$$

Each of the basic expansions to be obtained in the next section is the Maclaurin series for a particular elementary function.

45. Some Basic Expansions

An efficient way to get the Taylor and Maclaurin series for elementary functions is to obtain a set of basic expansions, (1)–(6) below, and then to use the manipulative techniques of Chapter 8 to derive other expansions from the basic ones. We shall find that

* Colin Maclaurin, 1698–1746.

(1) $$e^x = \sum_{n=0}^{\infty} \frac{x^n}{n!};\qquad \text{for all values of } x.$$

(2) $$\cos x = \sum_{n=0}^{\infty} \frac{(-1)^n x^{2n}}{(2n)!};\qquad \text{for all values of } x.$$

(3) $$\sin x = \sum_{n=0}^{\infty} \frac{(-1)^n x^{2n+1}}{(2n+1)!};\qquad \text{for all values of } x.$$

(4) $$\frac{1}{1-x} = \sum_{n=0}^{\infty} x^n;\qquad -1 < x < 1.$$

(5) $$\ln(1+x) = \sum_{n=1}^{\infty} \frac{(-1)^{n+1} x^n}{n};\qquad -1 < x \le 1.$$

(6) $$(1+x)^m = 1 + \sum_{n=1}^{\infty} \frac{m(m-1)(m-2)\cdots(m-n+1)x^n}{n!};\qquad |x| < 1.$$

First consider $f(x) = e^x$. We know that for all n,

$$f^{(n)}(x) = e^x.$$

Then, using $a = 0$, we have

$$e^x = 1 + \sum_{n=1}^{\infty} \frac{x^n}{n!}$$

if only

(7) $$\lim_{n \to \infty} \frac{x^{n+1} e^{x_1}}{(n+1)!} = 0,\qquad 0 < x_1 < x.$$

But (7) is true for any fixed x, so (1) is valid for all positive x. The same argument with x replaced by $(-x)$ yields the validity for negative x. At $x = 0$, the series terminates. Therefore the expansion (1) is valid for all finite x.

The interval of validity of a Taylor (or Maclaurin) series is symmetric about the point $x = a$ (or zero). We need not discuss negative x separately in our justification of the basic Maclaurin expansions.

Next consider at once both the functions $\sin x$ and $\cos x$. We know the derivatives are each either plus or minus $\sin x$ or $\cos x$. Hence, for all finite x_1,

$$|f^{(n+1)}(x_1)| \le 1.$$

It follows that $R_n \to 0$ as $n \to \infty$ for $f(x) = \cos x$ or $f(x) = \sin x$. By computing the values of the even and odd numbered derivatives of $\cos x$

and $\sin x$ at $x = 0$, we obtain the desired coefficients in the Maclaurin series and thus complete the justification of (2) and (3).

The sum of a geometric series is known as is its interval of convergence to that sum, so (4) is valid. Equation (5) may be obtained from (4) by the methods of Chapter 8. The proof of the validity of (6) is left as an exercise.

Again the student is warned that this direct approach to the expansion of functions in Taylor or Maclaurin series is cumbersome* and should be avoided whenever possible by using the methods of the next chapter. For this reason, the following set of exercises is a short one.

Exercises

1. Justify the expansion (5), page 119, for the range $|x| < 1$ by using Theorem 48. For justification at $x = 1$, see page 135.

2. From (1), page 119, with x replaced by $(x - a)$, obtain the Taylor series

$$e^x = e^a + \sum_{n=1}^{\infty} \frac{e^a(x - a)^n}{n!}.$$

3. Show that, if $f(x) = \sin x$,

$$f^{(2k)}(x) = (-1)^k \sin x$$

and

$$f^{(2k+1)}(x) = (-1)^k \cos x.$$

Then justify the Taylor expansion

$$\sin x = \sin a + \sum_{n=1}^{\infty} \frac{b_n(x - a)^n}{n!},$$

in which $b_{2k} = (-1)^k \sin a$ and $b_{2k+1} = (-1)^k \cos a$.

4. Show that, if $f(x) = \cos x$,

$$f^{(2k)}(x) = (-1)^k \cos x$$

and

$$f^{(2k+1)}(x) = (-)^{k+1} \sin x.$$

Then justify the Taylor expansion

$$\cos x = \cos a + \sum_{n=1}^{\infty} \frac{c_n(x - a)^n}{n!},$$

---

* Try this method for getting the general term of the series for $x^3(1 + x^2)^{-2}$ and compare with the neat device used in Example (b), page 138.

in which $c_{2k} = (-1)^k \cos a$ and $c_{2k+1} = (-1)^{k+1} \sin a$.

5. Use $a = \frac{1}{2}\pi$ in the result in Exercise 3 to obtain the series

$$\sin x = 1 + \sum_{k=1}^{\infty} \frac{(-1)^k (x - \frac{1}{2}\pi)^{2k}}{(2k)!}.$$

6. Obtain the series in Exercise 5 by using (2), page 119, and the fact that

$$\sin x = \cos(\tfrac{1}{2}\pi - x) = \cos(x - \tfrac{1}{2}\pi).$$

7. Use $a = \frac{1}{2}\pi$ in the result in Exercise 4 to obtain

$$\cos x = \sum_{k=0}^{\infty} \frac{(-1)^{k+1}(x - \frac{1}{2}\pi)^{2k+1}}{(2k+1)!}.$$

8. Obtain the series in Exercise 7 by using (3), page 119, and the fact that

$$\cos x = \sin(\tfrac{1}{2}\pi - x) = -\sin(x - \tfrac{1}{2}\pi).$$

9. Justify the expansion (6), page 119, by using Theorem 48.

In Exercies 10–14, use the Maclaurin expansion (16), page 118, directly to get a power series for the given function.

10. $\ln(1 - x)$.

11. $\dfrac{1}{1 + 5x}$.

12. $\exp(-\tfrac{1}{2}x)$.

13. $\sqrt{1 + x}$.   ANS. $1 + \dfrac{1}{2}x + \sum_{n=2}^{\infty} \dfrac{(-1)^{n+1} 1 \cdot 3 \cdot 5 \cdots (2n - 3)x^n}{2^n n!}$.

14. $\dfrac{1}{\sqrt{1 + x}}$.   ANS. $1 + \sum_{n=1}^{\infty} \dfrac{(-1)^n 1 \cdot 3 \cdot 5 \cdots (2n - 1)x^n}{2^n n!}$.

In Exercises 15–23, obtain the power series directly from the Taylor series (15), page 118.

15. e^x in powers of $(x - 2)$.   ANS. $\sum_{n=0}^{\infty} \dfrac{e^2(x - 2)^n}{n!}$.

16. $\ln x$ in powers of $(x - 3)$.

17. $\sin x$ in powers of $(x - \tfrac{1}{4}\pi)$.

18. $\sqrt{x}$ in powers of $(x - 2)$.

19. $\dfrac{1}{1 + x}$ in powers of $(x + 4)$.

20. e^x in powers of $(x + 1)$.

21. $\ln x$ in powers of $(x - \tfrac{1}{2})$.

22. $\cos x$ in powers of $(x + \tfrac{1}{4}\pi)$.

23. $\dfrac{1}{1-x}$ in powers of $(x-3)$.

In Exercises 24–30, obtain the desired series by making appropriate substitutions in the basic expansions (1)–(6), page 119.

24. $\dfrac{1}{1-x^2}$. Put x^2 for x in (4), page 119.

25. $\ln(1-x^2)$. Put $(-x^2)$ for x in (5), page 119.

26. $\exp(-\tfrac{1}{2}x^2)$.

27. $\cos 3x$.

28. $\sin 4x$.

29. $\ln(1+3x^2)$.

30. $(1+3x^2)^{-1}$.

31. Obtain the power series for $\dfrac{1}{\sqrt{1-x^2}}$ from the result of Exercise 14.

32. Obtain the power series for $\dfrac{x^4}{1-x^3}$.

33. Obtain the power series for $\dfrac{x^3}{\sqrt{1-x^3}}$ from Exercise 14.

34. Obtain the power series for $\ln(3-x)$ with the aid of the relation

$$\ln(3-x)=\ln\left[3\left(1-\frac{x}{3}\right)\right]=\ln 3+\ln\left(1-\frac{x}{3}\right).$$

35. Obtain the power series for $\ln(5-2x)$.

CHAPTER 8

Operations with Power Series

46. Addition and Multiplication

Within their common region of convergence two power series may be added, subtracted, or multiplied and the resultant power series will have as its sum the desired sum, difference, or product of the original two sums.

THEOREM 49. *If*

$$(1) \qquad f_1(x) = \sum_{n=0}^{\infty} a_n(x-a)^n, \quad in \ |x-a| < R_1,$$

and

$$(2) \qquad f_2(x) = \sum_{n=0}^{\infty} b_n(x-a)^n, \quad in \ |x-a| < R_2,$$

then

$$(3) \qquad f_1(x) + f_2(x) = \sum_{n=0}^{\infty} (a_n + b_n)x - a)^n, \quad in \ |x-a| < R,$$

and

$$(4) \qquad f_1(x)f_2(x) = \sum_{n=0}^{\infty} \sum_{k=0}^{n} a_k b_{n-k}(x-a)^n, \quad in \ |x-a| < R,$$

where $R = \mathrm{Min}(R_1, R_2)$.

Theorem 49 follows at once from the fact that power series are absolutely convergent inside the interval of convergence. See Section 28, page

67, for addition of series and Theorem 33, page 72, for multiplication of absolutely convergent series. The product in (4) is the Cauchy product of Section 31, page 72. Term-by-term subtraction is accomplished by changing signs throughout (2) and then performing addition of series.

EXAMPLE (a). Find a power series for $\cosh x$.

We know from calculus that

$$\cosh x = \tfrac{1}{2}(e^x + e^{-x}).$$

Since

$$e^x = \sum_{n=0}^{\infty} \frac{x^n}{n!}, \qquad |x| < \infty,$$

we obtain

$$\cosh x = \tfrac{1}{2}\sum_{n=0}^{\infty} \frac{x^n}{n!} + \tfrac{1}{2}\sum_{n=0}^{\infty} \frac{(-1)^n x^n}{n!},$$

(5)
$$\cosh x = \sum_{n=0}^{\infty} \frac{1+(-1)^n}{2} \cdot \frac{x^n}{n!}.$$

For n odd, $n = 2k+1$, the coefficients in (5) are zero. The only terms remaining are those with n even, $n = 2k$. Thus (5) reduces to

(6)
$$\cosh x = \sum_{k=0}^{\infty} \frac{x^{2k}}{(2k)!}, \qquad |x| < \infty.$$

EXAMPLE (b). Find a series for $e^{-x}\ln(1+3x)$.

We know that

(7)
$$e^{-x} = \sum_{n=0}^{\infty} \frac{(-1)^n x^n}{n!}, \qquad |x| < \infty.$$

From

$$\ln(1+y) = \sum_{n=1}^{\infty} \frac{(-1)^{n+1} y^n}{n}, \qquad |y| < 1,$$

with y replaced by $3x$ and n shifted to $(n+1)$, we obtain

(8)
$$\ln(1+3x) = \sum_{n=0}^{\infty} \frac{(-1)^n 3^{n+1} x^{n+1}}{n+1}, \qquad |x| < \frac{1}{3}.$$

The Cauchy product of the series in (7) and (8) yields

$$e^{-x}\ln(1+3x) = \sum_{n=0}^{\infty}\sum_{k=0}^{n} \frac{(-1)^k(-1)^{n-k}3^{n-k+1}x^{n+1}}{k!\,(n-k+1)}, \qquad |x| < \frac{1}{3},$$

(9) $\quad e^{-x}\ln(1+3x) = \sum_{n=0}^{\infty}\sum_{k=0}^{n}\frac{3^{n-k+1}}{k!(n-k+1)}(-1)^n x^{n+1}, \qquad |x| < \frac{1}{3}.$

The theorem on multiplication of absolutely convergent series, Theorem 33, page 72, permits any collection of the pertinent product terms into an infinite series of finite sums. When multiplying power series our purpose is to get a power series for the product. Therefore we use the arrangement of terms which collects all product terms containing the same power of the parameter.

Suppose we wish to multiply a series containing all powers of x by a series of only even powers of x,

(10) $\qquad\qquad \left(\sum_{n=0}^{\infty} a_n x^{2n}\right)\left(\sum_{n=0}^{\infty} b_n x^n\right).$

Consider the product terms that will contain the nth power of x. Any term

$$a_k x^{2k}$$

from the first series will contribute an x^n term if and only if it is multiplied by a term containing x^{n-2k} from the second series. In the second series, the subscript on the b is equal to the exponent on the x. The pertinent terms, those in which x appears with exponent n, are the products

$$a_k x^{2k} b_{n-2k} x^{n-2k} = a_k b_{n-2k} x^n.$$

The only remaining question is the range of the index k.

Since the subscripts on the coefficients in (10) range over the non-negative integers, we must use the integral values of k for which

$$k \geq 0 \quad \text{and} \quad n - 2k \geq 0.$$

Thus $0 \leq k \leq \frac{1}{2}n$, and k is integral. We may use a common notation*

$$[y] = \text{greatest integer} \leq y.$$

We thus obtain for the product (10) the form shown in (11) below.

LEMMA 9. *Within the common interval of convergence of the series being multiplied,*

(11) $\qquad \left(\sum_{n=0}^{\infty} a_n x^{2n}\right)\left(\sum_{n=0}^{\infty} b_n x^n\right) = \sum_{n=0}^{\infty}\sum_{k=0}^{[\frac{1}{2}n]} a_k b_{n-2k} x^n.$

* We do not wish to sacrifice square brackets for ordinary usage. Therefore we adopt the convention that square brackets denote the greatest integer symbol only when used in a limit of summation.

EXAMPLE (c). Find a series for $e^{-x} \cos 2x$.

Since

$$\cos 2x = \sum_{n=0}^{\infty} \frac{(-1)^n 2^{2n} x^{2n}}{(2n)!}, \qquad |x| < \infty,$$

and

$$e^{-x} = \sum_{n=0}^{\infty} \frac{(-1)^n x^n}{n!}, \qquad |x| < \infty,$$

we obtain, by Lemma 9,

$$e^{-x} \cos 2x = \sum_{n=0}^{\infty} \sum_{k=0}^{[\frac{1}{2}n]} \frac{(-1)^k 2^{2k} (-1)^{n-2k} x^n}{(2k)!\,(n-2k)!},$$

from which

$$(12) \qquad e^{-x} \cos 2x = \sum_{n=0}^{\infty} \sum_{k=0}^{[\frac{1}{2}n]} \frac{(-1)^{n+k} 2^{2k}}{(2k)!(n-2k)!} x^n, \qquad |x| < \infty.$$

The fact that the right member of (12) permits additional simplification is immaterial here.

EXAMPLE (d). Find a series for $\sin x \ln(1 + 4x)$.

We know that

$$(13) \qquad \sin x = \sum_{n=0}^{\infty} \frac{(-1)^n x^{2n+1}}{(2n+1)!}, \qquad |x| < \infty,$$

and can easily get, from the series for $\ln(1 + y)$, the result

$$(14) \qquad \ln(1 + 4x) = \sum_{n=0}^{\infty} \frac{(-1)^n 4^{n+1} x^{n+1}}{n+1}, \qquad |x| < \tfrac{1}{4}.$$

The series (14) contains all positive exponents on x; the series (13) only the odd exponents. The desired product will be obtainable from Lemma 9, if we mentally hold out a factor x from each of (13) and (14), then insert the two factors after forming the product. Thus we obtain

$$\sin x \ln(1 + 4x) = x^2 \left[\sum_{n=0}^{\infty} \frac{(-1)^n x^{2n}}{(2n+1)!} \right] \left[\sum_{n=0}^{\infty} \frac{(-1)^n 4^{n+1} x^n}{n+1} \right],$$

from which

$$\sin x \ln(1 + 4x) = x^2 \sum_{n=0}^{\infty} \sum_{k=0}^{[\frac{1}{2}n]} \frac{(-1)^k (-1)^{n-2k} 4^{n-2k+1} x^n}{(2k+1)!(n-2k+1)},$$

or

$$(15) \quad \sin x \ln(1+4x) = \sum_{n=0}^{\infty} \sum_{k=0}^{[\frac{1}{2}n]} \frac{(-1)^{n+k}4^{n+1-2k}}{(2k+1)!(n-2k+1)} x^{n+2}, \qquad |x| < \tfrac{1}{4}.$$

The power series thus obtained may be put in other forms by shifting indices. Replacing n by $(n-2)$ yields

$$(16) \quad \sin x \ln(1+4x) = \sum_{n=2}^{\infty} \sum_{k=0}^{[\frac{1}{2}n-1]} \frac{(-1)^{n+k}4^{n-1-2k}}{(2k+1)!(n-1-2k)} x^{n}, \qquad |x| < \tfrac{1}{4},$$

and an additional shift from k to $(k-1)$ gives us

$$(17) \quad \sin x \ln(1+4x) = \sum_{n=2}^{\infty} \sum_{k=1}^{[\frac{1}{2}n]} \frac{(-1)^{n+k+1}4^{n+1-2k}}{(2k-1)!(n+1-2k)} x^{n}, \qquad |x| < \tfrac{1}{4}.$$

Exercises

Use Theorem 49, or Lemma 9, to obtain Maclaurin series for the given function using the basic expansions of Section 45, page 119.

1. $\sinh x = \sum\limits_{n=0}^{\infty} \dfrac{x^{2n+1}}{(2n+1)!}, \qquad |x| < \infty.$

2. $\dfrac{1}{1-2x} + \dfrac{1}{1+4x} = \sum\limits_{n=0}^{\infty} 2^n\{1+(-2)^n\}x^n, \qquad |x| < \tfrac{1}{4}.$

3. $\dfrac{1}{1+3x} + \dfrac{1}{1+x}.$

4. $x \cos x - \sin x.$

5. $\dfrac{e^{2x}}{1-3x} = \sum\limits_{n=0}^{\infty} \sum\limits_{k=0}^{n} \dfrac{2^k}{3^k k!} 3^n x^n, \qquad |x| < \dfrac{1}{3}.$

6. $e^y \ln(1+y).$

7. $\dfrac{e^{-2y}}{1+y}.$

8. $\dfrac{\ln(1+x)}{1-x}.$

9. $\dfrac{\exp(-x^2)}{1+x} = \sum\limits_{n=0}^{\infty} \sum\limits_{k=0}^{[\frac{1}{2}n]} \dfrac{(-1)^{n+k}}{k!} x^n, \qquad |x| < 1.$

10. $e^{-2x} \sin 3x.$

11. $\cos x \ln(1-2x).$

12. $\dfrac{\cos 2x}{1-3x}.$

47. Uniqueness

If two infinite series of powers of the same quantity are equal throughout an interval, their coefficients are equal.

THEOREM 50. *If*

$$(1) \qquad \sum_{n=0}^{\infty} a_n x^n = \sum_{n=0}^{\infty} b_n x^n, \qquad in \ |x| < R,$$

then $a_n = b_n$ *for every n.*

The theorem can equally well be read: If

$$(2) \qquad \sum_{n=0}^{\infty} a_n (y-a)^n = \sum_{n=0}^{\infty} b_n (y-a)^n, \qquad |y-a| < R,$$

then $a_n = b_n$ for every *n.*

PROOF. By hypothesis, each of the series in (1) converges in the common region $|x| < R$. We may therefore use $x = 0$ in (1) and thus conclude that

$$a_0 = b_0.$$

Then (1) becomes

$$(3) \qquad \sum_{n=1}^{\infty} a_n x^n = \sum_{n=1}^{\infty} b_n x^n, \qquad in \ |x| < R.$$

For $x \neq 0$, (3) yields

$$(4) \qquad \sum_{n=1}^{\infty} a_n x^{n-1} = \sum_{n=1}^{\infty} b_n x^{n-1}, \qquad in \ 0 < |x| < R.$$

But each member of the equality (4) is a power series convergent for all $|x| < R$ by Theorem 45, page 109. Then in every closed region $|x| \leq r < R$, each of the series in (4) is uniformly convergent and so its sum is continuous throughout $|x| \leq r < R$. The sums of the two series in (4), being continuous in $|x| \leq r$ and equal for $0 < |x| \leq r$, are also equal at $x = 0$. Thus we may conclude that (4) is also valid at $x = 0$. Hence we are led to the identity

$$(5) \qquad \sum_{n=1}^{\infty} a_n x^{n-1} = \sum_{n=1}^{\infty} b_n x^{n-1}, \qquad in \ |x| < R.$$

For $x = 0$, (5) yields

$$a_1 = b_1,$$

and iteration of the argument leads to $a_n = b_n$ for every n.

As a special case of Theorem 50, we obtain the fact that if

$$\sum_{n=0}^{\infty} c_n x^n = 0, \qquad \text{in } |x| < R,$$

then $c_n = 0$ for every n.

If two power series are equal in some region, their coefficients are equal, by Theorem 50, and therefore the two series are equal throughout their common region of convergence.

48. Division

Division of power series can be performed but the result has two drawbacks. In general, the coefficients will not be obtained by an explicit formula and the interval of convergence of the quotient series is not necessarily as large as the common interval of convergence of the two original series.

THEOREM 51. *If*

(1) $$f_1(x) = \sum_{n=0}^{\infty} a_n x^n, \qquad \text{in } |x| < R_1,$$

and

(2) $$f_2(x) = \sum_{n=0}^{\infty} b_n x^n, \qquad \text{in } |x| < R_2,$$

and if $b_0 \neq 0$, then

(3) $$\frac{f_1(x)}{f_2(x)} = \sum_{n=0}^{\infty} q_n x^n, \qquad \text{in } |x| < R,$$

where $R = \text{Min}(R_1, R_2, |z|)$, with z being the zero of $f_2(x)$ nearest to $x = 0$. The q_n are determined as follows:

(4) $$q_0 = \frac{a_0}{b_0},$$

and, for $n \geq 1$,

(5) $$b_0 q_n = a_n - \sum_{k=1}^{n} b_k q_{n-k} .$$

Let us determine the coefficients q_n in the above quotient under the assumption that there does exist a region, or interval $|x| < R$ in which

(6)
$$\frac{\sum\limits_{n=0}^{\infty} a_n x^n}{\sum\limits_{n=0}^{\infty} b_n x^n} = \sum_{n=0}^{\infty} q_n x^n$$

is valid. From (6) it follows that

(7)
$$\sum_{n=0}^{\infty} a_n x^n = \left[\sum_{n=0}^{\infty} b_n x^n \right]\left[\sum_{n=0}^{\infty} q_n x^n \right].$$

The Cauchy product of two power series is then used to obtain

(8)
$$\sum_{n=0}^{\infty} a_n x^n = \sum_{n=0}^{\infty} \sum_{k=0}^{n} b_k q_{n-k} x^n.$$

By Theorem 50, we can equate coefficients of corresponding powers of x on the two sides of (8). Hence

(9)
$$a_n = \sum_{k=0}^{n} b_k q_{n-k}, \qquad \text{for } n \geq 0.$$

We seek to determine the q_n from (9). For $n = 0$, (9) yields

$$a_0 = b_0 q_0$$

from which (4) is obtained. For $n \geq 1$ in (9), we obtain

(10)
$$a_n = b_0 q_n + \sum_{k=1}^{n} b_k q_{n-k}$$

in which the summation includes only those q_i with index $i < n$. Hence, (10) gives us (5),

$$b_0 q_n = a_n - \sum_{k=1}^{n} b_k q_{n-k},$$

each q_n being thus determined from the known a_n and b_k and the q_i of index lower than n. In practice we could compute q_1 from

$$b_0 q_1 = a_1 - b_1 q_0,$$

then q_2 from

$$b_0 q_2 = a_2 - b_1 q_1 - b_2 q_0, \quad \text{etc.}$$

Showing that the series (3) has the radius of convergence designated in Theorem 51 is best done by using material from the theory of analytic functions of a complex variable, so we omit it here. One fact that should be noted is that the z in Theorem 51 is actually the zero of $f_2(x)$ nearest $x = 0$ after all zeros common to $f_1(x)$ and $f_2(x)$ have been removed.

The condition $b_0 \neq 0$ in Theorem 51 is easily relaxed. If $f_2(x)$ has a zero of order m at $x = 0$, write

$$f_2(x) = x^m f_3(x).$$

Then $f_3(0) \neq 0$ and Theorem 51 can be used to get the power series for the ratio $\dfrac{f_1(x)}{f_3(x)}$. That is, if

$$f_1(x) = \sum_{n=0}^{\infty} a_n x^n \quad \text{and} \quad f_2(x) = x^m \sum_{n=0}^{\infty} b_n x^n,$$

with $b_0 \neq 0$, then

$$\frac{f_1(x)}{f_2(x)} = \frac{1}{x^m} \sum_{n=0}^{\infty} q_n x^n.$$

and the q_n are precisely those of Theorem 51.

If very few terms of a quotient are needed, the ordinary long division process used to divide one polynomial by another can be employed efficiently, as in Example (b) below.

EXAMPLE (a). Find a power series for $\tan x$ and compute the terms out to the x^5 term, inclusive.

We may write

$$\tan x = \frac{\sin x}{\cos x} = \frac{\displaystyle\sum_{n=0}^{\infty} \frac{(-1)^n x^{2n+1}}{(2n+1)!}}{\displaystyle\sum_{n=0}^{\infty} \frac{(-1)^n x^{2n}}{(2n)!}},$$

or

$$\tan x = \frac{x \displaystyle\sum_{n=0}^{\infty} \frac{(-1)^n (x^2)^n}{(2n+1)!}}{\displaystyle\sum_{n=0}^{\infty} \frac{(-1)^n (x^2)^n}{(2n)!}} = x \sum_{n=0}^{\infty} q_n (x^2)^n.$$

We now apply Theorem 51, page 129, with

$$a_n = \frac{(-1)^n}{(2n+1)!}, \qquad b_n = \frac{(-1)^n}{(2n)!},$$

Thus we obtain

(11) $$\tan x = \sum_{n=0}^{\infty} q_n x^{2n+1},$$

in which $q_0 = 1$, and

(12) $$n \geqq 1: \qquad 1 \cdot q_n = \frac{(-1)^n}{(2n+1)!} - \sum_{k=1}^{n} \frac{(-1)^k q_{n-k}}{(2k)!}.$$

Then

$$q_1 = -\frac{1}{6} + \frac{q_0}{2} = -\frac{1}{6} + \frac{1}{2} = \frac{1}{3},$$

$$q_2 = \frac{1}{120} + \frac{q_1}{2} - \frac{q_0}{24} = \frac{1}{120} + \frac{1}{6} - \frac{1}{24} = \frac{2}{15}.$$

Therefore

$$\tan x = x + \frac{1}{3} x^3 + \frac{2}{15} x^5 + \cdots.$$

EXAMPLE (b). Do Example (a) by long division.

We set up the following numerical process:

$$
1 - \frac{x^2}{2} + \frac{x^4}{24} - \cdots \quad \Bigg) \quad \overline{
\begin{array}{l}
x + \dfrac{x^3}{3} + \dfrac{2x^5}{15} + \cdots \\[2mm]
x - \dfrac{x^3}{6} + \dfrac{x^5}{120} - \cdots \\[2mm]
x - \dfrac{x^3}{2} + \dfrac{x^5}{24} - \cdots \\ \hline
+ \dfrac{x^3}{3} - \dfrac{x^5}{30} + \cdots \\[2mm]
+ \dfrac{x^3}{3} - \dfrac{x^5}{6} + \cdots \\ \hline
+ \dfrac{2x^5}{15} - \cdots.
\end{array}
}
$$

See Section 54 for another way to solve Example (a).

49. Integration

A power series with radius of convergence R is uniformly convergent in the closed region

(1) $$0 \leq |x - a| \leq r < R,$$

so term-by-term integration yields the desired result in the closed region (1) by Theorem 42, page 98

THEOREM 52. *If*

(2) $$f(x) = \sum_{n=0}^{\infty} a_n(x - a)^n, \qquad in \ |x - a| < R,$$

then

(3) $$\int_a^x f(\beta) \, d\beta = \sum_{n=0}^{\infty} \frac{a_n(x - a)^{n+1}}{n + 1}, \qquad in \ |x - a| < R.$$

In rough language, power series may be integrated term-by-term and the resultant power series will have the same interval of convergence as the original. The expression "may be integrated term-by-term" means that the sum of the integrals is the integral of the sum. It follows from Theorem 52 and

$$\int_{x_1}^{x_2} f(\beta) \, d\beta = \int_a^{x_2} f(\beta) \, d\beta - \int_a^{x_1} f(\beta) \, d\beta,$$

that term-by-term integration of power series is legitimate between any two limits inside the interval of convergence.

EXAMPLE Obtain the Maclaurin series for Arctan x.
From

(4) $$\frac{1}{1 - x} = \sum_{n=0}^{\infty} x^n, \qquad |x| < 1,$$

we obtain

(5) $$\frac{1}{1 + y^2} = \sum_{n=0}^{\infty} (-1)^n y^{2n}, \qquad |y| < 1.$$

We integrate each member of (5) from $y = 0$ to $y = x$ and thus arrive at

(6) $$\text{Arctan } x = \sum_{n=0}^{\infty} \frac{(-1)^n x^{2n+1}}{2n + 1}, \qquad |x| < 1.$$

With the aid of Theorem 53 of the next section, the range of validity of (6) can be extended. Indeed,

$$(7) \qquad \text{Arctan } x = \sum_{n=0}^{\infty} \frac{(-1)^n x^{2n+1}}{2n+1}, \qquad -1 \leq x \leq 1.$$

50. Continuity; Abel's Theorem

Suppose the power series

$$(1) \qquad \sum_{n=0}^{\infty} a_n x^n$$

converges at $x = R$. Then, by Theorem 45, page 109, the series also converges for $|x| < R$. Let

$$(2) \qquad s(x) = \sum_{n=0}^{\infty} a_n x^n, \qquad -R < x < R,$$

and

$$(3) \qquad F(R) = \sum_{n=0}^{\infty} a_n R^n.$$

We shall show that

$$(4) \qquad \lim_{x \to R^-} s(x) = F(R).$$

If R is less than the radius of convergence of (1), the result (4) follows at once. A power series is uniformly convergent in any closed region inside its interval of convergence by Theorem 46, page 110. Therefore, by Theorem 41, page 94, the series has a continuous sum function inside the interval of convergence.

Now suppose R is the radius of convergence of the series (1). In Hardy's test for uniform convergence, Theorem 44, page 104, choose

$$(5) \qquad u_n(x) = \left(\frac{x}{R}\right)^n \quad \text{and} \quad c_n = a_n R^n.$$

For $0 \leq x \leq R$,

$$(6) \qquad 0 \leq u_{n+1}(x) \leq u_n(x) \leq 1,$$

and $\sum_{n=0}^{\infty} c_n$ converges because the series (1) converges at $x = R$.

Therefore, by Theorem 44, the series

(7) $$\sum_{n=0}^{\infty} a_n R^n \left(\frac{x}{R}\right)^n = \sum_{n=0}^{\infty} a_n x^n$$

converges uniformly over the interval $0 \leq x \leq R$. By Theorem 41, page 94, the sum of the series in (7) is continuous on the closed interval. This completes the proof of Abel's theorem.

THEOREM 53. *If* $\sum_{n=0}^{\infty} a_n x^n$ *converges at* $x = R$,

(8) $$\lim_{x \to R^-} \left[\sum_{n=0}^{\infty} a_n x^n \right] = \sum_{n=0}^{\infty} a_n R^n.$$

The theorem applies equally well, of course, to a series

(9) $$\sum_{n=0}^{\infty} b_n (y - a)^n$$

that converges at $y - a = R$. It is often convenient to state theorems for Maclaurin series, such as (2), and use a simple substitution, $x = y - a$, to convert the theorems into results on power series of the form (9).

EXAMPLE. Sum the series

(10) $$\sum_{n=1}^{\infty} \frac{(-1)^{n+1}}{n}.$$

The geometric series

$$\frac{1}{1+\beta} = \sum_{n=0}^{\infty} (-1)^n \beta^n, \qquad -1 < \beta < 1,$$

may be integrated term by term to obtain

$$\ln(1+x) = \sum_{n=0}^{\infty} \frac{(-1)^n x^{n+1}}{n+1} = \sum_{n=1}^{\infty} \frac{(-1)^{n+1} x^n}{n}, \qquad -1 < x < 1.$$

We know, from the alternating series test, that (10) converges, Then, by Theorem 53,

$$\sum_{n=1}^{\infty} \frac{(-1)^{n+1}}{n} = \lim_{x \to 1^-} \left[\sum_{n=1}^{\infty} \frac{(-1)^{n+1} x^n}{n} \right] = \lim_{x \to 1^-} \ln(1+x) = \ln 2,$$

the desired sum. We have thus derived (5), page 119,

$$\ln(1+x) = \sum_{n=1}^{\infty} \frac{(-1)^{n+1} x^n}{n}, \qquad -1 < x \leq 1.$$

51. Differentiation

Next, we show that term-by-term differentiation of power series is legitimate and that the derived series has the same radius of convergence as the original series. Use of the following lemma will simplify our work.

LEMMA 10. *If* $\sum\limits_{n=0}^{\infty} b_n y^n$ *converges at* $y = y_0$, *then* $\sum\limits_{n=1}^{\infty} n b_n y^n$ *converges for* $|y| < |y_0|$.

PROOF. The convergence of $\sum\limits_{n=0}^{\infty} b_n y_0^n$ implies that $\{b_n y_0^n\}$ is a null sequence and therefore bounded. Then a constant M, independent of n, exists such that

$$(1) \qquad\qquad |b_n y_0^n| \leq M.$$

For $0 < r < 1$, the series of non-negative terms

$$(2) \qquad\qquad \sum\limits_{n=1}^{\infty} n r^n$$

is convergent by D'Alembert's ratio test, Theorem 19, page 44. At $r = 0$, all terms of (2) are zero, so (2) converges for $0 \leq r < 1$.

Now, for $|y| < |y_0|$,

$$|n b_n y^n| = |n b_n y_0^n| \cdot \left|\frac{y}{y_0}\right|^n \leq M \cdot n \left|\frac{y}{y_0}\right|^n,$$

so Lemma 10 follows by comparison of the terms of

$$\sum\limits_{n=1}^{\infty} n b_n y^n, \qquad |y| < |y_0|,$$

with those of the known convergent series

$$\sum\limits_{n=1}^{\infty} n \left|\frac{y}{y_0}\right|^n.$$

THEOREM 54. *If*

$$(3) \qquad\qquad f(x) = \sum\limits_{n=0}^{\infty} b_n (x-a)^n, \qquad in \ |x-a| < R,$$

then

$$(4) \qquad\qquad f'(x) = \sum\limits_{n=1}^{\infty} n b_n (x-a)^{n-1}, \qquad in \ |x-a| < R.$$

PROOF. From the assumed convergence of the series (3) in the interval $|x - a| < R$, it follows from Lemma 10 that the series

$$(5) \qquad \sum_{n=1}^{\infty} nb_n(x - a)^{n-1}$$

also converges in $|x - a| < R$.

Call the sum of the series (5) $g(x)$:

$$(6) \qquad g(x) = \sum_{n=1}^{\infty} nb_n(x - a)^{n-1}, \qquad \text{in } |x - a| < R.$$

By Theorem 52, page 133, term-by-term integration of the power series (6) is legitimate. Hence,

$$(7) \qquad \int_a^x g(\beta) \, d\beta = \sum_{n=1}^{\infty} b_n(x - a)^n, \qquad \text{in } |x - a| < R.$$

We now compare the expansions (3) and (7) and use the uniqueness theorem, page 128, to conclude that

$$(8) \qquad \int_a^x g(\beta) \, d\beta = f(x) - b_0.$$

From (8) it follows at once that $g(x) = f'(x)$ and this concludes the proof of Theorem 54.

EXAMPLE (a). Obtain various expansions from

$$(9) \qquad \frac{1}{1 - x} = \sum_{n=0}^{\infty} x^n, \qquad |x| < 1.$$

Using Theorem 54 on (9) and noting that x^0 is constant, we obtain

$$\frac{1}{(1 - x)^2} = \sum_{n=1}^{\infty} nx^{n-1}, \qquad |x| < 1,$$

or

$$(10) \qquad \frac{1}{(1 - x)^2} = \sum_{n=0}^{\infty} (n + 1)x^n, \qquad |x| < 1.$$

From (10) it follows that

$$\frac{2}{(1 - x)^3} = \sum_{n=1}^{\infty} n(n + 1)x^{n-1}, \qquad |x| < 1,$$

or

(11) $$\frac{1}{(1-x)^3} = \tfrac{1}{2} \sum_{n=0}^{\infty} (n+1)(n+2)x^n, \qquad |x| < 1,$$

etc.

EXAMPLE (b). Expand $\dfrac{x^3}{(1+x^2)^2}$ in a Maclaurin series.

Here the computation of $f^{(n)}(0)$ from

$$f(x) = \frac{x^3}{(1+x^2)^2}$$

would be tedious. Instead of the brute strength procedure, we obtain

(12) $$\frac{1}{(1-x)^2} = \sum_{n=1}^{\infty} nx^{n-1}, \qquad |x| < 1,$$

as in Example (a). In (12), replace x by $(-x^2)$ to obtain

$$\frac{1}{(1+x^2)^2} = \sum_{n=1}^{\infty} (-1)^{n-1} n x^{2n-2}, \qquad |x| + 1,$$

from which it follows that

$$\frac{x^3}{(1+x^2)^2} = \sum_{n=1}^{\infty} (-1)^{n-1} n x^{2n+1}, \qquad |x| < 1,$$

or

$$\frac{x^3}{(1+x^2)^2} =: \sum_{n=0}^{\infty} (-1)^n (n+1) x^{2n+3}, \qquad |x| < 1.$$

Exercises

The solution of these exercises involves the use of the theorems developed so far in this chapter, not just the theorem of this section. An interval of convergence enclosed in parentheses was determined by methods more advanced than those given in this book.

1. Obtain the series for $\sinh x$ from the series for $\cosh x$ in two ways.
2. From the series for $(1 + x)^{-\frac{1}{2}}$, obtain the series for $(1 - y^2)^{-\frac{1}{2}}$, and then that for Arcsin x.

     ANS. $Arcsin\ x = x + \displaystyle\sum_{n=1}^{\infty} \frac{1 \cdot 3 \cdot 5 \cdots (2n-1)x^{2n+1}}{2^n n!(2n+1)}, \qquad |x| < 1.$

3. Investigate the result of integrating, term by term, the series for e^x.
4. Obtain the series for $\cos x$ by integration.

5. Show that

$$\ln\frac{1+x}{1-x} = 2\sum_{n=0}^{\infty}\frac{x^{2n+1}}{2n+1}, \qquad |x| < 1.$$

6. Show that

$$\ln(1-3x+2x^2) = -\sum_{n=1}^{\infty}\frac{(1+2^n)x^n}{n}, \qquad |x| < \tfrac{1}{2}.$$

7. Show that

$$\frac{x}{(1+8x^3)^2} = \sum_{n=0}^{\infty}(n+1)2^{3n}x^{3n+1}, \qquad |x| < \tfrac{1}{2}.$$

8. Obtain a power series for $x(1-3x^4)^{-2}$.

9. Show that

$$\ln^2(1+x) = \sum_{n=2}^{\infty}\sum_{k=2}^{n}\frac{(-1)^n x^n}{(k-1)(n+1-k)}, \qquad |x| < 1.$$

See also Exercise 16, page 163.

10. Use the result in Exercise 9 to obtain a series for

$$\frac{\ln(1+x)}{1+x}.$$

See also Exercise 15, page 163.

11. Use the formula $\cos^2 x = \tfrac{1}{2}(1+\cos 2x)$ to obtain

$$\cos^2 x = 1 + \sum_{n=1}^{\infty}\frac{(-1)^n 2^{2n-1}x^{2n}}{(2n)!}, \qquad |x| < \infty.$$

12. Use the formula $\sin^2 x = \tfrac{1}{2}(1-\cos 2x)$ to obtain a series for $\sin^2 x$ and check your result with that in Exercise 11.

In Exercises 13–21, obtain the series out to the term indicated. See also the results in Sections 54, page 146, and 56, page 148.

13. $\sec x$, to the term in x^6.

   ANS. $1 + \tfrac{1}{2}x^2 + \tfrac{5}{24}x^4 + \tfrac{61}{720}x^6 + \cdots$, $(|x| < \tfrac{1}{2}\pi)$.

14. $x \csc x$, to the term in x^4.

   ANS. $1 + \tfrac{1}{6}x^2 + \tfrac{7}{360}x^4 + \cdots$, $(|x| < \pi)$.

15. $\tan^2 x$, to the term in x^6.

   ANS. $x^2 + \tfrac{2}{3}x^4 + \tfrac{17}{45}x^6 + \cdots$, $(|x| < \tfrac{1}{2}\pi)$.

16. $\sec^2 x$, to the term in x^6, by squaring the answer to Exercise 13.

17. From the series for $\tan x$, Example (a), page 131, obtain the terms, out to the x^6 term, in the power series for $\ln \cos x$.

   ANS. $\ln \cos x = -\dfrac{x^2}{2} - \dfrac{x^4}{12} - \dfrac{x^6}{45} + \cdots$, $(|x| < \tfrac{1}{2}\pi)$.

18. Using the result in Exercise 13, obtain the power series for

$$\ln (\sec x + \tan x),$$

out to the term in x^7.

ANS. $\ln(\sec x + \tan x) = x + \dfrac{x^3}{6} + \dfrac{x^5}{24} + \dfrac{61x^7}{5040} + \cdots, \qquad (|x| < \tfrac{1}{2}\pi).$

19. In Exercise 15 we found that

$$\tan^2 x = x^2 + \tfrac{2}{3}x^4 + \tfrac{17}{45}x^6 + \cdots.$$

By integration of this series show that

$$\tan x = x + \frac{x^3}{3} + \frac{2x^5}{15} + \frac{17x^7}{315} + \cdots$$

and thus improve upon the result obtained in Example (a), page 131.

20. From Exercise 13, find the first three terms of the series for

$$\sec x \tan x.$$

Check your result by multiplication of series.

21. Show that

$$\csc x - \cot x = \tfrac{1}{2}x + \frac{1}{24}x^3 + \frac{1}{240}x^5 + \cdots, \qquad (|x| < \pi).$$

22. Show that $\sin^3 x = \dfrac{3}{4} \displaystyle\sum_{n=1}^{\infty} \dfrac{(-1)^{n-1}(3^{2n}-1)x^{2n+1}}{(2n+1)!}, \qquad |x| < \infty.$

23. Find, to three decimal places, the area under the curve $y = \exp(-x^2)$ from $x = 0$ to $x = \tfrac{1}{2}$.   ANS.   0.461.

24. Find the area under the curve $y = \exp(-x^3)$ from $x = 0$ to $x = 1$.   ANS.   0.807.

25. Find the area under the curve $y = \cos(x^2)$ from $x = 0$ to $x = 1$.   ANS.   0.9045.

26. Find the area under the curve $y = \sin(x^2)$ from $x = 0$ to $x = 1$.

27. Find, to two decimal places, the centroid of the area in Exercise 23.   ANS.   (0.24, 0.46).

28. Show that for values of x so small that the fourth and higher powers of $\dfrac{x}{a}$ may be neglected, the catenary $y = a \cosh \dfrac{x}{a}$ may be replaced by the parabola $x^2 = 2a(y - a)$.

29. Find the area under the curve $y = x^{-1}e^{-x}$ from $x = 0.001$ to $x = 0.002$.   ANS. $\ln 2 - 0.00100 = 0.69215.$

In Exercises 30–42, evaluate the limits with the aid of power series. Note that this is one application in which the general term of the series is not of use; a few terms suffice.

30. $\lim_{\theta \to 0} \dfrac{\theta - \sin \theta}{\theta^3}$. $\qquad$ ANS. $\frac{1}{6}$.

31. $\lim_{\theta \to 0} \dfrac{1 - \cos \theta}{\theta^2}$. $\qquad$ ANS. $\frac{1}{2}$.

32. $\lim_{x \to 0} \dfrac{(1+x)^m - (1-x)^m}{x}$. $\qquad$ ANS. $2m$.

33. $\lim_{x \to 0} \dfrac{\sinh x - \sin x}{x^3}$. $\qquad$ ANS. $\frac{1}{3}$.

34. $\lim_{x \to 0} \dfrac{\cosh x - \cos x}{x^2}$. $\qquad$ ANS. 1.

35. $\lim_{x \to 0} \dfrac{\sin x - \ln(1+x)}{x^2}$. $\qquad$ ANS. $\frac{1}{2}$.

36. $\lim_{x \to 0} \dfrac{\cos x - 1}{x \sin x}$. $\qquad$ ANS. $-\frac{1}{2}$.

37. $\lim_{\theta \to 0} \dfrac{\sin \theta - \theta \cos \theta}{\sin^3 \theta}$. $\qquad$ ANS. $\frac{1}{3}$.

38. $\lim_{\theta \to 0} \dfrac{\tan \theta - \theta}{\theta^3}$. $\qquad$ ANS. $\frac{1}{3}$.

39. $\lim_{\theta \to 0} \dfrac{\tan^2 \theta - \theta^2}{\theta^4}$. $\qquad$ ANS. $\frac{2}{3}$.

40. $\lim_{x \to 0} \dfrac{\tan^2 x - \sin^2 x.}{\sinh^3 x \ln(1+x)}$. $\qquad$ ANS. 1.

41. $\lim_{a \to 0} \dfrac{\tan 2\alpha - 2 \sin \alpha}{\alpha^3}$.

42. $\lim_{x \to 0} \dfrac{\sqrt{1-x} - \sqrt{1+x}}{x}$.

52. Harmonic Sums

On page 33 we showed that the harmonic series diverges and therefore that the harmonic sum

$$(1) \qquad H_n = \sum_{k=1}^{n} \frac{1}{k} = 1 + \frac{1}{2} + \frac{1}{3} + \cdots + \frac{1}{n}$$

approaches infinity, as $n \to \infty$. We are now in a position to examine H_n more closely. First, we show that the sequence with elements

$$(2) \qquad\qquad A_m = H_m - \ln m$$

converges to some limit γ. Our proof will also show that the constant γ, called the Euler or Mascheroni* constant, lies somewhere in the interval $0 \leq \gamma < 1$. An approximation to γ is

$$\gamma = 0.5772.$$

Since $\dfrac{1}{x}$ decreases steadily as x increases for $x \geq 1$, we obtain

$$(3) \qquad\qquad \frac{1}{k} < \int_{k-1}^{k} \frac{dx}{x} < \frac{1}{k-1}, \qquad k \geq 2.$$

Sum each member of (3) from $k = 2$ to $k = m$ to see that

$$\sum_{k=2}^{m} \frac{1}{k} < \sum_{k=2}^{m} \int_{k-1}^{k} \frac{dx}{x} < \sum_{k=2}^{m} \frac{1}{k-1}$$

so

$$H_m - 1 < \int_{1}^{m} \frac{dx}{x} < H_{m-1},$$

which yields

$$(4) \qquad\qquad H_m - 1 < \ln m < H_{m-1}.$$

By (4),

$$-1 < -H_m + \ln m < -\frac{1}{m}.$$

Therefore the A_m of (2) satisfies

$$(5) \qquad\qquad 1 > A_m > \frac{1}{m},$$

so $\{A_m\}$ is a bounded sequence of positive elements.

Next, we show that $\{A_m\}$ is strictly monotonic decreasing. Since

$$A_{m+1} - A_m = H_{m+1} - H_m - \ln(m+1) + \ln m$$

$$= \frac{1}{m+1} + \ln \frac{m}{m+1} = \frac{1}{m+1} + \ln\left(1 - \frac{1}{m+1}\right)$$

---

* L. Euler, 1707–1783; L. Mascheroni, 1750–1800.

and $m \geq 1$, we may use the power series expansion for $\ln(1-x)$ to obtain the relation

$$A_{m+1} - A_m = \frac{1}{m+1} - \sum_{k=1}^{\infty} \frac{1}{k(m+1)^k}$$

$$= -\sum_{k=2}^{\infty} \frac{1}{k(m+1)^k}.$$

Then $A_{m+1} < A_m$. The sequence $\{A_m\}$ is a bounded monotonic decreasing sequence and thus converges to some limit γ.

THEOREM 55. $\lim_{m \to \infty} (H_m - \ln m) = \gamma$.

The harmonic sum H_m does $\to \infty$ as $m \to \infty$, but somewhat slowly. From (5) we obtain

(6) $$H_m < 1 + \ln m.$$

For m equal to a billion, for instance, $m = 10^9$, so

$$\ln m = \frac{\log_{10} 10^9}{\log_{10} e} = 9(2.30259) = 20.7233,$$

and therefore

$$H_{1,000,000,000} < 22.$$

EXAMPLE. Simplify the sum

(7) $$\sum_{k=0}^{n} \frac{1}{2k+1} = 1 + \frac{1}{3} + \frac{1}{5} + \cdots + \frac{1}{2n+1}.$$

We fill in the sum of the reciprocals of even integers to bring the sum in (7) to proper form for a harmonic sum. Thus

$$1 + \frac{1}{3} + \frac{1}{5} + \cdots + \frac{1}{2n+1} = 1 + \frac{1}{2} + \frac{1}{3} + \frac{1}{4} + \frac{1}{5} + \cdots + \frac{1}{2n} + \frac{1}{2n+1}$$

$$- \left(\frac{1}{2} + \frac{1}{4} + \frac{1}{6} + \cdots + \frac{1}{2n} \right),$$

so

(8) $$\sum_{k=0}^{n} \frac{1}{2k+1} = H_{2n+1} - \tfrac{1}{2} H_n.$$

53. Bernoulli Numbers

We define a sequence of numbers $\{B_n\}$ by

(1)
$$\frac{x}{e^x - 1} = \sum_{n=0}^{\infty} \frac{B_n x^n}{n!}, \qquad |x| < 2\pi.$$

The numbers B_n are called the *Bernoulli* numbers*. We shall find that these numbers occur naturally in many power series expansions.

From (1) it follows that

$$x = \left[\sum_{n=0}^{\infty} \frac{x^n}{n!} \right] \left[\sum_{n=0}^{\infty} \frac{B_n x^n}{n!} \right] - \sum_{n=0}^{\infty} \frac{B_n x^n}{n!}$$

or

(2)
$$x = \sum_{n=0}^{\infty} \sum_{k=0}^{n} \frac{B_k x^n}{k!(n-k)!} - \sum_{n=0}^{\infty} \frac{B_n x^n}{n!}.$$

Equating coefficients of corresponding powers of x of the right- and left-hand members of (2) yields

$$n = 0: \qquad B_0 - B_0 = 0,$$

$$n = 1: \qquad B_0 + B_1 - B_1 = 1,$$

$$n \geq 2: \qquad \sum_{k=0}^{n} \frac{B_k}{k!(n-k)!} - \frac{B_n}{n!} = 0.$$

Thus we find that $B_0 = 1$ and the remaining B_n may be computed successively from

(3)
$$\sum_{k=0}^{n} \frac{n! \, B_k}{k!(n-k)!} = B_n, \qquad n \geq 2.$$

The coefficient of B_k in the summation on the left in (3) is the binomial coefficient. A popular symbolic notation replaces the equals sign $=$ by the symbol $\doteq$ to indicate that two expressions will be equal when exponents are lowered to subscripts. For example,

$$(1 + B)^3 \doteq B^0 + 3B^1 + 3B^2 + B^3,$$

so

---

* Named for Jakob (James) Bernoulli, 1654–1705, who introduced them in a work published in 1713. The reader is warned that varying notations exist for Bernoulli numbers. The notation used here is only one of the prevalent ones. Before using results on Bernoulli numbers, always check to see what that particular author means by B_n.

$$(1+B)^3 \doteq B_0 + 3B_1 + 3B_2 + B_3.$$

In this symbolic notation, (3) takes the form

(4) $$(1+B)^n \doteq B^n, \qquad n \geq 2.$$

In particular we obtain

(5) $$B_0 + 2B_1 + B_2 = B_2,$$

(6) $$B_0 + 3B_1 + 3B_2 + B_3 = B_3,$$

(7) $$B_0 + 4B_1 + 6B_2 + 4B_3 + B_4 = B_4,$$

(8) $$B_0 + 5B_1 + 10B_2 + 10B_3 + 5B_4 + B_5 = B_5, \quad \text{etc.}$$

Since $B_0 = 1$, we find that $B_1 = -\dfrac{1}{2}$, $B_2 = \dfrac{1}{6}$, $B_3 = 0$, $B_4 = -\dfrac{1}{30}$.

Using the known B_0 and B_1, we may write (1) in the form

$$\frac{x}{e^x - 1} = 1 - \tfrac{1}{2}x + \sum_{n=2}^{\infty} \frac{B_n x^n}{n!},$$

(9)
$$\frac{x}{e^x - 1} + \frac{x}{2} = 1 + \sum_{n=2}^{\infty} \frac{B_n x^n}{n!}.$$

Consider the left member of (9). Elementary manipulations give us

$$\frac{x}{e^x - 1} + \frac{x}{2} = \frac{\tfrac{1}{2}x + \tfrac{1}{2}xe^x}{e^x - 1} = \frac{x}{2} \cdot \frac{e^x + 1}{e^x - 1}.$$

But

$$\frac{e^x + 1}{e^x - 1} = \frac{\exp(\tfrac{1}{2}x) + \exp(-\tfrac{1}{2}x)}{\exp(\tfrac{1}{2}x) - \exp(-\tfrac{1}{2}x)} = \coth \frac{x}{2},$$

so

(10) $$\frac{x}{2} \coth \frac{x}{2} = 1 + \sum_{n=2}^{\infty} \frac{B_n x^n}{n!}.$$

The function on the left in (10) is an even function* of x and its power series expansion must contain only even powers of x. Hence, for $n \geq 2$, all Bernoulli numbers with odd subscripts are zero:

(11) $$B_{2k+1} = 0, \qquad \text{for } k \geq 1.$$

The only nonzero element of the sequence $\{B_{2k+1}\}$ is B_1.

* An even function of x is one possessing the property $f(-x) = f(x)$. See also Section 69, page 176.

Because of (11), and the fact that $B_0=1$, equation (10) takes the form

$$(12) \qquad \frac{x}{2} \coth \frac{x}{2} = \sum_{k=0}^{\infty} \frac{B_{2k}x^{2k}}{(2k)!}, \qquad |x| < 2\pi.$$

In (12) let us replace x by $(2x)$ and go back to the running index n. We thus obtain the expansion on which all the results in the next section will be based:

$$(13) \qquad x \coth x = \sum_{n=0}^{\infty} \frac{2^{2n}B_{2n}x^{2n}}{(2n)!}, \qquad |x| < \pi.$$

An interesting result, proof of which requires more background than is assumed or developed in this book, is that

$$(14) \qquad \sum_{k=1}^{\infty} \frac{1}{k^{2n}} = \frac{(-1)^{n+1}(2\pi)^{2n}B_{2n}}{2(2n)!}.$$

In our study of Fourier series, Chapter 11, we shall encounter the special cases $n = 1$ and $n = 2$ of (14),

$$\sum_{k=1}^{\infty} \frac{1}{k^2} = \frac{\pi^2}{6}, \qquad \sum_{k=1}^{\infty} \frac{1}{k^4} = \frac{\pi^4}{90}.$$

In the notation we are using, the first few nonzero Bernoulli numbers are

$$B_0 = 1, \quad B_1 = -\frac{1}{2}, \quad B_2 = \frac{1}{6}, \quad B_4 = \frac{-1}{30}, \quad B_6 = \frac{1}{42},$$

$$B_8 = \frac{-1}{30}, \quad B_{10} = \frac{5}{66}, \quad B_{12} = \frac{-691}{2730}, \quad B_{14} = \frac{7}{6}, \quad B_{16} = \frac{-3617}{510}.$$

54. Expansion of tan x

In the preceding section we obtained the expansion

$$(1) \qquad x \coth x = \sum_{n=0}^{\infty} \frac{2^{2n}B_{2n}x^{2n}}{(2n)!}, \qquad |x| < \pi,$$

in which the B_{2n} are Bernoulli numbers. We know that

$$\coth x = \frac{\cosh x}{\sinh x} = \frac{e^x + e^{-x}}{e^x - e^{-x}}$$

and

$$\cot x = \frac{\cos x}{\sin x} = \frac{i(e^{ix} + e^{-ix})}{e^{ix} - e^{-ix}}.$$

Then

$$(ix) \coth(ix) = x \cot x.$$

Let us replace x by ix throughout (1) and thus arrive at

(2) $$x \cot x = \sum_{n=0}^{\infty} \frac{(-1)^n 2^{2n} B_{2n} x^{2n}}{(2n)!}, \qquad |x| < \pi.$$

The trigonometric identity

(3) $$\tan x = \cot x - 2 \cot 2x$$

is easily verified. Using (3) in conjunction with (2), we obtain

$$x \tan x = \sum_{n=0}^{\infty} \frac{(-1)^n 2^{2n} B_{2n} x^{2n}}{(2n)!} - \sum_{n=0}^{\infty} \frac{(-1)^n 2^{2n} B_{2n} (2x)^{2n}}{(2n)!},$$

from which it follows that

(4) $$\tan x = \sum_{n=1}^{\infty} \frac{(-1)^{n+1} 2^{2n} (2^{2n} - 1) B_{2n} x^{2n-1}}{(2n)!}, \qquad |x| < \tfrac{1}{2}\pi.$$

Many other expansions can be obtained from (2) and (4); some of them appear in the exercises on pages 149–150.

55. Euler Numbers

In a manner paralleling our definition of Bernoulli numbers, we define the *Euler Numbers* E_n by

(1) $$\frac{2e^x}{e^{2x} + 1} = \sum_{n=0}^{\infty} \frac{E_n x^n}{n!}, \qquad |x| < \tfrac{1}{2}\pi.$$

Since

$$\frac{2e^x}{e^{2x} + 1} = \frac{2e^{-x}}{1 + e^{-2x}},$$

the left member of (1) is an even function of x. It follows that $E_{2n+1} = 0$ for all n and that

(2) $$\frac{2e^x}{e^{2x} + 1} = \sum_{n=0}^{\infty} \frac{E_{2n} x^{2n}}{(2n)!}, \qquad |x| < \tfrac{1}{2}\pi.$$

We know that

$$\frac{2e^x}{e^{2x}+1} = \frac{2}{e^x + e^{-x}} = \operatorname{sech} x,$$

so (2) may be written in the form

$$(3) \qquad \operatorname{sech} x = \sum_{n=0}^{\infty} \frac{E_{2n}x^{2n}}{(2n)!}, \qquad |x| < \tfrac{1}{2}\pi.$$

We shall use (3) in the next section.

Returning to equation (1) and proceeding as we did with Bernoulli numbers, we obtain

$$2\sum_{n=0}^{\infty}\frac{x^n}{n!} = \left[\sum_{n=0}^{\infty}\frac{2^n x^n}{n!}\right]\left[\sum_{n=0}^{\infty}\frac{E_n x^n}{n!}\right] + \sum_{n=0}^{\infty}\frac{E_n x^n}{n!}.$$

We perform the indicated product and then equate corresponding coefficients of x^n to arrive at $E_0 = 1$ and

$$(4) \qquad \sum_{k=0}^{n}\frac{n!\,2^{n-k}E_k}{k!\,(n-k)!} + E_n = 2, \qquad n \geq 1.$$

With the symbolic notation introduced on page 144, we may write (4) in the form

$$(5) \qquad (2+E)^n + E^n \doteq 2, \qquad n \geq 1.$$

We know that $E_{2k+1} = 0$. For odd n, (5) will lead to the same conclusion. For even n, we obtain

$$4E_0 + 4E_1 + E_2 + E_2 = 2,$$

$$2^4 E_0 + 2^3(4)E_1 + 2^2(6)E_2 + 2(4)E_3 + E_4 + E_4 = 2,$$

$$2^6 E_0 + 2^5(6)E_1 + 2^4(15)E_2 + 2^3(20)E_3 + 2^2(15)E_4 + 2(6)E_5 + E_6 + E_6 = 2,$$

etc. Then, from $E_0 = 1$, we obtain $E_2 = -1$, $E_4 = 5$, $E_6 = -61$.

56. Expansion of sec x

In terms of the Euler numbers, we have obtained

$$(1) \qquad \operatorname{sech} x = \sum_{n=0}^{\infty} \frac{E_{2n}x^{2n}}{(2n)!}, \qquad |x| < \tfrac{1}{2}\pi.$$

Since $\operatorname{sech}(ix) = \sec x$, it follows from (1) that

(2) $$\sec x = \sum_{n=0}^{\infty} \frac{(-1)^n E_{2n} x^{2n}}{(2n)!}, \qquad |x| < \tfrac{1}{2}\pi.$$

Other expansions, derived from (1) and (2) are contained in the exercises.

Exercises

1. Use the expansion for tan x, equation (4), page 147, to obtain
$$\sec^2 x = \sum_{n=1}^{\infty} \frac{(-1)^{n+1}(2n-1)2^{2n}(2^{2n}-1)B_{2n}x^{2n-2}}{(2n)!}, \qquad |x| < \tfrac{1}{2}\pi.$$

2. Use the expansion for tan x, equation (4), page 147, to obtain
$$\ln \cos x = \sum_{n=1}^{\infty} \frac{(-1)^n 2^{2n-1}(2^{2n}-1)B_{2n}x^{2n}}{n(2n)!}, \qquad |x| < \tfrac{1}{2}\pi.$$

3. Use the trigonometric identity
$$\csc 2x = \cot x - \cot 2x$$
and the expansion for $x \cot x$, equation (2), page 147, to conclude that
$$x \csc x = \frac{x}{\sin x} = \sum_{n=0}^{\infty} \frac{(-1)^{n+1}(2^{2n}-2)B_{2n}x^{2n}}{(2n)!}, \qquad |x| < \pi.$$

4. Show that
$$2 \coth 2x - \coth x = \tanh x$$
and then use the expansion for $x \coth x$, equation (1), page 146, to arrive at
$$\tanh x = \sum_{n=1}^{\infty} \frac{2^{2n}(2^{2n}-1)B_{2n}x^{2n-1}}{(2n)!}, \qquad |x| < \tfrac{1}{2}\pi.$$
Check your result with equation (4), page 147.

5. Use the result in Exercise 1 to obtain a series for $\sec^2 x \tan x$.

6. Obtain a series for $\sec^4 x$ by performing two differentiations of the result in Exercise 1.

7. By differentiation of equation (2), page 147, obtain a series for the function $x^2 \csc^2 x$.

8. Show that $\coth x - \coth 2x = \operatorname{csch} 2x$, and then from equation (1), page 146, obtain a series for $\operatorname{csch} x$.

9. Integrate both members of the expansion for sec x, equation (2), this page, and thus obtain
$$\ln (\sec x + \tan x) = \sum_{n=0}^{\infty} \frac{(-1)^n E_{2n} x^{2n+1}}{(2n+1)!}, \qquad |x| < \tfrac{1}{2}\pi.$$

10. Obtain the expansion

$$\sec x \tan x = \sum_{n=1}^{\infty} \frac{(-1)^n E_{2n} x^{2n-1}}{(2n-1)!}, \qquad |x| < \tfrac{1}{2}\pi.$$

11. Show that

$$\sec^3 x = \sum_{n=0}^{\infty} \frac{(-1)^{n+1}(E_{2n+2} - E_{2n}) x^{2n}}{2(2n)!}, \qquad |x| < \tfrac{1}{2}\pi.$$

CHAPTER 9

Functions Defined by Power Series

57. The Factorial Function

Before proceeding to the study of some functions defined by power series, we shall introduce a few tools to simplify the presentation.

It is convenient to use a standard notation for the product of n factors, each factor larger by unity than the preceding one. We put

$$(1) \qquad (\alpha)_n = \alpha(\alpha+1)(\alpha+2)\cdots(\alpha+n-1), \qquad \text{for } n \geq 1,$$

$$(\alpha)_0 = 1, \text{ for } \alpha \neq 0.$$

The function $(\alpha)_n$ thus defined is called the *factorial function* and it is a direct generalization of the simple factorial of Section 6, page 7. Indeed,

$$(2) \qquad\qquad\qquad n! = (1)_n.$$

EXAMPLE (a). Directly from the definition (1), we obtain

$$(6)_4 = 6\cdot 7\cdot 8\cdot 9,$$

$$(-7)_5 = (-7)(-6)(-5)(-4)(-3),$$

$$(\tfrac{1}{2})_3 = \left(\frac{1}{2}\right)\left(\frac{3}{2}\right)\left(\frac{5}{2}\right).$$

The following result is frequently useful and it should be derived by the student:

$$(a)_{2n} = 2^{2n}\left(\frac{a}{2}\right)_n \left(\frac{a+1}{2}\right)_n.$$

EXAMPLE (b). Evaluate the ratio $\dfrac{(\alpha)_{n+1}}{(\alpha)_n}$.

By (1) the subscript in $(\alpha)_n$ denotes the number of factors involved. Since each of the products $(\alpha)_n$ and $(\alpha)_{n+1}$ starts with the factor α, and $(\alpha)_{n+1}$ has one more factor than $(\alpha)_n$ has, we obtain

$$(\alpha)_{n+1} = (\alpha)_n(\alpha + n),$$

so

$$\frac{(\alpha)_{n+1}}{(\alpha)_n} = \alpha + n.$$

EXAMPLE (c). Evaluate $\dfrac{(\beta - 2)_n}{(\beta + 1)_n}$.

Here

$$(\beta - 2)_n = (\beta - 2)(\beta - 1)(\beta)(\beta + 1)_{n-3}$$

and, by (1),

$$(\beta + 1)_n = (\beta + 1)_{n-3}(\beta + 1 + n - 3)(\beta + 1 + n - 2)(\beta + 1 + n - 1),$$

so

$$\frac{(\beta - 2)_n}{(\beta + 1)_n} = \frac{(\beta - 2)(\beta - 1)\beta}{(\beta + n - 2)(\beta + n - 1)(\beta + n)}.$$

EXAMPLE (d). Show that

(3) $$(1 - y)^{-\alpha} = 1 + \sum_{n=1}^{\infty} \frac{(\alpha)_n y^n}{n!}, \qquad |y| < 1.$$

In the binomial expansion, equation (6), page 119, replace x by $(-y)$ and m by $(-\alpha)$ to obtain, for $|y| < 1$,

$$(1 - y)^{-\alpha} = 1 + \sum_{n=1}^{\infty} \frac{(-\alpha)(-\alpha - 1)(-\alpha - 2) \cdots (-\alpha - n + 1)(-y)^n}{n!}.$$

But

$$(-1)^n(-\alpha)(-\alpha - 1)(-\alpha - 2) \cdots (-\alpha - n + 1) = (\alpha)_n,$$

so

$$(1 - y)^{-\alpha} = 1 + \sum_{n=1}^{\infty} \frac{(\alpha)_n y^n}{n!},$$

as desired.

58. The Gamma Function

The Gamma function $\Gamma(x)$ is defined by

(1) $$\Gamma(x) = \int_0^\infty e^{-\beta}\beta^{x-1}\, d\beta, \qquad x > 0.$$

Substitution of $(x+1)$ for x in (1) gives

(2) $$\Gamma(x+1) = \int_0^\infty e^{-\beta}\beta^x\, d\beta.$$

An integration by parts, integrating $e^{-\beta}\, d\beta$ and differentiating β^x, yields

(3) $$\Gamma(x+1) = \left[-e^{-\beta}\beta^x \right]_0^\infty + x \int_0^\infty e^{-\beta}\beta^{x-1}\, d\beta.$$

Since $x > 0$, $\beta^x \to 0$ as $\beta \to 0$. Since x is fixed, $e^{-\beta}\beta^x \to 0$ as $\beta \to \infty$. Thus

(4) $$\Gamma(x+1) = x \int_0^\infty e^{-\beta}\beta^{x-1}\, d\beta = x\Gamma(x).$$

THEOREM 56. *For $x > 0$, $\Gamma(x+1) = x\Gamma(x)$.*

The definition (1) is equally useful for complex x with the restriction that the real part of x, $\operatorname{Re}(x)$, be positive,

(5) $$\Gamma(x) = \int_0^\infty e^{-\beta}\beta^{x-1}\, d\beta, \qquad \operatorname{Re}(x) > 0.$$

The condition $x > 0$ in Theorem 56 can be replaced by $\operatorname{Re}(x) > 0$.

By repeated use of Theorem 56, we obtain

$$\begin{aligned}
\Gamma(\alpha+n) &= (\alpha+n-1)\Gamma(\alpha+n-1) \\
&= (\alpha+n-1)(\alpha+n-2)\Gamma(\alpha+n-2) \\
&\quad \vdots \\
&= (\alpha+n-1)(\alpha+n-2)\cdots(\alpha)\Gamma(\alpha) \\
&= (\alpha)_n\Gamma(\alpha).
\end{aligned}$$

THEOREM 57. *If n is a positive integer and if α is neither zero nor a negative integer,*

(6) $$(\alpha)_n = \frac{\Gamma(\alpha+n)}{\Gamma(\alpha)}.$$

Equation (6), but not the proof given here, is valid for all complex α except zero and the negative integers.

It follows from (6) that

$$\Gamma(n+1) = n!\,\Gamma(1).$$

By definition

$$\Gamma(1) = \int_0^\infty e^{-\beta}\beta^0\,d\beta = \left[-e^{-\beta}\right]_0^\infty = 1.$$

Hence, for positive integral n (and also for $n = 0$)

(7) $$\Gamma(n+1) = n!.$$

An important property of the Gamma function, but a result we shall neither prove* nor use is the following:

If x is not an integer,

(8) $$\Gamma(x)\Gamma(1-x) = \frac{\pi}{\sin \pi x}.$$

59. The Beta Function

We define the Beta function $B(p, q)$ by

(1) $$B(p, q) = \int_0^1 t^{p-1}(1-t)^{q-1}\,dt, \qquad \mathrm{Re}(p) > 0,\ \mathrm{Re}(q) > 0.$$

Another useful form for this function can be obtained by putting $t = \sin^2 \varphi$, thus arriving at

(2) $$B(p, q) = 2\int_0^{\frac{1}{2}\pi} \sin^{2p-1}\varphi\,\cos^{2q-1}\varphi\,d\varphi, \qquad \mathrm{Re}(p) > 0,\ \mathrm{Re}(q) > 0.$$

The Beta function is intimately related to the Gamma function. Consider the product

(3) $$\Gamma(p)\Gamma(q) = \int_0^\infty e^{-t}t^{p-1}\,dt \cdot \int_0^\infty e^{-v}v^{q-1}\,dv.$$

In (3) use $t = x^2$ and $v = y^2$ to obtain

$$\Gamma(p)\Gamma(q) = 4\int_0^\infty \exp(-x^2)x^{2p-1}\,dx \cdot \int_0^\infty \exp(-y^2)y^{2q-1}\,dy,$$

---

* See, for example, E. D. Rainville, *Special Functions*, New York, The Macmillan Co., 1960, pp. 19–21.

$$\Gamma(p)\Gamma(q) = 4 \int_0^\infty \int_0^\infty \exp(-x^2 - y^2)x^{2p-1}y^{2q-1}\ dx\ dy.$$

Next turn to polar coordinates for the iterated integration over the first quadrant in the xy-plane. Using $x = r\cos\theta$, $y = r\sin\theta$, we may write

$$\Gamma(p)\Gamma(q) = 4 \int_0^\infty \int_0^{\frac{1}{2}\pi} \exp(-r^2)r^{2p+2q-2}\cos^{2p-1}\theta \sin^{2q-1}\theta\ r d\theta dr$$

$$= 2 \int_0^\infty \exp(-r^2)r^{2p+2q-1}dr \cdot 2\int_0^{\frac{1}{2}\pi} \cos^{2p-1}\theta \sin^{2q-1}\theta\ d\theta.$$

Now put $r = \sqrt{t}$ and $\theta = \frac{1}{2}\pi - \varphi$ to obtain

$$\Gamma(p)\Gamma(q) = \int_0^\infty e^{-t}t^{p+q-1}\ dt \cdot 2\int_0^{\frac{1}{2}\pi} \sin^{2p-1}\varphi \cos^{2q-1}\varphi\ d\varphi,$$

from which it follows that

$$\Gamma(p)\Gamma(q) = \Gamma(p+q)B(p, q).$$

THEOREM 58. *If* $\mathrm{Re}(p) > 0$ *and* $\mathrm{Re}(q) > 0$,

$$(4) \qquad\qquad B(p, q) = \frac{\Gamma(p)\Gamma(q)}{\Gamma(p+q)}.$$

By (4), $B(p, q) = B(q, p)$, a result just as easily obtained directly from (1) or (2).

Equations (2) and (4) yield a generalization of Wallis' formula of elementary calculus. In (2) put $2p - 1 = m$, $2q - 1 = n$, and use (4) to write

$$(5) \qquad \int_0^{\frac{1}{2}\pi} \sin^m\varphi \cos^n\varphi\ d\varphi = \frac{\Gamma\left(\dfrac{m+1}{2}\right)\Gamma\left(\dfrac{n+1}{2}\right)}{2\,\Gamma\left(\dfrac{m+n+2}{2}\right)},$$

valid for $\mathrm{Re}(m) > -1$, $\mathrm{Re}(n) > -1$.

EXAMPLE (a). Use the Beta function to evaluate $\Gamma(\frac{1}{2})$.

By Theorem 58,

$$(6) \qquad\qquad \frac{\Gamma(\frac{1}{2})\Gamma(\frac{1}{2})}{\Gamma(1)} = B(\tfrac{1}{2}, \tfrac{1}{2}),$$

and, by equation (2) of this section,

(7) $$B(\tfrac{1}{2}, \tfrac{1}{2}) = 2 \int_0^{\frac{1}{2}\pi} \sin^0 \varphi \cos^0 \varphi \, d\varphi = 2(\tfrac{1}{2}\pi) = \pi.$$

Since $\Gamma(\tfrac{1}{2})$ is positive, by its definition, (6) and (7) together yield the evaluation

$$\Gamma(\tfrac{1}{2}) = \sqrt{\pi}.$$

EXAMPLE (b). Prove that, if $\mathrm{Re}(\gamma) > \mathrm{Re}(\beta) > 0$, and if n is a non-negative integer,

(8) $$\frac{(\beta)_n}{(\gamma)_n} = \frac{\Gamma(\gamma)}{\Gamma(\beta)\Gamma(\gamma - \beta)} \int_0^1 t^{\beta+n-1}(1 - t)^{\gamma-\beta-1} \, dt.$$

By Theorem 57, page 153,

(9) $$\frac{(\beta)_n}{(\gamma)_n} = \frac{\Gamma(\beta + n)\Gamma(\gamma)}{\Gamma(\beta)\Gamma(\gamma + n)} = \frac{\Gamma(\gamma)}{\Gamma(\beta)\Gamma(\gamma - \beta)} \cdot \frac{\Gamma(\beta + n)\Gamma(\gamma - \beta)}{\Gamma(\gamma + n)}.$$

By Theorem 58,

$$\frac{\Gamma(\beta + n)\Gamma(\gamma - \beta)}{\Gamma(\gamma + n)} = B(\beta + n, \gamma - \beta)$$

$$= \int_0^1 t^{\beta+n-1}(1 - t)^{\gamma-\beta-1} \, dt,$$

which combines with (9) to yield (8).

60. The Hypergeometric Function

As our first illustration of the study of a function defined by power series, we choose the *hypergeometric function*

(1) $$F(\alpha, \beta; \gamma; x) = 1 + \sum_{n=1}^{\infty} \frac{(\alpha)_n(\beta)_n x^n}{(\gamma)_n n!}, \qquad |x| < 1,$$

in which γ must not be zero or a negative integer. If neither α nor β is zero, we may write

$$F(\alpha, \beta; \gamma; x) = \sum_{n=0}^{\infty} \frac{(\alpha)_n(\beta)_n x^n}{(\gamma)_n \, n!}, \qquad |x| < 1.$$

We shall obtain three properties of this function. For further study almost any book on *Special Functions* may be consulted.

A ratio test shows at once that the series in (1) has unity for its radius of convergence. Indeed, for $x \neq 0$,

$$\lim_{n \to \infty} \left| \frac{(\alpha)_{n+1}(\beta)_{n+1}x^{n+1}}{(\gamma)_{n+1}(n+1)!} \cdot \frac{(\gamma)_n \, n!}{(\alpha)_n(\beta)_n x^n} \right|$$

$$= \lim_{n \to \infty} \left| \frac{(\alpha+n)(\beta+n)x}{(\gamma+n)(n+1)} \right| = |x|.$$

The series (1) is absolutely convergent in $|x| < 1$, divergent in $|x| > 1$ unless it terminates, and is uniformly convergent in every closed region inside $|x| < 1$.

From (1) we obtain

$$\frac{d}{dx} F(\alpha, \beta; \gamma; x) = \sum_{n=1}^{\infty} \frac{(\alpha)_n(\beta)_n x^{n-1}}{(\gamma)_n(n-1)!}, \qquad |x| < 1.$$

A shift of index yields

$$\frac{d}{dx} F(\alpha, \beta; \gamma; x) = \sum_{n=0}^{\infty} \frac{(\alpha)_{n+1}(\beta)_{n+1} x^n}{(\gamma)_{n+1} \, n!}.$$

Now $(\alpha)_{n+1} = \alpha(\alpha+1)_n$, $(\beta)_{n+1} = \beta(\beta+1)_n$, etc. Hence,

$$\frac{d}{dx} F(\alpha, \beta; \gamma; x) = \frac{\alpha\beta}{\gamma} \sum_{n=0}^{\infty} \frac{(\alpha+1)_n(\beta+1)_n x^n}{(\gamma+1)_n \, n!}.$$

THEOREM 59. *In* $|x| < 1$,

$$(2) \qquad \frac{d}{dx} F(\alpha, \beta; \gamma; x) = \frac{\alpha\beta}{\gamma} F(\alpha+1, \beta+1,; \gamma+1; x).$$

Next, let us return to the definition (1) and use equation (8), page 156,

$$\frac{(\beta)_n}{(\gamma)_n} = \frac{\Gamma(\gamma)}{\Gamma(\beta)\Gamma(\gamma-\beta)} \int_0^1 t^{\beta+n-1}(1-t)^{\gamma-\beta-1} \, dt,$$

to arrive at

$$F(\alpha, \beta; \gamma; x) = \frac{\Gamma(\gamma)}{\Gamma(\beta)\Gamma(\gamma-\beta)} \sum_{n=0}^{\infty} \frac{(\alpha)_n x^n}{n!} \int_0^1 t^{\beta+n-1}(1-t)^{\gamma-\beta-1} \, dt.$$

For $|x| < 1$, $|xt| < 1$ and it is legitimate to interchange order of integration and summation. We thus obtain

$$F(\alpha, \beta; \gamma; x) = \frac{\Gamma(\gamma)}{\Gamma(\beta)\Gamma(\gamma - \beta)} \int_0^1 t^{\beta-1}(1 - t)^{\gamma-\beta-1} \sum_{n=0}^{\infty} \frac{(\alpha)_n(xt)^n}{n!} \, dt.$$

By equation (3), page 152,

$$\sum_{n=0}^{\infty} \frac{(\alpha)_n(xt)^n}{n!} = (1 - xt)^{-\alpha}.$$

THEOREM 60. *If* $|x| < 1$ *and if* $\mathrm{Re}(\gamma) > \mathrm{Re}(\beta) > 0$,

(3) $\qquad F(\alpha, \beta; \gamma; x) = \dfrac{\Gamma(\gamma)}{\Gamma(\beta)\Gamma(\gamma - \beta)} \displaystyle\int_0^1 t^{\beta-1}(1 - t)^{\gamma-\beta-1}(1 - xt)^{-\alpha} \, dt.$

We showed, pages 58–59, that if α, β, γ are positive and $(\gamma - \alpha - \beta) > 0$, the hypergeometric series in (1) converges at $x = 1$, a point on the boundary of the interval, or region, of convergence. Abel's Theorem, page 135, is applicable and we obtain

(4) $\qquad F(\alpha, \beta; \gamma; 1) = \dfrac{\Gamma(\gamma)}{\Gamma(\beta)\Gamma(\gamma - \beta)} \displaystyle\int_0^1 t^{\beta-1}(1 - t)^{\gamma-\alpha-\beta-1} \, dt.$

Now, by Theorem 58, page 155,

$$\int_0^1 t^{\beta-1}(1 - t)^{\gamma-\beta-1} \, dt = B(\beta, \gamma - \alpha - \beta) = \frac{\Gamma(\beta)\Gamma(\gamma - \alpha - \beta)}{\Gamma(\gamma - \alpha)},$$

which combines with (4) to give

$$F(\alpha, \beta; \gamma; 1) = \frac{\Gamma(\gamma)\Gamma(\gamma - \alpha - \beta)}{\Gamma(\gamma - \alpha)\Gamma(\gamma - \beta)}.$$

By more advanced methods, the conditions we have imposed can be relaxed to those stated in Theorem 61 below.

THEOREM 61. *If* $\mathrm{Re}(\gamma - \alpha - \beta) > 0$ *and if none of* $\gamma, \gamma - \alpha, \gamma - \beta$ *is zero or a negative integer,*

(5) $\qquad\qquad F(\alpha, \beta; \gamma; 1) = \dfrac{\Gamma(\gamma)\Gamma(\gamma - \alpha - \beta)}{\Gamma(\gamma - \alpha)\Gamma(\gamma - \beta)}.$

61. Two Fundamental Properties

We shall use Theorem 60 of the preceding section to obtain two basic results on the hypergeometric function. Theorem 60 may be applied to the function

$$F\left(\alpha, \gamma - \beta; \gamma; \frac{-x}{1-x}\right)$$

if we add the condition that $|-x| < |1-x|$. Replacing β by $(\gamma - \beta)$ and x by $\left[\dfrac{-x}{(1-x)}\right]$ in Theorem 60 yields

$$F\left(\alpha, \gamma - \beta; \gamma; \frac{-x}{1-x}\right) = \frac{\Gamma(\gamma)}{\Gamma(\gamma-\beta)\Gamma(\beta)} \int_0^1 t^{\gamma-\beta-1}(1-t)^{\beta-1}\left(1 - \frac{-xt}{1-x}\right)^{-\alpha} dt$$

$$= \frac{(1-x)^\alpha\Gamma(\gamma)}{\Gamma(\gamma-\beta)\Gamma(\beta)} \int_0^1 t^{\gamma-\beta-1}(1-t)^{\beta-1}(1-x+xt)^{-\alpha}\, dt.$$

Let us introduce a new variable of integration

$$v = 1 - t.$$

Then

$$t = 1 - v,\ dt = -dv,$$

and we obtain

$$(1-x)^{-\alpha}F\left(\alpha, \gamma-\beta; \gamma; \frac{-x}{1-x}\right)$$

$$= \frac{\Gamma(\gamma)}{\Gamma(\beta)\Gamma(\gamma-\beta)} \int_1^0 (1-v)^{\gamma-\beta-1}v^{\beta-1}(1-xv)^{-\alpha}(-dv)$$

$$= \frac{\Gamma(\gamma)}{\Gamma(\beta)\Gamma(\gamma-\beta)} \int_0^1 v^{\beta-1}(1-v)^{\gamma-\beta-1}(1-xv)^{-\alpha}\, dv$$

$$= F(\alpha, \beta; \gamma; x),$$

by Theorem 60.

THEOREM 62. *If* $|x| < 1$, *if* $|-x| < |1-x|$, *and if* $\mathrm{Re}(\gamma) > \mathrm{Re}(\beta) > 0$, *then*

(1) $$F(\alpha, \beta; \gamma; x) = (1-x)^{-\alpha}F\left(\alpha, \gamma-\beta; \gamma; \frac{-x}{1-x}\right).$$

The hypergeometric function is symmetric in its two numerator parameters,

$$F(\alpha, \beta; \gamma; x) = F(\beta, \alpha; \gamma; x),$$

as can be seen from the series definition of the function. We may therefore conclude from Theorem 62, by interchanging the roles of the two numerator parameters, that

(2) $$F(a, b; c; y) = (1 - y)^{-b} F\left(c - a, b; c; \frac{-y}{1-y}\right).$$

We shall employ equation (2) to transform the F in the right-hand member of equation (1). From

(3) $$y = \frac{-x}{1-x}$$

it follows that

$$1 - y = \frac{1}{1-x} \quad \text{and} \quad \frac{-y}{1-y} = x.$$

In (2), put $a = \alpha$, $b = \gamma - \beta$, $c = \gamma$, and use the y of (3) to obtain

(4) $$F\left(\alpha, \gamma - \beta; \gamma; \frac{-x}{1-x}\right) = (1 - x)^{\gamma-\beta} F(\gamma - \alpha, \gamma - \beta; \gamma; x).$$

By substituting from (4) on the right in equation (1), we are led to a result obtained by Euler.

THEOREM 63. *If $|x| < 1$ and if* $\mathrm{Re}(\gamma) > \mathrm{Re}(\beta) > 0$, *then*

(5) $$F(\alpha, \beta; \gamma; x) = (1 - x)^{\gamma-\alpha-\beta} F(\gamma - \alpha, \gamma - \beta; \gamma; x).$$

Note that the condition $|-x| < |1 - x|$, needed in Theorem 62, is not needed in Theorem 63 because of the result stated in the last paragraph of Section 47. See page 129.

62. Some Elementary Expansions

In Theorem 63 of the preceding section, choose $\alpha = \frac{1}{2}$, $\beta = \frac{1}{2}$, $\gamma = \frac{3}{2}$, to obtain

$$F(\tfrac{1}{2}, \tfrac{1}{2}; \tfrac{3}{2}; x) = (1 - x)^{1/2} F(1, 1; \tfrac{3}{2}; x),$$

or

(1) $$(1 - x)^{-1/2} F(\tfrac{1}{2}, \tfrac{1}{2}; \tfrac{3}{2}; x) = F(1, 1; \tfrac{3}{2}; x).$$

We know by equation (3), page 152, that

$$(1-x)^{-1/2} = \sum_{n=0}^{\infty} \frac{(\frac{1}{2})_n x^n}{n!}.$$

Then for the left member of equation (1), we obtain

$$(1-x)^{-1/2}F(\tfrac{1}{2}, \tfrac{1}{2}; \tfrac{3}{2}; x) = \left[\sum_{n=0}^{\infty} \frac{(\frac{1}{2})_n x^n}{n!}\right]\left[\sum_{n=0}^{\infty} \frac{(\frac{1}{2})_n(\frac{1}{2})_n x^n}{n!(\frac{3}{2})_n}\right]$$

$$= \sum_{n=0}^{\infty}\sum_{k=0}^{n} \frac{(\frac{1}{2})_k(\frac{1}{2})_k(\frac{1}{2})_{n-k}x^n}{k!(\frac{3}{2})_k(n-k)!}.$$

The right member of (1) is

$$F(1, 1; \tfrac{3}{2}; x) = \sum_{n=0}^{\infty} \frac{(1)_n(1)_n x^n}{(\frac{3}{2})_n n!} = \sum_{n=0}^{\infty} \frac{n!\, x^n}{(\frac{3}{2})_n}.$$

By equating coefficients of x^n in the power series for the two members of equation (1), we obtain a useful finite sum:

(2)
$$\sum_{k=0}^{n} \frac{(\frac{1}{2})_k(\frac{1}{2})_k(\frac{1}{2})_{n-k}}{k!(n-k)!(\frac{3}{2})_k} = \frac{n!}{(\frac{3}{2})_n}.$$

In Chapter 8 we found that

(3)
$$\frac{1}{\sqrt{1-x^2}} = \sum_{n=0}^{\infty} \frac{(\frac{1}{2})_n x^{2n}}{n!}, \qquad |x| < 1,$$

and

(4)
$$\text{Arcsin } x = \sum_{n=0}^{\infty} \frac{(\frac{1}{2})_n x^{2n+1}}{n!(2n+1)}, \qquad |x| < 1.$$

Now

$$\frac{(\frac{1}{2})_n}{(\frac{3}{2})_n} = \frac{\frac{1}{2}(\frac{3}{2})_{n-1}}{(\frac{3}{2})_{n-1}(\frac{3}{2}+n-1)} = \frac{\frac{1}{2}}{\frac{1}{2}+n} = \frac{1}{2n+1},$$

so the expansion (4) may be written in the form

(5)
$$\text{Arcsin } x = \sum_{n=0}^{\infty} \frac{(\frac{1}{2})_n(\frac{1}{2})_n x^{2n+1}}{n!(\frac{3}{2})_n}, \qquad |x| < 1.$$

The Cauchy product of the series in (3) and (5) yields

$$\frac{1}{\sqrt{1-x^2}}\text{Arcsin } x = \sum_{n=0}^{\infty}\sum_{k=0}^{n} \frac{(\frac{1}{2})_k(\frac{1}{2})_k(\frac{1}{2})_{n-k}x^{2n+1}}{k!(\frac{3}{2})_k(n-k)!}.$$

Therefore, because of equation (2),

(6)
$$\frac{1}{\sqrt{1-x^2}}\text{Arcsin } x = \sum_{n=0}^{\infty} \frac{n!\, x^{2n+1}}{(\frac{3}{2})_n}, \qquad |x| < 1.$$

Exercises

1. From the known expansion

$$\frac{1}{\sqrt{1+x^2}} = \sum_{n=0}^{\infty} \frac{(-1)^n(\frac{1}{2})_n x^{2n}}{n!}, \qquad |x| < 1,$$

obtain, using term-by-term integration, the result

$$\ln(x+\sqrt{1+x^2}) = \sum_{n=0}^{\infty} \frac{(-1)^n(\frac{1}{2})_n x^{2n+1}}{n!(2n+1)}, \qquad |x| < 1.$$

2. Follow the method of this section to obtain, from the two series in Exercise 1, the result

$$\frac{1}{\sqrt{1+x^2}} \ln(x+\sqrt{1+x^2}) = \sum_{n=0}^{\infty} \frac{(-1)^n n! \, x^{2n+1}}{(\frac{3}{2})_n}, \qquad |x| < 1.$$

3. From the result in Exercise 2 and the fact that

$$\frac{d}{dx}[\sqrt{1+x^2} \ln(x+\sqrt{1+x^2})] = 1 + \frac{x}{\sqrt{1+x^2}} \ln(x+\sqrt{1+x^2}),$$

obtain

$$\sqrt{1+x^2} \ln(x+\sqrt{1+x^2}) = x + \frac{1}{2}\sum_{n=0}^{\infty} \frac{(-1)^n n! \, x^{2n+3}}{(\frac{3}{2})_{n+1}}, \qquad |x| < 1.$$

4. From the result in Exercise 2, obtain

$$\ln^2(x+\sqrt{1+x^2}) = \sum_{n=0}^{\infty} \frac{(-1)^n n! \, x^{2n+2}}{(n+1)(\frac{3}{2})_n}, \qquad |x| < 1.$$

5. From equation (6), page 161, and the fact that

$$\frac{d}{dx}[\sqrt{1-x^2}\,\text{Arcsin}\,x] = 1 - \frac{x}{\sqrt{1-x^2}}\,\text{Arcsin}\,x,$$

show that

$$\sqrt{1-x^2}\,\text{Arcsin}\,x = x - \frac{1}{2}\sum_{n=0}^{\infty} \frac{n! \, x^{2n+3}}{(\frac{3}{2})_{n+1}}, \qquad |x| < 1.$$

6. From equation (6), page 161, obtain

$$(\text{Arcsin}\,x)^2 = \sum_{n=0}^{\infty} \frac{n! \, x^{2n+2}}{(n+1)(\frac{3}{2})_n}, \qquad |x| < 1.$$

In Exercises 7–13, obtain a check on the expansion to which reference is given by computing both members of the expansion for $x = \frac{1}{2}$.

7. Exercise 1.   ANS.   0.4812.

8. Exercise 2.   ANS. 0.4304.

9. Exercise 3.   ANS. 0.5380.

10. Exercise 4.   ANS. 0.2316.

11. Exercise 5.   ANS. 0.4535.

12. Exercise 6.   ANS. 0.2742.

13. Equation (6), page 161.   ANS. 0.6046.

14. Obtain the expansion

$$\ln \frac{1+\sqrt{1+x^2}}{2} = \sum_{n=1}^{\infty} \frac{(-1)^{n+1}(\frac{1}{2})_n x^{2n}}{2n(n!)}, \qquad |x| < 1.$$

15. Use multiplication of series to show that

$$\frac{\ln(1+x)}{1+x} = \sum_{n=1}^{\infty} (-1)^{n+1} H_n x^n, \qquad |x| < 1,$$

in which H_n is the harmonic sum of Section 52, page 141.

16. From the result in Exercise 15, obtain

$$\tfrac{1}{2} \ln^2(1+x) = \sum_{n=1}^{\infty} \frac{(-1)^{n+1} H_n x^{n+1}}{n+1} \qquad |x| < 1,$$

and compare this expansion with the one in Exercise 9, page 139.

17. Show that

$$\tfrac{1}{2} \sum_{k=2}^{n+1} \frac{1}{(k-1)(n+2-k)} = \frac{H_n}{n+1}$$

and thus demonstrate the identity of the results in Exercise 16 and Exercise 9, page 139.

63. A Bessel Function

Next let us define the *Bessel* function* $J_n(x)$ by

(1) $$J_n(x) = \sum_{k=0}^{\infty} \frac{(-1)^k x^{n+2k}}{2^{n+2k} k! \, \Gamma(k+n+1)}, \qquad |x| < \infty,$$

in which n is not to be a negative integer.

The series in (1) converges for all finite x. We may use the theorems of Chapter 8 to study $J_n(x)$. From (1) it follows that

* F. W. Bessel (1785–1846) encountered $J_n(x)$ in his study of the orbits of planets. Euler and Daniel Bernoulli (1700–1782) used $J_0(x)$ around 1750 and Euler worked with $J_n(x)$ long before Bessel was born.

$$x^n J_n(x) = \sum_{k=0}^{\infty} \frac{(-1)^k x^{2n+2k}}{2^{n+2k} k! \ \Gamma(k+n+1)},$$

so

$$\frac{d}{dx}[x^n J_n(x)] = \sum_{k=0}^{\infty} \frac{(-1)^k 2(n+k) x^{2n+2k-1}}{2^{n+2k} k! \ \Gamma(k+n+1)}.$$

But $\Gamma(k+n+1) = (k+n)\Gamma(k+n) = (n+k)\Gamma(k+n-1+1)$. Hence,

$$\frac{d}{dx}[x^n J_n(x)] = x^n \sum_{k=0}^{\infty} \frac{(-1)^k x^{n-1+2k}}{2^{n-1+2k} k! \ \Gamma(k+n-1+1)}$$

and the series on the right is the same as (1) with n replaced by $(n-1)$. Thus we obtain

(2) $$\frac{d}{dx}[x^n J_n(x)] = x^n J_{n-1}(x).$$

Let us carry out the indicated differentiation in (2) to obtain

$$x^n J_n'(x) + n x^{n-1} J_n(x) = x^n J_{n-1}(x),$$

from which

(3) $$x J_n'(x) = x J_{n-1}(x) - n J_n(x).$$

From (1) we also obtain

$$x^{-n} J_n(x) = \sum_{k=0}^{\infty} \frac{(-1)^k x^{2k}}{2^{n+2k} k! \ \Gamma(k+n+1)}$$

and therefore, since the $k=0$ term is independent of x,

(4) $$\frac{d}{dx}[x^{-n} J_n(x)] = \sum_{k=1}^{\infty} \frac{(-1)^k x^{2k-1}}{2^{n+2k-1}(k-1)! \ \Gamma(k+n+1)}.$$

On the right in (4) we shift index from k to $(k+1)$ to obtain

$$\frac{d}{dx}[x^{-n} J_n(x)] = \sum_{k=0}^{\infty} \frac{(-1)^{k+1} x^{2k+1}}{2^{n+2k+1} k! \ \Gamma(k+1+n+1)}.$$

from which it follows that

$$\frac{d}{dx}[x^{-n} J_n(x)] = -x^{-n} \sum_{k=0}^{\infty} \frac{(-1)^k x^{n+1+2k}}{2^{n+1+2k} k! \ \Gamma(k+n+1+1)}.$$

Comparison of the series on the right above with the series defining $J_n(x)$

yields

(5)
$$\frac{d}{dx}[x^{-n}J_n(x)] = -x^{-n}J_{n+1}(x).$$

From (5) we obtain

$$x^{-n}J_n'(x) - nx^{-n-1}J_n(x) = -x^{-n}J_{n+1}(x),$$

or

(6)
$$xJ_n'(x) = -xJ_{n+1}(x) + nJ_n(x).$$

Equation (6) and equation (3) combine to yield

(7)
$$2J_n'(x) = J_{n-1}(x) - J_{n+1}(x)$$

and

(8)
$$2nJ_n(x) = x[J_{n-1}(x) + J_{n+1}(x)].$$

From (3) we obtain

(9)
$$J_{n-1}(x) = J_n'(x) + \frac{n}{x}J_n(x).$$

In (6), replace n by $(n-1)$ to obtain

(10)
$$xJ_{n-1}'(x) = -xJ_n(x) + (n-1)J_{n-1}(x).$$

Insert the J_{n-1} of (9) into equation (10) to arrive at

$$x\left[J_n''(x) + \frac{n}{x}J_n'(x) - \frac{n}{x^2}J_n(x)\right] = -xJ_n(x) + (n-1)J_n'(x) + \frac{n(n-1)}{x}J_n(x)$$

in which the terms can be arranged to yield

(11)
$$x^2J_n''(x) + xJ_n'(x) + (x^2 - n^2)J_n(x) = 0.$$

Equation (11) is simply a statement that

$$y = J_n(x)$$

is one solution of Bessel's differential equation

(12)
$$x^2y'' + xy' + (x^2 - n^2)y = 0.$$

The material in this section is an indication of how the study of $J_n(x)$ may be started on the basis of the power series definition. Further results on $J_n(x)$ and functions associated with it may be found in hundreds of books and thousands of research papers.

Exercises

1. Define a modified Bessel function $I_n(x)$ by

$$I_n(x) = \sum_{k=0}^{\infty} \frac{x^{n+2k}}{2^{n+2k}k!\ \Gamma(k+n+1)},$$

in which n is not to be negative integer. Parallel the work in Section 63 and obtain the results:

$$xI_n'(x) = xI_{n-1}(x) - nI_n(x),$$

$$xI_n'(x) = xI_{n+1}(x) + nI_n(x),$$

$$2I_n'(x) = I_{n-1}(x) + I_{n+1}(x),$$

$$2nI_n(x) = x[I_{n-1}(x) - I_{n+1}(x)].$$

2. Show that in the notation of Exercise 1, $y = I_n(x)$ is a solution of the differential equation

$$x^2 y'' + xy' - (x^2 + n^2)y = 0.$$

3. Show that $J_n(-x) = (-1)^n J_n(x)$ and obtain a similar result for $I_n(x)$ of Exercise 1.

4. Show that

$$\gamma F(\alpha, \beta+1; \gamma; x) - \gamma F(\alpha, \beta; \gamma; x) = \alpha x F(\alpha+1, \beta+1; \gamma+1; x).$$

In Exercises 5–11, reduce the known power series for the function on the left to the hypergeometric form given.

5. $\ln(1+x) = xF(1, 1; 2; -x).$

6. $\text{Arcsin } x = xF(\frac{1}{2}, \frac{1}{2}; \frac{3}{2}; x^2).$

7. $\text{Arctan } x = xF(\frac{1}{2}, 1; \frac{3}{2}; -x^2).$

8. $\frac{1}{2}\ln\frac{1+x}{1-x} = xF(\frac{1}{2}, 1; \frac{3}{2}; x^2).$

9. $(1-x^2)^{-1/2}\text{ Arcsin } x = xF(1, 1; \frac{3}{2}; x^2).$

10. $\ln(x + \sqrt{1+x^2}) = xF(\frac{1}{2}, \frac{1}{2}; \frac{3}{2}; -x^2).$

11. $(1+x^2)^{-1/2}\ln(x + \sqrt{1+x^2}) = xF(1, 1; \frac{3}{2}; -x^2).$

CHAPTER 10

Orthogonal Sets of Functions

64. Orthogonality and Formal Expansions

Consider a sequence of functions $\{\varphi_n(x)\}$, one function for each non-negative integer, $n = 0, 1, 2, \ldots$. If there exists an interval (a, b) and a function $w(x)$, independent of n, such that

(1)
$$\int_a^b w(x)\varphi_n(x)\varphi_m(x)\,dx = 0, \qquad m \neq n,$$
$$\neq 0, \qquad m = n,$$

we say that the set $\{\varphi_n(x)\}$ is *orthogonal* with respect to the weight function $w(x)$ over the interval (a, b).

The concept of an orthogonal set of functions plays an important role in analysis. We seek expansions of the form

(2)
$$f(x) = \sum_{n=0}^{\infty} c_n\varphi_n(x)$$

for some class of functions $f(x)$ of a nature to be determined.

First we determine, under the assumption that the expansion (2) exists and is well behaved in every respect, what the coefficients c_n must be. Then we attempt to prove that with those coefficients the series on the right in (2) does actually converge to the function on the left in (2). The first step is simple; the second is usually difficult.

By the definition of orthogonality, the integral from a to b of the product of $w(x)$ and any two different elements of the set $\{\varphi_n(x)\}$ is zero. If we put

$$(3) \qquad g_n = \int_a^b w(x)\varphi_n^2(x)\,dx,$$

then $g_n \neq 0$, by the same definition of orthogonality.

We now proceed to find the c_n in a purely formal manner. No justification is needed because we are merely determining what c_n should be used in the series in attempting to prove that the series converges to the desired sum. All we need at present is the assumption that $f(x)$ is sufficiently well behaved on (a, b) to make the integrals

$$\int_a^b f(x)w(x)\varphi_n(x)\,dx$$

exist for every n.

We multiply each term in the assumed equation

$$f(x) = \sum_{n=0}^{\infty} c_n\varphi_n(x)$$

by $w(x)\varphi_k(x)\,dx$, and then integrate throughout from a to b. The order of integration and summation can be interchanged here because the work is, as yet, formal. We are not proving anything; we are finding the coefficients which are needed in a proof.

In the formal identity

$$(4) \qquad \int_a^b f(x)w(x)\varphi_k(x)\,dx = \sum_{n=0}^{\infty} c_n \int_a^b w(x)\varphi_k(x)\varphi_n(x)\,dx,$$

every term on the right is zero except the term in which $n = k$. This follows from the orthogonality of the $\varphi_n(x)$. Thus equation (4) degenerates to the form

$$(5) \qquad \int_a^b f(x)w(x)\varphi_k(x)\,dx = c_k \int_a^b w(x)\varphi_k^2(x)\,dx.$$

By the definition of g_n in (3), we have

$$(6) \qquad g_k = \int_a^b w(x)\varphi_k^2(x)\,dx \neq 0.$$

so that (5) yields

$$(7) \qquad c_k = g_k^{-1}\int_a^b f(x)w(x)\varphi_k(x)\,dx.$$

Let us replace the index k in (7) by n, and let us change the variable of integration from x to β to avoid any danger of confusion.

We may conclude that an assumed expansion

(8)
$$f(x) = \sum_{n=0}^{\infty} c_n \varphi_n(x)$$

leads in a formal manner to the choice

(9)
$$c_n = g_n^{-1} \int_a^b f(\beta) w(\beta) \varphi_n(\beta) \, d\beta$$

$$= \frac{\displaystyle\int_a^b f(\beta) w(\beta) \varphi_n(\beta) \, d\beta}{\displaystyle\int_a^b w(\beta) \varphi_n^2(\beta) \, d\beta}.$$

Since we have no proof of equality in (8), it is customary to reword our result. We say that the series on the right in (8) with coefficients given by (9) is the series associated with $f(x)$ and we use the symbol $\sim$ to replace the equals sign in (8).

DEFINITION. Let the sequence $\{\varphi_n(x)\}$ be orthogonal with respect to the weight function $w(x)$ over the interval (a, b). Let $f(x)$ be such that the integrals

$$\int_a^b f(x) w(x) \varphi_n(x) \, dx$$

exist. We write

(10)
$$f(x) \sim \sum_{n=0}^{\infty} c_n \varphi_n(x),$$

where

(11)
$$c_n = \frac{\displaystyle\int_a^b f(\beta) w(\beta) \varphi_n(\beta) \, d\beta}{\displaystyle\int_a^b w(\beta) \varphi_n^2(\beta) \, d\beta},$$

and say that the series on the right in (10) is the *φ-series associated with* $f(x)$ on the interval (a, b).

The major problem, of course, is to find conditions under which we can prove that the series associated with $f(x)$ actually converges to $f(x)$ on (a, b).

65. Normalization

Suppose we have a sequence of functions $\{\varphi_n(x)\}$ orthogonal with respect to a weight function $w(x)$ over an interval (a, b). Then

$$(1) \qquad \int_a^b w(x)\varphi_n(x)\varphi_m(x)\, dx = 0, \qquad m \neq n,$$

$$(2) \qquad \int_a^b w(x)\varphi_n^2(x)\, dx = g_n \neq 0.$$

It is convenient to replace $\varphi_n(x)$ by $\psi_n(x)$ defined by

$$(3) \qquad \psi_n(x) = g_n^{-1/2}\varphi_n(x).$$

Then the sequence $\{\psi_n(x)\}$ has the properties

$$(4) \qquad \int_a^b w(x)\psi_n(x)\psi_m(x)\, dx = 0, \qquad m \neq n,$$

$$(5) \qquad \int_a^b w(x)\psi_n^2(x)\, dx = 1.$$

This process is called normalization. The $\psi_n(x)$ are normalized. We say that the set $\{\psi_n(x)\}$ is *orthonormal* with respect to the weight function $w(x)$ over the interval (a, b).

For an orthonormal set, the formula corresponding to equation (11) of the preceding section is simplified by having the denominator on the right reduce to unity.

Further simplification for theoretical work is often obtained by stipulating that $w(x)$ is non-negative on (a, b) and then putting

$$(6) \qquad \sigma_n(x) = [w(x)]^{1/2}\psi_n(x) = [w(x)]^{1/2}g_n^{-1/2}\varphi_n(x).$$

so the set $\sigma_n(x)$ will be orthonormal with respect to the weight function unity over the interval (a, b).

66. A Least Square Property

Consider a sequence $\{\psi_n(x)\}$ orthonormal with respect to a non-negative weight function $w(x)$ over the interval (a, b). As usual, all variables and functions are to be real. Let

$$(1) \qquad f(x) \sim \sum_{n=0}^{\infty} b_n\psi_n(x)$$

in the sense of the definition on page 169. Then

(2)
$$b_n = \int_a^b w(x)f(x)\psi_n(x)\,dx,$$

(3)
$$\int_a^b w(x)\psi_n(x)\psi_m(x)\,dx = 0, \qquad m \neq n,$$

(4)
$$\int_a^b w(x)\psi_n^2(x)\,dx = 1.$$

We shall now demonstrate that (1), the formal ψ-series associated with (x) over the interval (a, b), is worthy of study even without an expansion theorem to tell us when the series actually converges to $f(x)$.

Define $T_n(x)$ by

(5)
$$T_n(x) = \sum_{k=0}^n a_k\psi_k(x)$$

and consider the problem of choosing the coefficients a_k to make

(6)
$$B = \int_a^b w(x)[f(x) - T_n(x)]^2\,dx$$

a minimum. This is related to the problem of selecting the a_k to make $T_n(x)$ the best fit, in the sense of least squares, to $f(x)$ over (a, b).

From (6) we obtain

(7)
$$B = \int_a^b w(x)f^2(x)\,dx - 2\int_a^b w(x)f(x)T_n(x)\,dx + \int_a^b w(x)T_n^2(x)\,dx.$$

Now, by (5) and then by (2),

(8)
$$\int_a^b w(x)f(x)T_n(x)\,dx = \sum_{k=0}^n a_k \int_a^b w(x)f(x)\psi_k(x)\,dx = \sum_{k=0}^n a_k b_k.$$

In the last integral in (7),

$$\int_a^b w(x)T_n^2(x)\,dx = \int_a^b w(x)\left[\sum_{k=0}^n a_k\psi_k(x)\right]^2\,dx,$$

we expand the square of the sum involved and note that each time a term involves two different ψ's, the corresponding integral is zero,

$$\int_a^b w(x)a_k a_s\psi_k(x)\psi_s(x)\,dx = 0, \qquad s \neq k.$$

Therefore only those terms involving squares of ψ's are left and we obtain

(9)
$$\int_a^b w(x)T_n^2(x)\,dx = \sum_{k=0}^n a_k^2 \int_a^b w(x)\psi_k^2(x)\,dx = \sum_{k=0}^n a_k^2,$$

because the ψ-set is orthonormal with respect to $w(x)$ over (a, b).

Using (8) and (9), we rewrite (7) in the form

$$(10) \qquad B = \int_a^b w(x)f^2(x)\,dx - 2\sum_{k=0}^n a_k b_k + \sum_{k=0}^n a_k^2.$$

We add and subtract the sum of the squares of the b's on the right in (10) to complete the square and obtain

$$(11) \qquad B = \int_a^b w(x)f^2(x)\,dx + \sum_{k=0}^n (a_k - b_k)^2 - \sum_{k=0}^n b_k^2.$$

On the right side of (11) the only variables, once $f(x)$, $w(x)$, and $\{\psi_n(x)\}$ are stipulated, are the coefficients a_k. Since all functions and variables are to be real and $w(x)$ is non-negative over (a, b), the B of (11) will be a minimum if and only if

$$(12) \qquad a_k = b_k$$

for every k.

THEOREM 64. *Let $\{\psi_n(x)$ be orthonormal with respect to the non-negative weight function $w(x)$ over the interval (a, b). Let $f(x)$ be such that*

$$b_k = \int_a^b w(x)f(x)\psi_k(x)\,dx \qquad and \qquad \int_a^b w(x)f^2(x)\,dx$$

exist. Let

$$T_n(x) = \sum_{k=0}^n a_k \psi_k(x).$$

Then a necessary and sufficient that

$$B = \int_a^b w(x)[f(x) - T_n(x)]^2\,dx$$

be a minimum is that $a_k = b_k$.

67. Bessel's Inequality

Let the set $\{\psi_n(x)\}$ be orthonormal with respect to the non-negative weight function $w(x)$ over the interval (a, b). Let $f(x)$ be such that

$$b_k = \int_a^b w(x)f(x)\psi_k(x)\,dx \qquad and \qquad \int_a^b w(x)f^2(x)\,dx$$

exist. Define $S_n(x)$ by

(1) $$S_n(x) = \sum_{k=0}^{n} b_k \psi_k(x).$$

In the terminology of the preceding section, $S_n(x)$ is that one of the sums $T_n(x)$ which makes the integral B a minimum. Indeed,

(2) $$\text{Min } B = \int_a^b w(x)[f(x) - S_n(x)]^2 \, dx$$

and by (11) and (12) of the preceding section,

(3) $$\text{Min } B = \int_a^b w(x) f^2(x) \, dx - \sum_{k=0}^{n} b_k^2.$$

It follows from (2) and the non-negative character of $w(x)$ that Min B is never negative. Therefore, from (3),

$$\sum_{k=0}^{n} b_k^2 \leq \int_a^b w(x) f^2(x) \, dx,$$

which is known as Bessel's inequality.

THEOREM 65. *Let $\{\psi_n(x)\}$ be orthonormal with respect to the non-negative weight function $w(x)$ over the interval (a, b). Let $f(x)$ be such that*

$$b_k = \int_a^b w(x) f(x) \psi_k(x) \, dx \qquad \text{and} \qquad \int_a^b w(x) f^2(x) \, dx$$

exist. Then, for every n, the b_k satisfy Bessel's inequality,

(4) $$\sum_{k=0}^{n} b_k^2 \leq \int_a^b w(x) f^2(x) \, dx.$$

The right member of (4) is independent of n, so the partial sums of

$$\sum_{n=0}^{\infty} b_n^2$$

form a bounded monotonic increasing sequence.

THEOREM 66. *With the hypotheses of Theorem 65,*

$$\sum_{n=0}^{\infty} b_n^2$$

converges and

(5) $$\sum_{n=0}^{\infty} b_n^2 \leq \int_a^b w(x) f^2(x) \, dx.$$

A necessary condition for convergence of a series is that the general term $\to 0$ as the index of summation $\to \infty$. Also $b_n^2 \to 0$ implies $b_n \to 0$. Thus from Theorem 66 we get a weaker, but useful, result stated in the theorem below.

THEOREM 67. *With the hypotheses of Theorem 65,*

$$(6) \qquad \lim_{n \to \infty} b_n = 0.$$

Although the orthonormal set $\{\psi_n(x)\}$ was a handy tool for our excursion into the theory, we may wish to use the results directly on the original orthogonal set $\{\varphi_n(x)\}$. Recall that we put

$$(7) \qquad \psi_n(x) = g_n^{-1/2} \varphi_n(x), \qquad g_n = \int_a^b w(x)\varphi_n^2(x) \, dx.$$

We now use (7) to restate some of our results.

THEOREM 68. *Let the set $\{\varphi_n(x)\}$ be orthogonal with respect to the non-negative weight function $w(x)$ over the interval (a, b). Let $f(x)$ be such that the integrals*

$$b_n = \int_a^b w(x)f(x)\varphi_n(x) \, dx \qquad and \qquad \int_a^b w(x)f^2(x) \, dx$$

exist. Define

$$(8) \qquad g_n = \int_a^b w(x)\varphi_n^2(x) \, dx.$$

Then it follows that

$$(9) \qquad \sum_{k=0}^n g_k^{-1} b_k^2 \leqq \int_a^b w(x)f^2(x) \, dx,$$

that $\sum\limits_{n=0}^\infty g_n^{-1} b_n^2$ converges, that

$$(10) \qquad \sum_{n=0}^\infty g_n^{-1} b_n^2 \leqq \int_a^b w(x)f^2(x) \, dx,$$

and that

$$(11) \qquad \lim_{n \to \infty} g_n^{-1/2} b_n = \lim_{n \to \infty} \frac{\displaystyle\int_a^b w(x)f(x)\varphi_n(x) \, dx}{\left[\displaystyle\int_a^b w(x)\varphi_n^2(x) \, dx\right]^{1/2}} = 0.$$

68. The Convergence Problem

Let the set $\{\sigma_n(x)\}$ be orthonormal with respect to the weight function unity over the interval (a, b). See (6), page 170, for the definition of $\sigma_n(x)$ in terms of any orthogonal set on the same interval. Let the σ-series associated with a function $f(x)$ be

$$(1) \qquad f(x) \sim \sum_{n=0}^{\infty} b_n \sigma_n(x).$$

Let

$$(2) \qquad S_n(x) = \sum_{k=0}^{n} b_k \sigma_k(x).$$

The problem of showing that the series in (1) converges to some function $H(x)$ over the interval (a, b) is the problem of showing that

$$(3) \qquad \lim_{n \to \infty}[H(x) - S_n(x)] = 0,$$

for each fixed x in $a \leq x \leq b$. Naturally, we expect that the series, if it is convergent, will converge to $f(x)$; we hope for $H(x) = f(x)$.

We know the coefficients in (2) are given by

$$(4) \qquad b_k = \int_a^b f(y)\sigma_k(y)\, dy.$$

Then

$$S_n(x) = \sum_{k=0}^{n} \int_a^b f(y)\sigma_k(y)\sigma_k(x)\, dy$$

$$= \int_a^b f(y) \sum_{k=0}^{n} \sigma_k(x)\sigma_k(y)\, dy.$$

Define the function $K_n(x, y)$, called the *kernel* of the set $\{\sigma_n(x)\}$, by

$$K_n(x, y) = \sum_{k=0}^{n} \sigma_k(x)\sigma_k(y).$$

Then

$$(5) \qquad S_n(x) = \int_a^b f(y)K_n(x, y)\, dy.$$

The series in (1) will converge to $H(x)$ if and only if

$$(6) \qquad \lim_{n \to \infty}\left[H(x) - \int_a^b f(y)K_n(x, y)\, dy\right] = 0.$$

69. Even and Odd Functions

A function $f(x)$ that *remains unchanged* when x is replaced by $-x$,

(1) $$f(-x) = f(x),$$

is called an *even function*. This means geometrically that the curve

$$y = f(x)$$

is symmetric with respect to the y-axis. Familiar examples of even functions are x^{2n} (n an integer), $\cos \theta$, $t \sin t$, etc.

A function such that

(2) $$f(-x) = -f(x)$$

is called an *odd function*. Geometrically, the curve $y = f(x)$ is symmetric with respect to the origin. Examples are x^{2n+1}, $x^{1/3}$, $\sin \theta$, $\tan \theta$.

THEOREM 69. *Any function defined throughout an interval $-a \leq x \leq a$ can be expressed as the sum of an even function and an odd function in that interval.*

PROOF. We prove that this can be done by doing it. For x in the interval $-a \leq x \leq a$, write

(3) $$f(x) = \tfrac{1}{2}[f(x) + f(-x)] + \tfrac{1}{2}[f(x) - f(-x)],$$

an identity. The introduction of $f(-x)$ is permissible because our interval is symmetric with respect to $x = 0$; both $f(x)$ and $f(-x)$ exist for any x in that interval.

It is important that the separation (3) of a function into its even and odd parts is unique.

THEOREM 70. *If $E_1(x)$ and $E_2(x)$ are even functions of x and $O_1(x)$ and $O_2(x)$ are odd functions of x, then from*

(4) $$E_1(x) + O_1(x) = E_2(x) + O_2(x)$$

in some interval, it follows that in the same interval

(5) $$E_1(x) = E_2(x), \qquad O_1(x) = O_2(x).$$

PROOF. In (4) change x to $(-x)$ to get

(6) $$E_1(x) - O_1(x) = E_2(x) - O_2(x).$$

Add and subtract the members of (4) and (6) to arrive at (5).

THEOREM 71. *If $f(x)$ is an even function of x and $f(x)$ has a derivative $f'(x)$, then $f'(x)$ is an odd function of x. If $f(x)$ is an odd function of x and $f(x)$ has a derivative $f'(x)$, then $f'(x)$ is an even function of x.*

Proof of Theorem 71. We know that

(7) $$f'(x) = \lim_{\Delta x \to 0} \frac{f(x + \Delta x) - f(x)}{\Delta x},$$

(8) $$\lim_{h \to 0} g(h) = \lim_{h \to 0} g(-h).$$

From (7) and (8) it follows that

$$f'(-x) = \lim_{\Delta x \to 0} \frac{f(-x + \Delta x) - f(-x)}{\Delta x}$$

$$= \lim_{\Delta x \to 0} \frac{f(-x - \Delta x) - f(-x)}{-\Delta x}.$$

If $f(x)$ is an even function of x, $f(-x - \Delta x) = f(x + \Delta x)$, and therefore

$$f'(-x) = \lim_{\Delta x \to 0} \frac{f(x + \Delta x) - f(x)}{-\Delta x} = -f'(x),$$

so that $f'(x)$ is an odd function of x. If $f(x)$ is an odd function of x,

$$f(-x - \Delta x) = -f(x + \Delta x),$$

$$f'(-x) = \lim_{\Delta x \to 0} \frac{-f(x + \Delta x) + f(x)}{-\Delta x} = f'(x),$$

so that $f'(x)$ is an even function of x.

The student should prove the following lemma by first separating $H(x)$ into its even and odd parts and then employing Theorems 70 and 71.

LEMMA 11. *If $H'(x)$ is an even function of x, $H(x)$ is the sum of a constant $H(0)$ and an odd function of x; if $H'(x)$ is an odd function of x, $H(x)$ is an even function of x.*

THEOREM 72. *If $f(x)$ is an even function of x,*

$$\int_{-a}^{a} f(x)\, dx = 2 \int_{0}^{a} f(x)\, dx.$$

If $f(x)$ is an odd function of x,

$$\int_{-a}^{a} f(x)\, dx = 0.$$

In Theorem 72 it is assumed that the integrals involved exist.

Proof of Theorem 72. Let the indefinite integral of $f(x)\,dx$ be denoted by

(9)
$$\int f(x)\,dx = H(x) + C.$$

We know that $H'(x) = f(x)$ and that

(10)
$$\int_{-a}^{a} f(x)\,dx = H(a) - H(-a).$$

If $f(x)$ is an even function in the interval $-a \leq x \leq a$, $H'(x)$ is an even function, and by Lemma 11, $H(x)$ is an odd function of x plus the constant $H(0)$. Put

(11)
$$H(x) = O(x) + H(0).$$

Then, by (10),

$$\int_{-a}^{a} f(x)\,dx = O(a) + H(0) - O(-a) - H(0) = 2O(a)$$

or

$$\int_{-a}^{a} f(x)\,dx = 2[H(a) - H(0)] = 2\int_{0}^{a} f(x)\,dx,$$

by (11).

If $f(x)$ is an odd function of x, $H'(x)$ is odd, so $H(x)$ is an even function of x. Then $H(-a) = H(a)$ and the second part of Theorem 72 follows from equation (10).

70. Orthogonality of a Set of Sines and Cosines

We shall show that the set of functions,

(A)
$$\begin{cases} \sin (n\pi x/c), & n = 1, 2, 3 \dots, \\ \cos (n\pi x/c, & n = 0, 1, 2, \dots, \end{cases}$$

or

(A)
$$\begin{cases} \sin (\pi x/c),\ \sin (2\pi x/c),\ \sin (3\pi x/c),\ \dots,\ \sin (n\pi x/c),\ \dots, \\ 1,\ \cos (\pi x/c),\ \cos (2\pi x/c),\ \cos (3\pi x/c),\ \dots,\ \cos (n\pi x/c),\ \dots, \end{cases}$$

is orthogonal with respect to the weight function $w(x) = 1$ *over the interval* $-c \leq x \leq c$. That is, we shall prove that the integral from $x = -c$ to $x = +c$ of the product of any two different members of the set (A) is zero.

First consider the integral of the product of any of the sine functions in (A) and any of the cosine functions in (A). The result

$$I_1 = \int_{-c}^{c} \sin \frac{n\pi x}{c} \cos \frac{k\pi x}{c} \, dx = 0$$

follows at once from the fact that the integrand is an odd function of x; in this instance the result does not depend upon the fact that k and n are integers.

Next consider the integral of the product of two different sine functions from the set (A),

$$I_2 = \int_{-c}^{c} \sin \frac{n\pi x}{c} \sin \frac{k\pi x}{c} \, dx, \qquad k \neq n.$$

Let us introduce a new variable of integration for simplicity in writing; put

$$\frac{\pi x}{c} = \beta,$$

from which

$$dx = \frac{c}{\pi} \, d\beta.$$

Then I_2 can be written

$$I_2 = \frac{c}{\pi} \int_{-\pi}^{\pi} \sin n\beta \, \sin k\beta \, d\beta.$$

Now from trigonometry we get the formula

$$\sin n\beta \sin k\beta = \tfrac{1}{2}[\cos (n - k)\beta - \cos (n + k)\beta]$$

which is useful in performing the desired integration. Thus it follows that the integral becomes

$$I_2 = \frac{c}{2\pi} \int_{-\pi}^{\pi} [\cos (n - k)\beta - \cos (n + k)\beta] \, d\beta$$

$$= \frac{c}{2\pi} \left[\frac{\sin (n - k)\beta}{n - k} - \frac{\sin (n + k)\beta}{n + k} \right]_{-\pi}^{\pi},$$

since neither $(n - k)$ nor $(n + k)$ can be zero. Because n and k are positive integers, $\sin (n - k)\beta$ and $\sin (n + k)\beta$ each vanish at $\beta = \pi$ and $\beta = -\pi$; then

$$I_2 = 0$$

for $n, k = 1, 2, 3, \ldots,$ and $k \neq n$.

Finally, consider the integral of the product of two different cosine functions from the set (A),

$$I_3 = \int_{-c}^{c} \cos \frac{n\pi x}{c} \cos \frac{k\pi x}{c} \, dx,$$

where $n, k = 0, 1, 2, 3, \ldots$; $k \neq n$. The method used on I_2 works equally well here to yield

$$I_3 = \frac{c}{2\pi} \left[\frac{\sin (n-k)\beta}{n-k} + \frac{\sin (n+k)\beta}{n+k} \right]_{-\pi}^{\pi} = 0.$$

We shall evaluate the integrals of the squares of the functions in the set (A). The integral

$$I_4 = \int_{-c}^{c} \sin^2 \frac{n\pi x}{c} \, dx$$

has an even integrand. Hence it can be written as

$$I_4 = 2 \int_{0}^{c} \sin^2 \frac{n\pi x}{c} \, dx.$$

Elementary methods of integration yield

$$I_4 = \int_{0}^{c} \left(1 - \cos \frac{2n\pi x}{c} \right) dx$$

$$= \left[x - \frac{c}{2n\pi} \sin \frac{2n\pi x}{c} \right]_{0}^{c} = c.$$

Therefore

$$\int_{-c}^{c} \sin^2 \frac{n\pi x}{c} \, dx = c \text{ for } n = 1, 2, 3, \ldots.$$

In the same way it follows that, for $n > 0$, n integral,

$$I_5 = \int_{-c}^{c} \cos^2 \frac{n\pi x}{c} \, dx$$

$$= \left[x + \frac{c}{2n\pi} \sin \frac{2n\pi x}{c} \right]_{0}^{c} = c.$$

For $n = 0$ the integral I_5 becomes

$$I_6 = \int_{-c}^{c} 1 \cdot dx = 2c.$$

Thus

$$\int_{-c}^{c} \cos^2 \frac{n\pi x}{c}\, dx = c \text{ for } n = 1, 2, 3, \dots ,$$

$$= 2c \text{ for } n = 0.$$

We have shown that the set

(A) $\begin{cases} \sin(n\pi x/c), & n = 1, 2, 3, \dots , \\ \cos(m\pi x/c), & m = 0, 1, 2, \dots , \end{cases}$

is orthogonal with respect to the weight function $w(x) = 1$ over the interval $-c \le x \le c$. We have also evaluated the integrals of the squares of the functions of the set (A). The set (A) can now be normalized so that it fits into the discussion in Section 68.

An expansion associated with $f(x)$ on the interval $(-c, c)$ in a series of the elements of (A) is called a Fourier* series for $f(x)$. Such series will be discussed in the next chapter.

* J. Fourier, 1768–1830.

CHAPTER 11

Fourier Series

71. The Fourier Coefficients

The Fourier series associated with $f(x)$ on the interval $(-c, c)$ may be written

$$(1)^* \qquad f(x) \sim \tfrac{1}{2}a_0 + \sum_{n=1}^{\infty} \left(a_n \cos \frac{n\pi x}{c} + b_n \sin \frac{n\pi x}{c} \right),$$

Although the formal expansion (1) fits into the theory developed in Chapter 10, we shall determine the coefficients a_n and b_n without recourse to the formulas developed earlier. For the sole purpose of getting the coefficients, we assume that (1) is an equality and proceed in the usual formal manner.

Multiply each term of equation (1) by $\sin (k\pi x/c) \, dx$, where k is a positive integer, and then integrate each term from $-c$ to $+c$, thus arriving at

$$(2) \qquad \int_{-c}^{c} f(x) \sin \frac{k\pi x}{c} \, dx = \tfrac{1}{2}a_0 \int_{-c}^{c} \sin \frac{k\pi x}{c} \, dx$$

$$+ \sum_{n=1}^{\infty} \left[a_n \int_{-c}^{c} \cos \frac{n\pi x}{c} \sin \frac{k\pi x}{c} \, dx \right.$$

$$\left. + b_n \int_{-c}^{c} \sin \frac{n\pi x}{c} \sin \frac{k\pi x}{c} \, dx \right].$$

* A reason for the apparently peculiar notation, $\tfrac{1}{2}a_0$, for the constant term will be seen soon, page 184.

As seen earlier,

(3) $$\int_{-c}^{c} \cos\frac{n\pi x}{c} \sin\frac{k\pi x}{c}\, dx = 0 \qquad \text{for all } k \text{ and } n,$$

and

(4) $$\int_{-c}^{c} \sin\frac{n\pi x}{c} \sin\frac{k\pi x}{c}\, dx = 0 \qquad \text{for } k \neq n; \quad k, n = 1, 2, 3, \ldots.$$

Therefore each term on the right-hand side of equation (2) is zero except for the term $n = k$. Thus equation (2) reduces to

(5) $$\int_{-c}^{c} f(x) \sin\frac{k\pi x}{c}\, dx = b_k \int_{-c}^{c} \sin^2\frac{k\pi x}{c}\, dx.$$

Since

$$\int_{-c}^{c} \sin^2\frac{k\pi x}{c}\, dx = c,$$

$$b_k = \frac{1}{c}\int_{-c}^{c} f(x) \sin\frac{k\pi x}{c}\, dx, \qquad k = 1, 2, 3, \ldots,$$

from which the coefficients b_n in equation (1) follow by mere replacement of k with n; that is,

(6) $$b_n = \frac{1}{c}\int_{-c}^{c} f(x) \sin\frac{n\pi x}{c}\, dx, \qquad n = 1, 2, 3, \ldots.$$

Let us obtain the a_n in a like manner. Using the multiplier $\cos(k\pi x/c)\, dx$ throughout equation (1) and then integrating term by term from $x = -c$ to $x = +c$, we get

(7) $$\int_{-c}^{c} f(x) \cos\frac{k\pi x}{c}\, dx = \tfrac{1}{2}a_0 \int_{-c}^{c} \cos\frac{k\pi x}{c}\, dx$$

$$+ \sum_{n=1}^{\infty} \left[a_n \int_{-c}^{c} \cos\frac{n\pi x}{c} \cos\frac{k\pi x}{c}\, dx \right.$$

$$\left. + b_n \int_{-c}^{c} \sin\frac{n\pi x}{c} \cos\frac{k\pi x}{c}\, dx \right].$$

The coefficient of b_n in (7) is zero for all n and k. If $k \neq 0$, we know that

$$\int_{-c}^{c} \cos\frac{n\pi x}{c} \cos\frac{k\pi x}{c}\, dx = 0 \qquad \text{for } n \neq k,$$

$$= c \qquad \text{for } n = k,$$

and also the coefficient of $\frac{1}{2}a_0$ is zero. Thus, for $k \neq 0$, equation (7) reduces to

$$\int_{-c}^{c} f(x) \cos \frac{k\pi x}{c} \, dx = a_k \int_{-c}^{c} \cos^2 \frac{k\pi x}{c} \, dx,$$

from which a_k, and therefore a_n, can be found in the way b_k was determined. Thus we get

(8) $$a_n = \frac{1}{c} \int_{-c}^{c} f(x) \cos \frac{n\pi x}{c} \, dx, \qquad n = 1, 2, 3, \ldots.$$

Next let us determine a_0. Suppose $k = 0$ in equation (7) so we have the equation

$$\int_{-c}^{c} f(x) \, dx = \frac{1}{2}a_0 \int_{-c}^{c} dx + \sum_{n=1}^{\infty} \left[a_n \int_{-c}^{c} \cos \frac{n\pi x}{c} \, dx + b_n \int_{-c}^{c} \sin \frac{n\pi x}{c} \, dx \right].$$

The terms involving $n \geq 1$ are each zero. Hence

$$\int_{-c}^{c} f(x) \, dx = \frac{1}{2}a_0(2c),$$

from which we obtain

(9) $$a_0 = \frac{1}{c} \int_{-c}^{c} f(x) \, dx.$$

Equation (9) fits in with equation (8) as the special case $n = 0$. Had the factor $\frac{1}{2}$ not been inserted as in equation (1), a separate formula would have been needed. As it is, we may write the formal expansion as follows:

(10) $$f(x) = \frac{1}{2}a_0 + \sum_{n=1}^{\infty} \left(a_n \cos \frac{n\pi x}{c} + b_n \sin \frac{n\pi x}{c} \right)$$

with

(11) $$a_n = \frac{1}{c} \int_{-c}^{c} f(x) \cos \frac{n\pi x}{c} \, dx, \qquad n = 0, 1, 2, \ldots,$$

(12) $$b_n = \frac{1}{c} \int_{-c}^{c} f(x) \sin \frac{n\pi x}{c} \, dx, \qquad n = 1, 2, 3, \ldots.$$

When a_n and b_n are given by (11) and (12) above, then the right-hand member of equation (10) is called the *Fourier series, over the interval $-c \leq x \leq c$, for the function $f(x)$.* A statement of conditions sufficient to insure that the Fourier series in (10) represents the function $f(x)$ in a reasonably meaningful manner follows.

72. An Expansion Theorem

For the Fourier series (10), of the preceding section, let

$$(1) \qquad s_n(x) = \tfrac{1}{2}a_0 + \sum_{k=1}^{n} \left(a_k \cos \frac{k\pi x}{c} + b_k \sin \frac{k\pi x}{c} \right),$$

$$(2) \qquad a_k = \frac{1}{c} \int_{-c}^{c} f(y) \cos \frac{k\pi y}{c} \, dy, \qquad k \geq 0,$$

$$(3) \qquad b_k = \frac{1}{c} \int_{-c}^{c} f(y) \sin \frac{k\pi y}{c} \, dy, \qquad k \geq 1,$$

It follows that

$$s_n(x) = \frac{1}{c} \int_{-c}^{c} f(y) \left[\tfrac{1}{2} + \sum_{k=1}^{n} \left(\cos \frac{k\pi y}{c} \cos \frac{k\pi x}{c} + \sin \frac{k\pi x}{c} \sin \frac{k\pi x}{c} \right) \right] dy.$$

Then

$$(4) \qquad s_n(x) = \frac{1}{c} \int_{-c}^{c} f(y) K_n(x, y) \, dy$$

in which

$$(5) \qquad K_n(x, y) = \tfrac{1}{2} + \sum_{k=1}^{n} \cos \frac{k\pi(y - x)}{c}.$$

To sum the finite series we use $\cos k\varphi = \tfrac{1}{2}(e^{ki\varphi} + e^{-ki\varphi})$ to get

$$(6) \qquad \tfrac{1}{2} + \sum_{k=1}^{n} \cos k\varphi = \frac{\sin(n + \tfrac{1}{2})\varphi}{2 \sin \tfrac{1}{2}\varphi}.$$

Because of (5) and (6), we may now put equation (4) into the form

$$(7) \qquad s_n(x) = \frac{1}{c} \int_{-c}^{c} f(y) \frac{\sin \dfrac{(n + \tfrac{1}{2})\pi(y - x)}{c}}{2 \sin \dfrac{\pi(y - x)}{2c}} \, dy.$$

It can be proved* that if $f(x)$ is sufficiently well behaved, the $s_n(x)$ of (7) converges to $f(x)$ at points of continuity of $f(x)$ and to the average value of the function at points where $f(x)$ has a finite jump. We now state such a "Fourier Theorem."

---

* Proof is omitted here. See R. V. Churchill, *Fourier Series and Boundary Value Problems*, 2nd ed., New York, McGraw-Hill Book Co., 1963, pp. 85–93; E. T. Whittaker and G. N. Watson, *Modern Analysis*, 4th ed., Cambridge, Cambridge University Press, 1927, pp. 164 and 175–179.

THEOREM 73. *Let $f(x)$ be continuous and differentiable at every point of the interval $-c \leqq x \leqq c$ except for at most a finite number of points, and at those points let $f(x)$ and $f'(x)$ have right- and left-hand limits. Then the Fourier series for $f(x)$,*

$$(8) \qquad f(x) \sim \tfrac{1}{2}a_0 + \sum_{n=1}^{\infty} \left(a_n \cos \frac{n\pi x}{c} + b_n \sin \frac{n\pi x}{c} \right),$$

with coefficients given by

$$(9) \qquad a_n = \frac{1}{c} \int_{-c}^{c} f(x) \cos \frac{n\pi x}{c} \, dx, \qquad n \geqq 0,$$

$$(10) \qquad b_n = \frac{1}{c} \int_{-c}^{c} f(x) \sin \frac{n\pi x}{c} \, dx, \qquad n \geqq 1,$$

converges to $f(x)$ at each point of continuity of $f(x)$. At each point of discontinuity of $f(x)$, the Fourier series converges to the arithmetic mean of the values approached by $f(x)$ from the right and the left.

The kind of function described in Theorem 73 is exhibited in Figure 5.

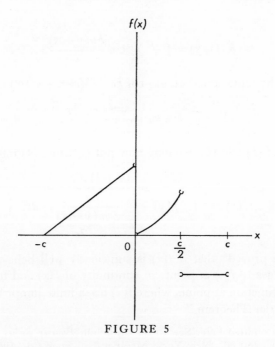

FIGURE 5

An interesting fact and one often useful as a check in numerical problems is that $\tfrac{1}{2}a_0$ is the average value of $f(x)$ over the interval $-c < x < c$.

The sine and cosine functions are periodic with period 2π, so the terms in the Fourier series (8) for $f(x)$ are periodic with period $2c$. Therefore the series represents (converges to) a function that is as described above for the interval $-c < x < c$ and repeats that structure over and over outside that interval. For the function exhibited in Figure 5, the corresponding Fourier series would converge to the periodic function shown in Figure 6. Note the convergence to the average value at discontinuities,

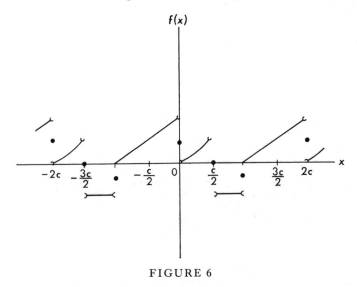

FIGURE 6

the periodicity, and the way in which the two together determine the value to which the series converges at $x = c$ and $x = -c$.

These statements will be amply illustrated in the numerical examples and exercises of the next section.

73. Numerical Examples of Fourier Series

We shall now construct the Fourier series for specific functions.

EXAMPLE (a). Construct the Fourier series, over the interval

$$-2 \leqq x \leqq 2$$

for the function defined by

$$(1) \qquad\qquad f(x) = 2, \qquad -2 < x \leqq 0,$$
$$= x, \qquad\quad 0 < x < 2,$$

and sketch the function to which the series converges.

First we sketch $f(x)$ itself, the result being exhibited in Figure 7. Note that $f(x)$ is undefined except for x between $x = -2$ and $x = +2$.

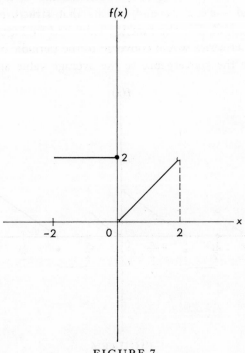

FIGURE 7

For the function described in (1),

$$f(x) \sim \tfrac{1}{2}a_0 + \sum_{n=1}^{\infty} \left(a_n \cos \frac{n\pi x}{2} + b_n \sin \frac{n\pi x}{2} \right),$$

in which

(2) $a_n = \tfrac{1}{2} \displaystyle\int_{-2}^{2} f(x) \cos \frac{n\pi x}{2} \, dx; \qquad n = 0, 1, 2, \ldots,$

and

(3) $b_n = \tfrac{1}{2} \displaystyle\int_{-2}^{2} f(x) \sin \frac{n\pi x}{2} \, dx; \qquad n = 1, 2, 3, \ldots.$

Since in the description of $f(x)$, different formulas were used in the two intervals $-2 < x < 0$ and $0 < x < 2$, it is convenient to separate the integrals in (2) and (3) into corresponding parts. Thus inserting the

$f(x)$ of (1) into the integral (2) leads us to the form

$$(4) \qquad a_n = \tfrac{1}{2} \int_{-2}^{0} 2 \cos \frac{n\pi x}{2}\, dx + \tfrac{1}{2}\int_{0}^{2} x \cos \frac{n\pi x}{2}\, dx.$$

For these integrals, the method of integration will differ according to whether $n = 0$ or $n \neq 0$.

If $n \neq 0$, then

$$a_n = \frac{2}{n\pi}\left[\sin\frac{n\pi x}{2}\right]_{-2}^{0} + \tfrac{1}{2}\left[\frac{2}{n\pi}\, x \sin\frac{n\pi x}{2} + \left(\frac{2}{n\pi}\right)^2 \cos\frac{n\pi x}{2}\right]_{0}^{2},$$

or

$$a_n = \frac{2}{n\pi}\,[0-0] + \tfrac{1}{2}\left[0 + \left(\frac{2}{n\pi}\right)^2 \cos n\pi - 0 - \left(\frac{2}{n\pi}\right)^2\right].$$

Hence for $n \neq 0$, the a_n are given by the formula

$$(5) \qquad a_n = \frac{-2(1-\cos n\pi)}{n^2\pi^2}, \qquad n = 1, 2, 3, \ldots.$$

For $n = 0$ the above integrations are not valid (division by n), but we return to (4), put $n = 0$, and get

$$a_0 = \tfrac{1}{2}\int_{-2}^{0} 2\, dx + \tfrac{1}{2}\int_{0}^{2} x\, dx,$$

from which

$$a_0 = \left[x\right]_{-2}^{0} + \tfrac{1}{4}\left[x^2\right]_{0}^{2} = 2 + 1 = 3.$$

The b_n may be obtained in a like manner. From (3) and (1) it follows that

$$b_n = \tfrac{1}{2}\int_{-2}^{0} 2 \sin\frac{n\pi x}{2}\, dx + \tfrac{1}{2}\int_{0}^{2} x \sin\frac{n\pi x}{2}\, dx.$$

Thus

$$b_n = \frac{2}{n\pi}\left[-\cos\frac{n\pi x}{2}\right]_{-2}^{0} + \tfrac{1}{2}\left[-\left(\frac{2}{n\pi}\right) x \cos\frac{n\pi x}{2} + \left(\frac{2}{n\pi}\right)^2 \sin\frac{n\pi x}{2}\right]_{0}^{2},$$

from which, since $\cos(-n\pi) = \cos n\pi$,

$$b_n = \frac{2}{n\pi}\,[-1 + \cos n\pi] + \tfrac{1}{2}\left[-\frac{2}{n\pi}\cdot 2 \cos n\pi + 0 + 0 - 0\right],$$

or

(6) $$b_n = -\frac{2}{n\pi}, \qquad n = 1, 2, 3, \ldots.$$

For integral n, $\cos n\pi = (-1)^n$, as is seen by examining both sides for even and odd n. Therefore the formula (5) above can also be written

(7) $$a_n = \frac{-2[1-(-1)^n]}{n^2\pi^2}, \qquad n = 1, 2, 3, \ldots.$$

We can now write the Fourier series, over the interval $-2 < x < 2$ for the $f(x)$ of this example,

(8) $$f(x) \sim \tfrac{3}{2} - 2 \sum_{n=1}^{\infty} \left[\frac{1-(-1)^n}{n^2\pi^2} \cos \frac{n\pi x}{2} + \frac{1}{n\pi} \sin \frac{n\pi x}{2} \right].$$

Several pertinent remarks can be made about (8). The right-hand member of (8) converges to the function shown in the sketch in Figure 8.

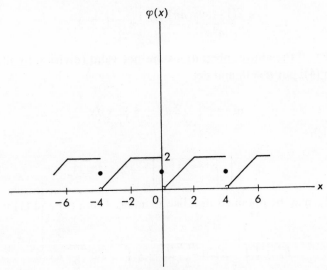

FIGURE 8

It converges to $f(x)$ at each point where $f(x)$ is defined except at the discontinuity at $x = 0$. Though $f(0) = 2$, the series converges to unity at $x = 0$.

We may therefore write

(9) $$f(x) = \tfrac{3}{2} - 2 \sum_{n=1}^{\infty} \left[\frac{1-(-1)^n}{n^2\pi^2} \cos \frac{n\pi x}{2} + \frac{1}{n\pi} \sin \frac{n\pi x}{2} \right]$$

for $-2 < x < 0$ and for $0 < x < 2$.

It is sometimes desirable to define a new function $\varphi(x)$ as follows:

$$\varphi(x) = f(x), \qquad -2 < x < 0,$$
$$= 1, \qquad x = 0,$$
$$= f(x), \qquad 0 < x < 2,$$

and

$$\varphi(x + 4) = \varphi(x).$$

This $\varphi(x)$ is the function exhibited in Figure 8. If $\varphi(x)$ is put in the place of $f(x)$ in (8) above, then the symbol $\sim$ may be replaced by the symbol $=$ for all x.

Because $[1 - (-1)^n]$ is zero for even n, the Fourier series on the right in (8) may be written in the somewhat more compact form

$$(10) \qquad f(x) \sim \tfrac{3}{2} - \frac{4}{\pi^2} \sum_{k=0}^{\infty} \frac{\cos[(2k+1)\pi x/2]}{(2k+1)^2} - \frac{2}{\pi} \sum_{n=1}^{\infty} \frac{\sin(n\pi x/2)}{n}.$$

This is one instance in which an infinite rearrangement in the order of terms, passing from (8) to (10), is easily justified. Consider (10) again after studying the sections on Fourier sine series and Fourier cosine series.

Let us next use the expansion in (8) or (10) to sum two numerical series. For instance, if we put $x = 0$ in (10), then the series has the sum unity as indicated above. Hence

$$1 = \tfrac{3}{2} - \frac{4}{\pi^2} \sum_{k=0}^{\infty} \frac{1}{(2k+1)^2} - \frac{2}{\pi} \sum_{n=1}^{\infty} \frac{0}{n},$$

or

$$(11) \qquad \sum_{k=0}^{\infty} \frac{1}{(2k+1)^2} = \frac{\pi^2}{8}.$$

For $x = 1$, the series in (10) has the sum unity again. Using $x = 1$ in (10) we are led to

$$1 = \tfrac{3}{2} - \frac{4}{\pi^2} \sum_{k=0}^{\infty} \frac{\cos[(2k+1)\pi/2]}{(2k+1)^2} - \frac{2}{\pi} \sum_{n=1}^{\infty} \frac{\sin(n\pi/2)}{n}.$$

Now $\cos[(2k+1)\pi/2] = 0$ and $\sin(n\pi/2)$ may be obtained as follows. For even n, $n = 2k$, we get

$$\sin \frac{2k\pi}{2} = \sin k\pi = 0.$$

For odd n, $n = 2k + 1$,

$$\sin\frac{(2k+1)\pi}{2} = \sin(k\pi + \tfrac{1}{2}\pi) = \cos k\pi = (-1)^k.$$

Thus we arrive at the equation

$$1 = \tfrac{3}{2} - \frac{2}{\pi}\sum_{k=0}^{\infty}\frac{(-1)^k}{2k+1},$$

or

(12)
$$\sum_{k=0}^{\infty}\frac{(-1)^k}{2k+1} = \frac{\pi}{4},$$

which can be verified also by the fact that the left-hand member represents Arctan 1.

EXAMPLE (b). Obtain the Fourier series over the interval $-\pi$ to π for the function x^2. We know that

(13)
$$x^2 \sim \tfrac{1}{2}a_0 + \sum_{n=1}^{\infty}[a_n\cos nx + b_n\sin nx]$$

for $-\pi < x < \pi$, where

(14)
$$a_n = \frac{1}{\pi}\int_{-\pi}^{\pi}x^2\cos nx\,dx; \qquad n = 0, 1, 2, \ldots,$$

(15)
$$b_n = \frac{1}{\pi}\int_{-\pi}^{\pi}x^2\sin nx\,dx; \qquad n = 1, 2, 3, \ldots.$$

Now x^2 is an even function of x and $\sin nx$ is an odd function of x, so the product $x^2\sin nx$ is an odd function of x. Therefore $b_n = 0$ for every n. Since $x^2\cos nx$ is an even function of x,

(16)
$$a_n = \frac{2}{\pi}\int_{0}^{\pi}x^2\cos nx\,dx; \qquad n = 0, 1, 2, \ldots.$$

For $n \neq 0$,

$$a_n = \frac{2}{\pi}\left[\frac{x^2\sin nx}{n} + \frac{2x\cos nx}{n^2} - \frac{2\sin nx}{n^3}\right]_0^{\pi},$$

from which

$$a_n = \frac{2}{\pi}\left[\frac{2\pi\cos n\pi}{n^2}\right] = \frac{4(-1)^n}{n^2}, \qquad n = 1, 2, 3, \ldots.$$

A separate integration is needed for a_0. We get

$$a_0 = \frac{2}{\pi}\int_0^{\pi} x^2\, dx = \frac{2}{\pi}\cdot\frac{\pi^3}{3} = \frac{2\pi^2}{3}.$$

Therefore, in the interval $-\pi < x < \pi$,

$$x^2 \sim \frac{\pi^2}{3} + 4\sum_{n=1}^{\infty}\frac{(-1)^n\cos nx}{n^2}.$$

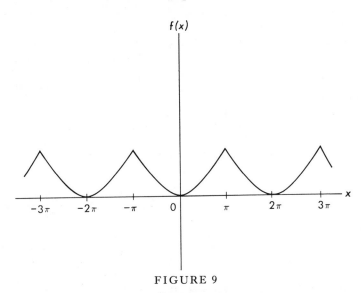

FIGURE 9

Indeed, because of continuity of the function involved, we may write

(17) $$x^2 = \frac{\pi^2}{3} + 4\sum_{n=1}^{\infty}\frac{(-1)^n\cos nx}{n^2}, \qquad \text{for } -\pi \leq x \leq \pi.$$

Beyond the indicated interval, the series on the right in equation (17) represents the periodic extension of the original function. The sum of the series is sketched in Figure 9.

Exercises

In Exercises 1–22, obtain the Fourier series, over the indicated interval, for the given function. Always sketch the function that is the sum of the series obtained.

   1. Interval, $-c < x < c$; function, $f(x) = 0, \qquad -c < x < 0,$
   $$\qquad\qquad\qquad\qquad = c - x, \qquad 0 < x < c.$$

   ANS. $$f(x) \sim \frac{c}{4} + \frac{c}{\pi^2}\sum_{n=1}^{\infty}\frac{1}{n^2}\left[\{1 - (-1)^n\}\cos\frac{n\pi x}{c} + n\pi\sin\frac{n\pi x}{c}\right].$$

2. Interval, $-c < x < c$; function, $f(x) = x$.

$$\text{ANS.} \quad f(\dot{x}) \sim \frac{2c}{\pi} \sum_{n=1}^{\infty} \frac{(-1)^{n+1} \sin(n\pi x/c)}{n}.$$

3. Interval, $-c < x < c$; function, $f(x) = x^2$. Check your answer with that in Example (b) in the text.

$$\text{ANS.} \quad f(x) \sim \frac{c^2}{3} + \frac{4c^2}{\pi^2} \sum_{n=1}^{\infty} \frac{(-1)^n \cos(n\pi x/c)}{n^2}.$$

4. Interval, $-c < x < c$; function, $f(x) = 0$, $\qquad -c < x < 0$,
    $\qquad\qquad\qquad\qquad\qquad\quad = (c-x)^2$, $\qquad 0 < x < c$.

$$\text{ANS.} \quad f(x) \sim \frac{c^2}{6}.$$

$$+ \frac{c^2}{\pi^3} \sum_{n=1}^{\infty} \frac{1}{n^3} \left[2n\pi \cos \frac{n\pi x}{c} + \{n^2\pi^2 - 2 + 2(-1)^n\} \sin \frac{n\pi x}{c} \right].$$

5. Interval, $-c < x < c$; function, $f(x) = 0$, $\quad -c < x < 0$,
    $\qquad\qquad\qquad\qquad\qquad\quad = 1$, $\qquad 0 < x < c$.

$$\text{ANS.} \quad f(x) \sim \tfrac{1}{2} + \sum_{n=1}^{\infty} \frac{1-(-1)^n}{n\pi} \sin \frac{n\pi x}{c},$$

or

$$f(x) \sim \tfrac{1}{2} + \frac{2}{\pi} \sum_{k=0}^{\infty} \frac{\sin[(2k+1)\pi x/c]}{2k+1}.$$

6. Interval, $-c < x < x$; function, $f(x) = x^3$.

$$\text{ANS.} \quad f(x) \sim \frac{2c^3}{\pi^3} \sum_{n=1}^{\infty} (-1)^{n+1} \frac{(n^2\pi^2 - 6) \sin(n\pi x/c)}{n^3}.$$

7. Interval, $-\pi < x < \pi$; function, $f(x) = 3\pi + 2x$, $\qquad -\pi < x < 0$,
    $\qquad\qquad\qquad\qquad\qquad\qquad = \pi + 2x$, $\qquad 0 < x < \pi$.

$$\text{ANS.} \quad f(x) \sim 2\pi - 2 \sum_{k=1}^{\infty} \frac{\sin 2kx}{k}.$$

8. Interval, $-c < x < c$; function, $f(x) = x(c+x)$, $\quad -c < x < 0$,
    $\qquad\qquad\qquad\qquad\qquad\qquad = (c-x)^2$, $\qquad 0 < x < c$.

$$\text{ANS.} \quad f(x) \sim \frac{c^2}{12} + \frac{c^2}{\pi^2} \sum_{n=1}^{\infty} \frac{1}{n^2} \left[\{3 + (-1)^n\} \cos \frac{n\pi x}{c} + n\pi \sin \frac{n\pi x}{c} \right].$$

9. Interval, $-2 < x < 2$; function, $f(x) = x+1$, $\qquad -2 < x < 0$,
    $\qquad\qquad\qquad\qquad\qquad\qquad = 1$, $\qquad 0 \leq x < 2$.

$$\text{ANS.} \quad f(x) \sim \tfrac{1}{2}.$$

$$+ \frac{2}{\pi^2} \sum_{n=1}^{\infty} \frac{1}{n^2} [\{1 - (-1)^n\} \cos \tfrac{1}{2} n\pi x + n\pi(-1)^{n+1} \sin \tfrac{1}{2} n\pi x].$$

10. Interval, $-1 < x < 1$; function, $f(x) = 0$, $\qquad -1 < x < 0$,
$$= 1, \qquad 0 < x < \tfrac{1}{2},$$
$$= 0, \qquad \tfrac{1}{2} < x < 1.$$

ANS. $f(x) \sim \tfrac{1}{4} + \dfrac{1}{\pi} \displaystyle\sum_{n=1}^{\infty} \dfrac{1}{n} \left[\sin \dfrac{n\pi}{2} \cos n\pi x + \left(1 - \cos \dfrac{n\pi}{2} \right) \sin n\pi x \right].$

11. Interval, $-\pi < x < \pi$; function, $f(x) = 0$, $\qquad -\pi < x < 0$,
$$= x^2, \qquad 0 < x < \pi.$$

ANS. $f(x) \sim \dfrac{\pi^2}{6} + 2 \displaystyle\sum_{n=1}^{\infty} \dfrac{(-)^n \cos nx}{n^2}.$

$$+ \dfrac{1}{\pi} \sum_{n=1}^{\infty} \dfrac{1}{n^3} [(-1)^{n+1} n^2 \pi^2 - 2 + 2(-1)^n] \sin nx.$$

12. Interval, $-\pi < x < \pi$; function, $f(x) = \cos 2x$. ANS. $f(x) \sim \cos 2x$.

13. Interval, $-\pi < x < \pi$; function, $f(x) = \cos (x/2)$.

ANS. $f(x) \sim \dfrac{2}{\pi} + \dfrac{4}{\pi} \displaystyle\sum_{n=1}^{\infty} \dfrac{(-1)^{n+1} \cos nx}{(2n-1)(2n+1)}.$

14. Interval, $-\pi < x < \pi$; function, $f(x) = \sin^2 x$.

ANS. $\sin^2 x \sim \tfrac{1}{2} - \tfrac{1}{2} \cos 2x.$

15. Interval, $-c < x < c$; function, $f(x) = e^x$.

ANS. $f(x) \sim \dfrac{\sinh c}{c}.$

$$+ \sum_{n=1}^{\infty} \dfrac{2(-1)^n \sinh c[c \cos(n\pi x/c) - n\pi \sin(n\pi x/c)]}{c^2 + n^2 \pi^2}.$$

16. Interval, $-c < x < c$; function, $f(x) = 0$, $\qquad -c < x < 0$,
$$= e^{-x}, \qquad 0 < x < c.$$

ANS. $f(x) \sim \dfrac{1 - e^{-c}}{2c}.$

$$+ \sum_{n=1}^{\infty} \dfrac{1 - (-1)^n e^{-c}}{c^2 + n^2 \pi^2} \left(c \cos \dfrac{n\pi x}{c} + n\pi \sin \dfrac{n\pi x}{c} \right).$$

17. Interval, $-c < x < c$; function, $f(x) = 0$, $\qquad -c < x < \tfrac{1}{2}c$,
$$= 1, \qquad \tfrac{1}{2}c < x < c.$$

ANS. $f(x) \sim \tfrac{1}{4}.$

$$- \dfrac{1}{\pi} \sum_{n=1}^{\infty} \dfrac{1}{n} \left[\sin \tfrac{1}{2} n\pi \cos \dfrac{n\pi x}{c} + (\cos n\pi - \cos \tfrac{1}{2} n\pi) \sin \dfrac{n\pi x}{c} \right].$$

18. Interval, $-c < x < c$; function, $f(x) = 0$, $\qquad -c < x < 0$,
$$= x, \qquad 0 < x < c.$$

ANS. $f(x) \sim \tfrac{1}{4}c.$

$$-\frac{c}{\pi^2}\sum_{n=1}^{\infty}\frac{1}{n^2}\left[\{1-(-1)^n\}\cos\frac{n\pi x}{c}+n\pi(-1)^n\sin\frac{n\pi x}{c}\right].$$

19. Interval, $-4 < x < 4$; function, $f(x) = 1, \qquad -4 < x < 2,$
$$= 0, \qquad 2 < x < 4.$$

20. Interval, $-c < x < c$; function, $f(x) = 0, \qquad\qquad -c < x < 0,$
$$= x(c - x), \qquad 0 < x < c.$$

21. Interval, $-c < x < c$; function, $f(x) = c + x, \quad -c < x < 0,$
$$= 0, \qquad\qquad 0 < x < c.$$

22. Interval, $-c < x < c$; function, $f(x) = x^4$.

      ANS. $\quad f(x) \sim \dfrac{c^4}{5} + 8c^4 \displaystyle\sum_{n=1}^{\infty} (-1)^n \, \dfrac{n^2\pi^2 - 6}{n^4\pi^4} \cos \dfrac{n\pi x}{c}.$

23. Use the answer to Exercise 3 to show that $\displaystyle\sum_{n=1}^{\infty} \frac{(-1)^{n+1}}{n^2} = \frac{\pi^2}{12}.$

24. Use the answer to Exercise 8 to show that $\displaystyle\sum_{n=1}^{\infty} \frac{1}{n^2} = \frac{\pi^2}{6}.$

25. Use the answer to Exercise 22 to show that

$$\sum_{n=1}^{\infty} \frac{1}{n^4} = \frac{\pi^4}{90}.$$

26. Use $x = 0$ in the answer to Exercise 15 to sum the series $\displaystyle\sum_{n=1}^{\infty} \frac{(-1)^n}{c^2 + n^2\pi^2}.$

                                         ANS. $\quad \dfrac{c - \sinh c}{2c^2 \sinh c}.$

27. Let $c \to 0$ in the result of Exercise 26 and check with Exercise 23.

28. From the results in Exercises 22 and 23, show that

$$\sum_{n=1}^{\infty} \frac{(-1)^{n+1}}{n^4} = \frac{7\pi^4}{720}.$$

29. Prove the validity of equation (6), page 185.

74. Fourier Sine Series

It is often desirable to have an expansion of a function $f(x)$ in a series involving only sine functions, the expansion to represent the original $f(x)$ in an interval $0 < x < c$. With the notation we have been using, the Fourier series

$$\tfrac{1}{2}a_0 + \sum_{n=1}^{\infty} \left(a_n \cos \frac{n\pi x}{c} + b_n \sin \frac{n\pi x}{c} \right)$$

will reduce to a series with each term containing a sine function if somehow the a_n; $n = 0, 1, 2, \ldots$, can be made to be zero. Examining the formula for a_n, page 186, reveals that the a_n will vanish if the function being expanded is an odd function over the interval $-c < x < c$.

Therefore, to get a sine series for $f(x)$ we introduce a new function $g(x)$ defined to equal $f(x)$ in the interval $0 < x < c$ and to be the odd extension of that function in the remaining interval, $-c < x < 0$. That is, we define $g(x)$ by

$$g(x) = f(x), \qquad\qquad 0 < x < c,$$
$$\quad = -f(-x), \quad -c < x < 0.$$

Then $g(x)$ is an odd function over the interval $-c < x < c$. Hence from

$$g(x) \sim \tfrac{1}{2}a_0 + \sum_{n=1}^{\infty} \left(a_n \cos \frac{n\pi x}{c} + b_n \sin \frac{n\pi x}{c} \right)$$

it follows that

$$a_n = \frac{1}{c} \int_{-c}^{c} g(x) \cos \frac{n\pi x}{c}\, dx = 0, \qquad n = 0, 1, 2, \ldots,$$

and that

$$b_n = \frac{1}{c} \int_{-c}^{c} g(x) \sin \frac{n\pi x}{c}\, dx = \frac{2}{c} \int_{0}^{c} f(x) \sin \frac{n\pi x}{c}\, dx.$$

The resultant series represents $f(x)$ in the interval $0 < x < c$, since $g(x)$ and $f(x)$ are identical over that portion of the whole interval.

Thus we have

(1) $$f(x) \sim \sum_{n=1}^{\infty} b_n \sin \frac{n\pi x}{c}, \qquad 0 < x < c,$$

in which

(2) $$b_n = \frac{2}{c} \int_{0}^{c} f(x) \sin \frac{n\pi x}{c}\, dx, \quad n = 1, 2, 3, \ldots.$$

The representation (1) is called the *Fourier sine series* for $f(x)$ over the interval $0 < x < c$.

It should be realized that the device of introducing the function $g(x)$ was a tool for arriving at (1) and (2); there is no need to repeat it in specific problems. Those we handle by direct use of (1) and (2) above.

EXAMPLE. Expand $f(x) = x^2$ in a Fourier sine series over the interval $0 < x < 1$.

At once we may write, for $0 < x < 1$,

(3) $$x^2 \sim \sum_{n=1}^{\infty} b_n \sin n\pi x,$$

in which

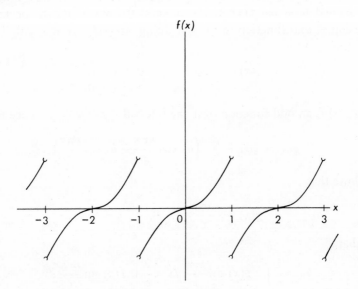

FIGURE 10

(4) $$b_n = 2 \int_0^1 x^2 \sin n\pi x \, dx$$

$$= 2 \left[-\frac{x^2 \cos n\pi x}{n\pi} + \frac{2x \sin n\pi x}{(n\pi)^2} + \frac{2 \cos n\pi x}{(n\pi)^3} \right]_0^1$$

$$= 2 \left[-\frac{\cos n\pi}{n\pi} + \frac{2 \cos n\pi}{n^3\pi^3} - \frac{2}{n^3\pi^3} \right].$$

Hence the Fourier sine series, over $0 < x < 1$, for x^2 is

(5) $$x^2 \sim 2 \sum_{n=1}^{\infty} \left[\frac{(-1)^{n+1}}{n\pi} - \frac{2\{1 - (-1)^n\}}{n^3\pi^3} \right] \sin n\pi x.$$

The series on the right in (5) converges to the function exhibited in Figure 10, that function being called the odd periodic extension, with period 2, of the function

$$f(x) = x^2, \qquad 0 < x < 1.$$

Exercises

In each exercise, obtain the Fourier sine series over the stipulated interval for the function given. Sketch the function that is the sum of the series obtained.

1. Interval, $0 < x < c$; function, $f(x) = 1$.

$$\text{ANS.}\quad f(x) \sim \frac{4}{\pi} \sum_{k=0}^{\infty} \frac{\sin[(2k+1)\pi x/c]}{2k+1}.$$

2. Interval, $0 < x < c$; function, $f(x) = x$. Compare your result with that in Exercise 2, page 194.

3. Inverval, $0 < x < c$; function, $f(x) = x^2$. Check your answer with that for the example in the text above.

$$\text{ANS.}\quad f(x) \sim 2c^2 \sum_{n=1}^{\infty} \left[\frac{(-1)^{n+1}}{n\pi} - \frac{2\{1-(-1)^n\}}{n^3\pi^3} \right] \sin \frac{n\pi x}{c}.$$

4. Interval, $0 < x < c$; function, $f(x) = c - x$.

$$\text{ANS.}\quad f(x) \sim \frac{2c}{\pi} \sum_{n=1}^{\infty} \frac{1}{n} \sin \frac{n\pi x}{c}.$$

5. Interval $0 < x < 2c$; function, $f(x) = c - x$.

$$\text{ANS.}\quad \text{Same as in Exercise 4.}$$

6. Interval, $0 < x < 4c$; function, $f(x) = c - x$. Compare with Exercises 4 and 5.

$$\text{ANS.}\quad f(x) \sim \frac{2c}{\pi} \sum_{n=1}^{\infty} \frac{1+3(-1)^n}{n} \sin \frac{n\pi x}{4c}.$$

7. Interval, $0 < x < c$; function, $f(x) = x(c - x)$.

$$\text{ANS.}\quad f(x) \sim \frac{8c^2}{\pi^3} \sum_{k=0}^{\infty} \frac{\sin[(2k+1)\pi x/c]}{(2k+1)^3}.$$

8. Interval $0 < x < 2$; function $f(x) = x,\qquad 0 < x < 1,$
    $$= 2 - x,\ 1 < x < 2.$$

$$\text{ANS.}\quad f(x) \sim \frac{8}{\pi^2} \sum_{k=0}^{\infty} \frac{(-1)^k}{(2k+1)^2} \sin\,[(2k+1)\pi x/2].$$

9. Interval, $0 < t < t_1$; function, $f(t) = 1,\quad 0 < t < t_0,$
    $$= 0,\quad t_0 < t < t_1.$$

$$\text{ANS.}\quad f(t) \sim \frac{2}{\pi} \sum_{n=1}^{\infty} \frac{1}{n}\left(1 - \cos \frac{n\pi t_0}{t_1}\right) \sin \frac{n\pi t}{t_1}.$$

10. Interval, $0 < x < 1$; function, $f(x) = 0, \qquad 0 < x < \frac{1}{2},$
$$= 1, \qquad \tfrac{1}{2} < x < 1.$$

ANS. $f(x) \sim \dfrac{2}{\pi} \displaystyle\sum_{n=1}^{\infty} \dfrac{1}{n} \left(\cos \dfrac{n\pi}{2} - \cos n\pi \right) \sin n\pi x.$

11. Interval, $0 < x < 1$; function, $f(x) = 0, \qquad 0 < x < \frac{1}{2},$
$$= x - \tfrac{1}{2}, \qquad \tfrac{1}{2} < x < 1.$$

ANS. $f(x) \sim \displaystyle\sum_{n=1}^{\infty} \left[\dfrac{(-1)^{n+1}}{n\pi} - \dfrac{2 \sin (n\pi/2)}{n^2\pi^2} \right] \sin n\pi x.$

12. Interval, $0 < x < \pi$; function, $f(x) = \sin 3x.$ ANS. $f(x) \sim \sin 3x.$

13. Interval, $0 < x < \pi$; function, $f(x) = \cos 2x.$ Note the special treatment necessary for the evaluation of b_2.

ANS. $f(x) \sim \dfrac{4}{\pi} \displaystyle\sum_{k=0}^{\infty} \dfrac{(2k+1) \sin[(2k+1)x]}{(2k-1)(2k+3)}.$

14. Interval, $0 < x < \pi$; function, $f(x) = \cos x.$

ANS. $f(x) \sim \dfrac{8}{\pi} \displaystyle\sum_{k=1}^{\infty} \dfrac{k \sin 2kx}{4k^2 - 1}.$

15. Interval, $0 < x < c$; function, $f(x) = e^{-x}.$

ANS. $f(x) \sim \displaystyle\sum_{n=1}^{\infty} \dfrac{2n\pi[1 - (-1)^n e^{-c}] \sin(n\pi x/c)}{c^2 + n^2\pi^2}.$

16. Interval, $0 < x < c$; function $f(x) = \sinh kx.$

ANS. $f(x) \sim \sinh kc \displaystyle\sum_{n=1}^{\infty} \dfrac{(-1)^{n+1} 2n\pi}{(kc)^2 + (n\pi)^2} \sin \dfrac{n\pi x}{c}.$

17. Interval, $0 < x < c$; function, $f(x) = \cosh kx.$

ANS. $f(x) \sim \displaystyle\sum_{n=1}^{\infty} \dfrac{2n\pi[1 + (-1)^{n+1} \cosh kc]}{(kc)^2 + (n\pi)^2} \sin \dfrac{n\pi x}{c}.$

18. Interval, $0 < x < c$; function, $f(x) = x^3.$ ANS. See Exercise 6, p. 194.

19. Interval, $0 < x < c$; function, $f(x) = x^4.$

ANS. $f(x) \sim \dfrac{2c^4}{\pi} \displaystyle\sum_{n=1}^{\infty} \left[(-1)^{n+1} \left\{ \dfrac{1}{n} - \dfrac{12}{\pi^2 n^3} + \dfrac{24}{\pi^4 n^5} \right\} + \dfrac{24}{\pi^4 n^5} \right] \sin \dfrac{n\pi x}{c}.$

20. Interval, $0 < x < c$; function, $f(x) = x, \qquad 0 < x < \frac{1}{2}c,$
$$= 0, \qquad \tfrac{1}{2}c < x < c.$$

ANS. $f(x) \sim \dfrac{c}{\pi^2} \displaystyle\sum_{n=1}^{\infty} \left(\dfrac{2}{n^2} \sin \dfrac{n\pi}{2} - \dfrac{\pi}{n} \cos \dfrac{n\pi}{2} \right) \sin \dfrac{n\pi x}{c}.$

21. Interval, $0 < x < 1$; function, $f(x) = (x - 1)^2.$

ANS. $f(x) \sim \dfrac{2}{\pi^3} \displaystyle\sum_{n=1}^{\infty} \dfrac{1}{n^3} [n^2\pi^2 - 2 + 2(-1)^n] \sin n\pi x.$

75. Fourier Cosine Series

In a manner entirely similar to that used to obtain the Fourier sine series, it is possible to obtain for a function defined over the interval $0 < x < c$ a series of cosine terms including a constant term. Indeed, given $f(x)$ defined over the interval $0 < x < c$ and satisfying there the conditions stipulated in Theorem 73, we may define an auxiliary function $h(x)$ by

$$h(x) = f(x), \qquad 0 < x < c,$$
$$= f(-x), \qquad -c < x < 0.$$

Then $h(x)$ is an even function of x and, of course, it is equal to $f(x)$ over the interval where $f(x)$ was defined. Since $h(x)$ is even, it follows that in its ordinary Fourier expansion over the interval $-c < x < c$, the b_n are all zero,

$$b_n = \frac{1}{c} \int_{-c}^{c} h(x) \sin \frac{n\pi x}{c} \, dx = 0,$$

because of the oddness of the integrand. Furthermore, since $h(x)$ is even, $h(x) \cos(n\pi x/c)$ is also even and

$$a_n = \frac{2}{c} \int_{0}^{c} h(x) \cos \frac{n\pi x}{c} \, dx = \frac{2}{c} \int_{0}^{c} f(x) \cos \frac{n\pi x}{c} \, dx.$$

Since $h(x)$ and $f(x)$ are identical over the interval $0 < x < c$, we may write what is customarily called the *Fourier cosine series* for $f(x)$ over that interval, namely,

$$(1) \qquad f(x) \sim \tfrac{1}{2}a_0 + \sum_{n=1}^{\infty} a_n \cos \frac{n\pi x}{c}, \quad 0 < x < c,$$

in which

$$(2) \qquad a_n = \frac{2}{c} \int_{0}^{c} f(x) \cos \frac{n\pi x}{c} \, dx.$$

EXAMPLE. Find the Fourier cosine series over the interval $0 < x < c$ for the function $f(x) = x$.

At once we have

$$f(x) \sim \tfrac{1}{2}a_0 + \sum_{n=1}^{\infty} a_n \cos \frac{n\pi x}{c},$$

in which

$$a_n = \frac{2}{c} \int_0^c x \cos \frac{n\pi x}{c} \, dx.$$

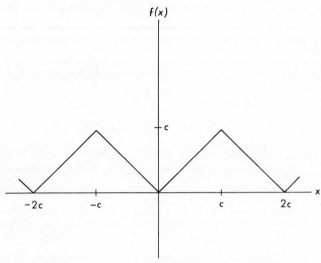

FIGURE 11

For $n \neq 0$, the a_n may be evaluated as follows:

$$a_n = \frac{2}{c} \left[\frac{c}{n\pi} x \sin \frac{n\pi x}{c} + \left(\frac{c}{n\pi} \right)^2 \cos \frac{n\pi x}{c} \right]_0^c$$

$$= \frac{2}{c} \left[\left(\frac{c}{n\pi} \right)^2 \cos n\pi - \left(\frac{c}{n\pi} \right)^2 \right]$$

$$= -\frac{2c}{n^2\pi^2} (1 - \cos n\pi), \qquad n \neq 0.$$

The remaining coefficient a_0 is readily obtained;

$$a_0 = \frac{2}{c} \int_0^c x \, dx = \frac{2}{c} \cdot \frac{c^2}{2} = c.$$

Thus the Fourier cosine series over the internal $0 < x < c$ for $f(x) = x$ is

$$f(x) \sim \tfrac{1}{2}c - \frac{2c}{\pi^2} \sum_{n=1}^{\infty} \frac{1 - (-1)^n}{n^2} \cos \frac{n\pi x}{c},$$

which may also be written in the form

(3) $$f(x) \sim \tfrac{1}{2}c - \frac{4c}{\pi^2} \sum_{k=0}^{\infty} \frac{\cos[(2k+1)\pi x/c]}{(2k+1)^2}.$$

In Figure 11 there is exhibited the sum of the series on the right in (3), often called the even periodic extension of the function x. The sum of the series is, of course, periodic with period $2c$.

Exercises

In Exercises 1–16 obtain the Fourier cosine series for the given function over the stipulated interval and sketch the function to which the series converges.

1. Interval, $0 < x < 2$; function, $f(x) = x$, $0 < x < 1$,
                                   $= 2 - x$, $1 < x < 2$.

ANS. $f(x) \sim \frac{1}{2} + \frac{4}{\pi^2} \sum_{n=1}^{\infty} \frac{1}{n^2} \left[2 \cos \frac{n\pi}{2} - 1 - (-1)^n \right] \cos \frac{n\pi x}{2}.$

2. Interval, $0 < t < t_1$; function, $f(t) = 1$, $0 < t < t_0$,
                                     $= 0$, $t_0 < t < t_1$.

ANS. $f(t) \sim \frac{t_0}{t_1} + \frac{2}{\pi} \sum_{n=1}^{\infty} \frac{1}{n} \sin \frac{n\pi t_0}{t_1} \cos \frac{n\pi t}{t_1}.$

3. Interval, $0 < x < 1$; function, $f(x) = (x - 1)^2$.

ANS. $f(x) \sim \frac{1}{3} + \frac{4}{\pi^2} \sum_{n=1}^{\infty} \frac{\cos n\pi x}{n^2}.$

4. Interval, $0 < x < c$; function, $f(x) = x(c - x)$.

ANS. $f(x) \sim \frac{c^2}{6} - \frac{c^2}{\pi^2} \sum_{k=1}^{\infty} \frac{\cos(2k\pi x/c)}{k^2}.$

5. Interval, $0 < x < c$; function, $f(x) = c - x$.

ANS. $f(x) \sim \frac{1}{2}c + \frac{4c}{\pi^2} \sum_{k=0}^{\infty} \frac{\cos[(2k+1)\pi x/c]}{(2k+1)^2}.$

6. Interval, $0 < x < 1$; function, $f(x) = 0$, $0 < x < \frac{1}{2}$,
                                     $= 1$, $\frac{1}{2} < x < 1$.

ANS. $f(x) \sim \frac{1}{2} - \frac{2}{\pi} \sum_{k=0}^{\infty} \frac{(-1)^k \cos[(2k+1)\pi x]}{2k+1}.$

7. Interval, $0 < x < 1$; function, $f(x) = 0$, $0 < x < \frac{1}{2}$,
                                     $= x - \frac{1}{2}$, $\frac{1}{2} < x < 1$.

ANS. $f(x) \sim \frac{1}{8} + \frac{2}{\pi^2} \sum_{n=1}^{\infty} \frac{1}{n^2} \left(\cos n\pi - \cos \frac{n\pi}{2} \right) \cos n\pi x.$

8. Interval, $0 < x < 1$; function, $f(x) = \frac{1}{2} - x$, $0 < x < \frac{1}{2}$,
                                     $= 0$, $\frac{1}{2} < x < 1$.

ANS. $f(x) \sim \frac{1}{8} + \frac{2}{\pi^2} \sum_{n=1}^{\infty} \frac{1}{n^2} \left(1 - \cos \frac{n\pi}{2} \right) \cos n\pi x.$

9. Interval, $0 < x < \pi$; function, $f(x) = \cos 2x$.   ANS. $f(x) \sim \cos 2x$.

10. Interval, $0 < x < \pi$; function, $f(x) = \sin 2x$.

$$\text{ANS.} \quad f(x) \sim -\frac{8}{\pi} \sum_{k=0}^{\infty} \frac{\cos[(2k+1)x]}{(2k-1)(2k+3)}.$$

11. Interval, $0 < x < c$; function, $f(x) = x, \qquad 0 < x < \tfrac{1}{2}c,$
    $$= 0, \qquad \tfrac{1}{2}c < x < c.$$

$$\text{ANS.} \quad f(x) \sim \frac{c}{8} + \frac{c}{\pi^2} \sum_{n=1}^{\infty} \frac{1}{n^2} \left[n\pi \sin \tfrac{1}{2}n\pi - 2(1 - \cos \tfrac{1}{2}n\pi) \right] \cos \frac{n\pi x}{c}.$$

12. Interval, $0 < x < c$; function, $f(x) = e^{-x}$. Notice how the a_0 term fits in with the others this time, making separate integration unnecessary.

$$\text{ANS.} \quad f(x) \sim \frac{1 - e^{-c}}{c} + 2c \sum_{n=1}^{\infty} \frac{1 - (-1)^n e^{-c}}{c^2 + n^2 \pi^2} \cos \frac{n\pi x}{c}.$$

13. Interval, $0 < x < c$; function, $f(x) = \cosh kx$.

$$\text{ANS.} \quad f(x) \sim \frac{\sinh kc}{kc} + \sinh kc \sum_{n=1}^{\infty} \frac{2kc(-1)^n}{(kc)^2 + (n\pi)^2} \cos \frac{n\pi x}{c}.$$

14. Interval, $0 < x < c$; function, $f(x) = \sinh kx$.

$$\text{ANS.} \quad f(x) \sim \frac{\cosh kc - 1}{kc} + \sum_{n=1}^{\infty} \frac{2kc[(-1)^n \cosh kc - 1]}{(kc)^2 + (n\pi)^2} \cos \frac{n\pi x}{c}.$$

15. Interval, $0 < x < c$; function, $f(x) = x^3$.

$$\text{ANS.} \quad f(x) \sim \frac{c^3}{4} + \frac{6c^3}{\pi^2} \sum_{n=1}^{\infty} \left[\frac{(-1)^n}{n^2} + \frac{2}{\pi^2} \cdot \frac{1 - (-1)^n}{n^4} \right] \cos \frac{n\pi x}{c}.$$

16. Interval, $0 < x < c$; function, $f(x) = x^4$.

ANS. See Exercise 22, p. 196.

17. Show that if

$$f(x) \sim \tfrac{1}{2}a_0 + \sum_{n=1}^{\infty} a_n \cos \frac{n\pi x}{c}, \qquad 0 < x < c,$$

then

$$f(c - x) \sim \tfrac{1}{2}a_0 + \sum_{n=1}^{\infty} (-1)^n a_n \cos \frac{n\pi x}{c}, \qquad 0 < x < c.$$

18. Show that if

$$f(x) \sim \sum_{n=1}^{\infty} b_n \sin \frac{n\pi x}{c}, \qquad 0 < x < c,$$

then

$$f(c - x) \sim \sum_{n=1}^{\infty} (-1)^{n+1} b_n \sin \frac{n\pi x}{c}, \qquad 0 < x < c.$$

76. Integration of Fourier Series

Let $f(x)$ satisfy the conditions of Theorem 73, page 186. Then

$$(1) \quad f(x) \sim \tfrac{1}{2}a_0 + \sum_{n=1}^{\infty} \left(a_n \cos \frac{n\pi x}{c} + b_n \sin \frac{n\pi x}{c} \right), \qquad -c \leq \dot{x} \leq c,$$

and

$$(2) \qquad a_n = \frac{1}{c} \int_{-c}^{c} f(y) \cos \frac{n\pi y}{c} \, dy, \qquad n \geq 0,$$

$$(3) \qquad b_n = \frac{1}{c} \int_{-c}^{c} f(y) \sin \frac{n\pi y}{c} \, dy, \qquad n \geq 1.$$

Because $f(x)$ is continuous except for a finite number of finite jumps, the function

$$(4) \qquad g(x) = \int_{-c}^{x} [f(y) - \tfrac{1}{2}a_0] \, dy$$

is continuous on the closed interval $-c \leq x \leq c$. By (4),

$$(5) \qquad g'(x) = f(x) - \tfrac{1}{2}a_0,$$

so $g(x)$ also satisfies the conditions of Theorem 73. Also

$$g(-c) = 0$$

and

$$g(c) = \int_{-c}^{c} f(y) \, dy - \tfrac{1}{2}a_0 \int_{-c}^{c} dy = ca_0 - \tfrac{1}{2}a_0(2c) = 0.$$

Therefore, $g(x)$ is continuous throughout the closed interval and the values of $g(x)$ at the endpoints are equal, so the periodic extension of $g(x)$ is continuous for all finite x. The Fourier series for $g(x)$ converges to the function at every point in the interval,

$$(6) \quad g(x) = \tfrac{1}{2}d_0 + \sum_{n=1}^{\infty} \left(d_n \cos \frac{n\pi x}{c} + e_n \sin \frac{n\pi x}{c} \right), \qquad -c \leq x \leq c,$$

with

$$(7) \qquad d_n = \frac{1}{c} \int_{-c}^{c} g(\beta) \cos \frac{n\pi\beta}{c} \, d\beta, \qquad n \geq 0,$$

$$(8) \qquad e_n = \frac{1}{c} \int_{-c}^{c} g(\beta) \sin \frac{n\pi\beta}{c} \, d\beta, \qquad n \geq 1.$$

We obtain d_0 by using $x = c$ and $g(c) = 0$ in (6):

$$(9) \qquad\qquad 0 = \tfrac{1}{2}d_0 + \sum_{n=1}^{\infty} d_n \cos n\pi.$$

Next, we integrate by parts in (7) and (8) and use the fact that

$$g'(\beta) = f(\beta) - \tfrac{1}{2}a_0.$$

An integration by parts performed on (7) yields, for $n \geq 1$,

$$d_n = \frac{1}{c}\left[\left(\frac{c}{n\pi}\right) g(\beta) \sin\frac{n\pi\beta}{c} \right]_{-c}^{c} - \frac{1}{c}\left(\frac{c}{n\pi}\right)\int_{-c}^{c} [f(\beta) - \tfrac{1}{2}a_0] \sin\frac{n\pi\beta}{c}\, d\beta.$$

Using (3) and the fact that $\sin x$ is an odd function of x, we obtain

$$(10) \qquad\qquad d_n = -\frac{c}{n\pi} b_n, \qquad n \geq 1.$$

An integration by parts performed on (8) yields

$$e_n = \frac{1}{c}\left[\left(\frac{-c}{n\pi}\right) g(\beta) \cos\frac{n\pi\beta}{c} \right]_{-c}^{c} + \frac{1}{c}\left(\frac{c}{n\pi}\right)\int_{-c}^{c} [f(\beta) - \tfrac{1}{2}a_0] \cos\frac{n\pi\beta}{c}\, d\beta.$$

But $g(c) = 0$, $g(-c) = 0$, and the term containing a_0 is also zero. Thus we obtain, with the aid of (2),

$$(11) \qquad\qquad e_n = \frac{c}{n\pi} a_n, \qquad n \geq 1.$$

Because of (10), we may rewrite equation (9) as

$$(12) \qquad\qquad \tfrac{1}{2}d_0 = \sum_{n=1}^{\infty} \left(\frac{c}{n\pi}\right) b_n \cos n\pi.$$

Finally, we make appropriate substitutions from equations (4), (10), (11), and (12) into the expansion (6) and thus obtain

$$(13) \quad \int_{-c}^{x} [f(y) - \tfrac{1}{2}a_0]\, dy = \sum_{n=1}^{\infty} \frac{c}{n\pi}\left[a_n \sin\frac{n\pi x}{c} + b_n\left\{\cos n\pi - \cos\frac{n\pi x}{c}\right\} \right],$$

valid throughout $-c \leq x \leq c$. A comparison of (13) with the Fourier series for $f(x)$, equation (1), page 205, shows that (13) is precisely the result of integrating the two members of (1) over the range $(-c)$ to x.

THEOREM 74. *If $f(x)$ satisfies the conditions imposed in Theorem 73, page 186, over the interval $-c \leq x \leq c$, then term-by-term integration of the Fourier series for $f(x)$ is legitimate in that interval.*

EXAMPLE. In Exercise 22, page 196, we found that

$$(14) \qquad x^4 = \frac{c^4}{5} + 8c^4 \sum_{n=1}^{\infty} (-1)^n \frac{n^2\pi^2 - 6}{n^4\pi^4} \cos \frac{n\pi x}{c}, \qquad -c \leq x \leq c,$$

the equality entering as a result of the continuity of the periodic extension of x^4.

Applying Theorem 74 to the expansion (14), we arrive at

$$\int_{-c}^{x} y^4 \, dy = \frac{c^4}{5} \int_{-c}^{x} dy + 8c^4 \sum_{n=1}^{\infty} (-1)^n \frac{n^2\pi^2 - 6}{n^4\pi^4} \int_{-c}^{x} \cos \frac{n\pi y}{c} \, dy.$$

Thus we obtain the expansion

$$\frac{1}{5}(x^5 + c^5) = \frac{c^4}{5}(x + c) + \frac{8c^5}{\pi^5} \sum_{n=1}^{\infty} (-1)^n \frac{n^2\pi^2 - 6}{n^5} \sin \frac{n\pi x}{c}$$

and from it

$$(15) \qquad x^5 = xc^4 + \frac{40c^5}{\pi^5} \sum_{n=1}^{\infty} (-1)^n \frac{n^2\pi^2 - 6}{n^5} \sin \frac{n\pi x}{c}, \qquad -c \leq x \leq c.$$

If $\dfrac{x}{c}$ is replaced by a new x, equation (15) takes on a simpler and just as useful form

$$(16) \qquad x^5 - x = \frac{40}{\pi^5} \sum_{n=1}^{\infty} (-1)^n \frac{n^2\pi^2 - 6}{n^5} \sin n\pi x, \qquad -1 \leq x \leq 1.$$

Retention of c in the above example, as well as in Exercise 22, page 196, does give us a mild dimensional check at each stage of the work.

77. Differentiation of Fourier Series

Suppose a Fourier series has a sum function that is continuous on the closed interval. Let

$$(1) \qquad f(x) = \tfrac{1}{2}a_0 + \sum_{n=1}^{\infty} \left(a_n \cos \frac{n\pi x}{c} + b_n \sin \frac{n\pi x}{c} \right), \qquad -c \leq x \leq c.$$

Suppose also that the derivative $f'(x)$ satisfies the conditions imposed on f in Theorem 73, page 186. Then

$$(2) \qquad f'(x) \sim \tfrac{1}{2}g_0 + \sum_{n=1}^{\infty} \left(g_n \cos \frac{n\pi x}{c} + h_n \sin \frac{n\pi x}{c} \right), \qquad -c \leq x \leq c.$$

We know that

(3) $$a_n = \frac{1}{c}\int_{-c}^{c} f(y)\cos\frac{n\pi y}{c}\,dy, \qquad n \geq 0,$$

(4) $$b_n = \frac{1}{c}\int_{-c}^{c} f(y)\sin\frac{n\pi y}{c}\,dy, \qquad n \geq 1,$$

(5) $$g_n = \frac{1}{c}\int_{-c}^{c} f'(y)\cos\frac{n\pi y}{c}\,dy, \qquad n \geq 0,$$

(6) $$h_n = \frac{1}{c}\int_{-c}^{c} f'(y)\sin\frac{n\pi y}{c}\,dy, \qquad n \leq 1.$$

We seek conditions that will force the series in (2) to be the term-by-term derivative of the series in (1). For $n = 0$,

(7) $$g_0 = \frac{1}{c}\int_{-c}^{c} f'(y)\,dy = \frac{1}{c}[f(c^-)-f(-c^+)].$$

We wish to have $g_0 = 0$, the derivative of the constant a_0. Therefore we impose the condition that the value approached by $f(x)$ as $x \to -c$ from the right equals the value approached by $f(x)$ as $x \to c$ from the left,

(8) $$f(c^-) = f(-c^+).$$

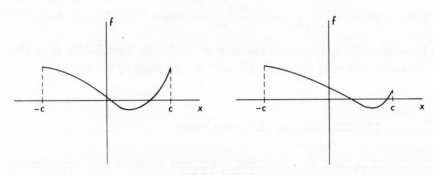

FIGURE 12

Of the continuous functions exhibited in Figure 12, the one on the left satisfies the condition (8), the one on the right does not satisfy (8).

An integration by parts performed on the integral in (5), for $n \geq 1$, yields

$$f_n = \frac{1}{c}\left[f(y)\cos\frac{n\pi y}{c}\right]_{-c}^{c} + \frac{1}{c}\left(\frac{n\pi}{c}\right)\int_{-c}^{c} f(y)\sin\frac{n\pi y}{c}\,dy,$$

$$g_n = \frac{1}{c} \cos n\pi [f(c^-) - f(-c^+)] + \frac{n\pi}{c} b_n.$$

Because of (8), we thus obtain

(9) $$g_n = \frac{n\pi}{c} b_n, \qquad n \geq 1.$$

An integration by parts performed on the integral in (6) yields

$$h_n = \frac{1}{c} \left[f(y) \sin \frac{n\pi y}{c} \right]_{-c}^{c} - \frac{1}{c} \left(\frac{n\pi}{c} \right) \int_{-c}^{c} f(y) \cos \frac{n\pi y}{c} \, dy,$$

from which it follows that

(10) $$h_n = -\frac{n\pi}{c} a_n, \qquad n \geq 1.$$

The relations (9) and (10) along with $g_0 = 0$ are precisely the ones needed to make the series in (2) be the term-by-term derivative of the series in (1).

Since the sum of the Fourier series (1) must be periodic in x with period $2c$,

(11) $$f(x + 2c) = f(x),$$

the result of adding the condition (8) to the requirement that $f(x)$ be continuous on the closed interval $-c \leq x \leq c$ is equivalent to requiring that the periodic extension of $f(x)$ be continuous for all finite x.

THEOREM 75. *If the sum function $f(x)$ of a Fourier series*

(12) $$f(x) = \tfrac{1}{2} a_0 + \sum_{n=1}^{\infty} \left(a_n \cos \frac{n\pi x}{c} + b_n \sin \frac{n\pi x}{c} \right), \qquad -c \leq x \leq c,$$

is continuous for all finite x, and if $f'(x)$ satisfies the conditions imposed on f in Theorem 73, page 186, then term-by-term differentiation of the series in (12) is legitimate.

Notice that the conditions imposed in Theorem 75 are *conditions on the sum of the Fourier series*, not on the function which led to that series. Indeed, the original function is most often not even defined outside the original interval and the original function could have missing point discontinuities, as it has in the example below.

EXAMPLE. Examine for term-by-term differentiability the Fourier series associated on $(-c, c)$ with the function

$$g(x) = 0, \qquad -c < x < 0,$$

(13)

$$= x(c - x), \qquad 0 < x < c.$$

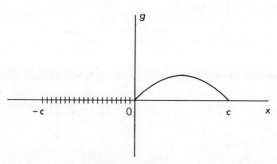

FIGURE 13

This $g(x)$ is not defined at $x = 0$, c, $-c$. But $g(x)$ does satisfy the conditions in Theorem 73, page 186. By performing the required integrations to get the coefficients we obtain

$$(14) \quad g(x) \sim \frac{c^2}{12} + c^2 \sum_{n=1}^{\infty} \left[-\frac{1 + (-1)^n}{n^2 \pi^2} \cos \frac{n\pi x}{c} + \frac{2[1 - (-1)^n]}{n^3 \pi^3} \sin \frac{n\pi x}{c} \right]$$

on $-c \leq x \leq c$.

The series in (14) converges for all x to the function defined by

(15) $$f(x) = 0, \qquad -c \leq x < 0,$$

$$= x(c - x), \qquad 0 \leq x \leq c,$$

$$f(x + 2c) = f(x), \qquad \text{for all } x.$$

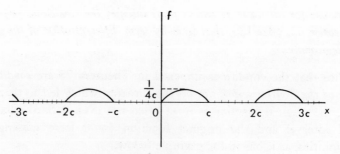

FIGURE 14

Indeed, $f(x)$ is continuous for all x,

$$(16) \qquad f'(x) = 0, \qquad -c < x < 0,$$
$$= c - 2x, \qquad 0 < x < c,$$

and f' does not exist at $x = 0$, c, $-c$, but the right- and left-hand limits of f' at each point do exist. Furthermore,

$$(17) \qquad f''(x) = 0, \qquad -c < x < 0,$$
$$= -2, \qquad 0 < x < c.$$

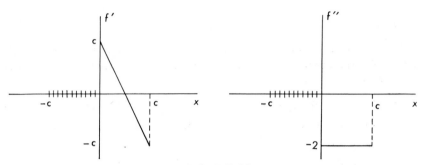

FIGURE 15

Hence $f'(x)$ satisfies the conditions of Theorem 73 and $f(x)$ satisfies the conditions of Theorem 75.

We obtain

$$(18) \quad f(x) = \frac{c^2}{12} + c^2 \sum_{n=1}^{\infty} \left[-\frac{1+(-1)^n}{n^2\pi^2} \cos\frac{n\pi x}{c} + \frac{2[1-(-1)^n]}{n^3\pi^3} \sin\frac{n\pi x}{c} \right]$$

for all x, and

$$(19) \quad f'(x) \sim c \sum_{n=1}^{\infty} \left[\frac{1+(-1)^n}{n\pi} \sin\frac{n\pi x}{c} + \frac{2[1-(-1)^n]}{n^2\pi^2} \cos\frac{n\pi x}{c} \right],$$

in $-c \leq x \leq c$. The series in (19) converges to $f'(x)$ throughout the interval except at $x = 0$, c, $-c$. At $x = 0$, the series in (19) converges to the mean value $\frac{1}{2}c$ and at $x = c$ and $x = -c$, the series in (19) converges to $(-\frac{1}{2}c)$.

If we try term-by-term differentiation on the derived series (19) we arrive at

$$(20) \qquad \sum_{n=1}^{\infty} \left[\{1+(-1)^n\} \cos\frac{n\pi x}{c} - \frac{2[1-(-1)^n]}{n\pi} \sin\frac{n\pi x}{c} \right],$$

a series which diverges because its general term does not approach zero as $n \to \infty$. Of course, no filling in of missing points can convert the $f'(x)$ of (16) to a continuous function. The series in (19) converges for all x, but not to a continuous function. Hence Theorem 75 cannot be applied to the series in (19).

The theorem on integration of Fourier series, Theorem 74, page 206, is applicable to all the Fourier series in the exercises at the end of Sections 73, 74, and 75. Therefore the following set contains only a few exercises that explicitly call for integration of series. The reader can obtain further practice by using items in the Table of Fourier Series, pages 256–259, and the answer will often be found in that same table.

Exercises

In Exercises 1–14, show that the Fourier series converges to a sum function that satisfies the conditions in Theorem 75, page 209. Obtain the derived series and its sum.

1.	Example (b), page 192.	**2.**	Exercise 3, page. 194.
3.	Exercise 13, page 195.	**4.**	Exercise 22, page 196.
5.	Exercise 7, page 199.	**6.**	Exercise 8, page 199.
7.	Example, page 201.	**8.**	Exercise 3, page 203.
9.	Exercise 4, page 203.	**10.**	Exercise 5, page 203.
11.	Exercise 8, page 203.	**12.**	Exercise 10, page 204.
13.	Exercise 13, page 204.	**14.**	Exercise 15, page 204.

In Exercises 15–39, show that the series has a sum function that does not satisfy the conditions of Theorem 75, page 209, and further show that term-by-term differentiation produces a divergent series.

15.	Example (a), page 187.	**16.**	Exercise 1, page 193.
17.	Exercise 2, page 194.	**18.**	Exercise 4, page 194.
19.	Exercise 5, page 194.	**20.**	Exercise 6, page 194.
21.	Exercise 7, page 194.	**22.**	Exercise 8, page 194.
23.	Exercise 9, page 194.	**24.**	Exercise 10, page 195.
25.	Exercise 11, page 195.	**26.**	Exercise 15, page 195.
27.	Exercise 16, page 195.	**28.**	Exercise 17, page 195.
29.	Exercise 18, page 195.	**30.**	Example, page 197.
31.	Exercise 1, page 199.	**32.**	Exercise 3, page 199.
33.	Exercise 4, page 199.	**34.**	Exercise 6, page 199.
35.	Exercise 9, page 199.	**36.**	Exercise 10, page 200.
37.	Exercise 2, page 203.	**38.**	Exercise 6, page 203.
39.	Exercise 11, page 204.		

40.   In Exercise 1, page 193, we found, in different notation, that the function

$$g(y) = 0, \qquad -c < y < 0,$$
$$= c - y, \qquad 0 < y < c,$$

has for its Fourier series in $(-c, c)$

$$g(y) \sim \frac{c}{4} + \frac{c}{\pi^2} \sum_{n=1}^{\infty} \frac{1}{n^2} \left[\{1 - (-1)^n\} \cos \frac{n\pi y}{c} + n\pi \sin \frac{n\pi y}{c} \right].$$

Integrate the above series from $y = -c$ to $y = x$ and conclude that the function

$$f(x) = 0, \qquad -c \leq x \leq 0,$$
$$= cx - \tfrac{1}{2}x^2, \qquad 0 \leq x \leq c,$$

has the expansion

$$f(x) = \frac{c}{4}(x + c) + \frac{c^2}{\pi^3} \sum_{n=1}^{\infty} \frac{1}{n^3} \left[\{1 - (-1)^n\} \sin \frac{n\pi x}{c} \right.$$
$$\left. - n\pi \left(\cos \frac{n\pi x}{c} - \cos n\pi \right) \right],$$

valid in $-c \leq x \leq c$. Note also the simplification that can be accomplished by using, from Exercise 23, page 196,

$$\sum_{n=1}^{\infty} \frac{\cos n\pi}{n^2} = -\frac{\pi^2}{12}.$$

In Exercises 41–44, obtain a series by performing integration of the series to which reference is given.

41.   Example (b), page 192.

42.   Exercise 2, page 194.

43.   Exercise 3, page 203.

44.   Exercise 5, page 203.

CHAPTER **12**

Computations

78. Improvement in Rapidity of Convergence

In practical problems, trigonometric series occur sometimes without the sum function being known in any other form. Computations with such series can be irksome unless the series converge with reasonable rapidity.

Suppose that it is desired to compute, at several points in the interval $0 < x < \pi$, the sum of the series

(1)
$$\sum_{n=1}^{\infty} \frac{(-1)^n n \cos nx}{n^3 + 7}.$$

The series in (1) converges absolutely since its general term is less in absolute value than $\dfrac{1}{n^2}$ and $\displaystyle\sum_{n=1}^{\infty} \frac{1}{n^2}$ converges. Let the sum of the series in (1) be denoted by $\varphi(x)$.

For large n the coefficients in the series (1) are well approximated by $\dfrac{(-1)^n}{n^2}$. But we know the sum of the corresponding series with those coefficients; on pages 192–193 we showed that

(2)
$$x^2 = \frac{\pi^2}{3} + 4 \sum_{n=1}^{\infty} \frac{(-1)^n \cos nx}{n^2}, \qquad \text{for } -\pi \leq x \leq \pi.$$

Therefore,

(3)
$$\tfrac{1}{4}\left(x^2 - \frac{\pi^2}{3}\right) = \sum_{n=1}^{\infty} \frac{(-1)^n \cos nx}{n^2}, \qquad -\pi \leq x \leq \pi.$$

214

Since the coefficients in the series in (3) and those in the series for $\varphi(x)$,

(4) $$\varphi(x) = \sum_{n=1}^{\infty} \frac{(-1)^n n \cos nx}{n^3 + 7}, \qquad 0 < x < \pi,$$

are nearly equal for large n, it follows that the difference of those coefficients should be small. So we subtract the members of equation (3) from the corresponding ones of equation (4) and get

$$\varphi(x) - \tfrac{1}{4}\left(x^2 - \frac{\pi^2}{3}\right) = \sum_{n=1}^{\infty} (-1)^n \left[\frac{n}{n^3 + 7} - \frac{1}{n^2}\right] \cos nx$$

$$= \sum_{n=1}^{\infty} \frac{7(-1)^{n+1} \cos nx}{n^2(n^3 + 7)}.$$

Thus we obtain for $\varphi(x)$ the formula

(5) $$\varphi(x) = \tfrac{1}{4}\left(x^2 - \frac{\pi^2}{3}\right) + 7 \sum_{n=1}^{\infty} \frac{(-1)^{n+1} \cos nx}{n^2(n^3 + 7)}, \qquad 0 < x < \pi,$$

with which computation of $\varphi(x)$ is simplified, since the coefficients of $\cos nx$ in (5) get small more rapidly than those in (4) as n increases.

The device employed above is also useful for series other than trigonometric series. The method is largely dependent upon the availability of a collection of series of known sums.

Less elementary methods exist. Transformations of series into forms which may converge more rapidly than the original series have received attention since the days of Euler, more than two centuries ago. For a discussion of such transformations, see Konrad Knopp, *Theory and Application of Infinite Series*, London, Blackie and Son, Ltd., 1928, pp. 240–273.

79. Numerical Computations

When computing the sum of a convergent series of constants

(1) $$s = \sum_{n=0}^{\infty} a_n$$

by using the partial sums

(2) $$s_n = \sum_{k=0}^{n} a_k,$$

it is highly desirable to be able to bound the error, or remainder,

(3) $$E_n = s - s_n.$$

For alternating series bounds on E_n appear in Theorem 36, page 75, and Theorem 37, page 76. Sometimes a simple device may enable us to bound the error (3) for positive term series. No systematic treatment of such processes can be studied here. We must content ourselves with simple examples.

EXAMPLE (a). Compute cosh 1 to five decimal places.

We know that the series

$$(4) \qquad\qquad \cosh 1 = \sum_{n=0}^{\infty} \frac{1}{(2n)!}$$

is absolutely convergent. Let $a_n = \dfrac{1}{(2n)!}$. Then

$$\frac{a_{n+1}}{a_n} = \frac{1}{(2n+1)(2n+2)}.$$

We compute each term from the one preceding it:

$$
\begin{array}{r}
1.000\ 000 \\
+0.500\ 000 \\
+0.041\ 667 \\
+0.001\ 389 \\
+0.000\ 025 \\
\hline
\end{array}
$$

$$s_4 = 1.543\ 081.$$

The error made by stopping with the term in which $n = 4$ is

$$E_4 = \cosh 1 - s_4 = \sum_{n=5}^{\infty} a_n.$$

Now, for $n \geq 5$,

$$a_n = \frac{1}{(2n)!} = \frac{1}{8!} \cdot \frac{1}{9 \cdot 10 \cdot 11 \cdot 12 \cdots (2n-1)(2n)}$$

so

$$a_n \leq a_4 \frac{1}{(90)^{n-4}}, \qquad n \geq 5,$$

with equality occurring only at $n = 5$. Therefore,

$$E_4 < a_4 \sum_{n=5}^{\infty} \frac{1}{(90)^{n-4}}.$$

We can sum the geometric series involved and thus get

$$E_4 < a_4 \frac{1}{90} \cdot \frac{1}{1 - \dfrac{1}{90}},$$

so

$$E_4 < \frac{a_4}{89} = \frac{0.000\ 025}{89} < 0.000\ 000\ 3.$$

We may therefore conclude that

$$\cosh 1 = 1.543\ 08$$

correct to five decimal places.

EXAMPLE (b). Compute to four decimal places the sum of the series

(5) $$A = \sum_{n=0}^{\infty} \frac{1}{(2n+1)^2 \cdot 5^n}.$$

The series may be written as

$$A = \frac{1}{1^2 \cdot 5^0} + \frac{1}{3^2 \cdot 5^1} + \frac{1}{5^2 \cdot 5^2} + \frac{1}{7^2 \cdot 5^3} + \cdots + \frac{1}{(2n+1)^2 5^n} + \cdots.$$

We compute

$$\begin{aligned}
a_0 &= 1.000\ 000 \\
a_1 &= 0.022\ 222 \\
a_2 &= 0.001\ 600 \\
a_3 &= 0.000\ 163 \\
\hline
s_3 &= 1.023\ 985.
\end{aligned}$$

Now

$$A - s_3 = \sum_{n=4}^{\infty} \frac{1}{(2n+1)^2 5^n} < \sum_{n=4}^{\infty} \frac{1}{9^2 \cdot 5^n}.$$

Hence

$$A - s_3 < \frac{1}{81} \cdot \frac{1}{5^4} \cdot \frac{1}{1 - \dfrac{1}{5}} = \frac{1}{81(5)^3 \cdot 4} = \frac{0.012\ 345\ 7}{500},$$

so

$$E_3 = A - s_3 < 0.000\ 025.$$

Then $A = 1.0240$, correct to four decimal places.

Exercises

In each exercise, find the sum of the series to the number of decimal places shown in the answer. Use the technique of Examples (a) and (b) above or Theorem 37, page 76, to get the necessary bounds on the remainders.

1. Compute $e^{-1/2}$ from

$$e^{-1/2} = \sum_{n=0}^{\infty} \frac{(-\frac{1}{2})^n}{n!}.$$
      ANS.   0.6065.

2. Compute $\sinh 0.4$ from

$$\sinh 0.4 = \sum_{n=0}^{\infty} \frac{(0.4)^{2n+1}}{(2n+1)!}.$$
      ANS.   0.4108.

3. Compute $\sin \frac{1}{2}$ from

$$\sin \tfrac{1}{2} = \sum_{n=0}^{\infty} \frac{(-1)^n (\frac{1}{2})^{2n+1}}{(2n+1)!}.$$
      ANS.   0.4794.

4. Compute $\cos \frac{1}{2}$.   ANS.   0.8776.

5. Compute $\text{Arctan } \frac{1}{7}$ from

$$\text{Arctan } \tfrac{1}{7} = \sum_{n=0}^{\infty} \frac{(-1)^n (\frac{1}{7})^{2n+1}}{2n+1}.$$
      ANS.   0.1419.

6. Compute $\cosh \frac{1}{4}$.   ANS.   1.0314.

7. $1 - \dfrac{1}{10} + \dfrac{2}{10^2} - \dfrac{3}{10^3} + \cdots + \dfrac{(-1)^n \cdot n}{10^n} + \cdots.$ ANS.   0.91736.

8. $1 - \dfrac{1}{3!} + \dfrac{1}{5!} - \cdots + \dfrac{(-1)^{n-1}}{(2n-1)!} + \cdots.$ ANS.   0.84147.

9. $1 - \dfrac{1}{2!} + \dfrac{2}{3!} - \dfrac{3}{4!} + \cdots + \dfrac{(-1)^{n-1}(n-1)}{n!} + \cdots.$ ANS.   0.736.

10. $\dfrac{1}{10} - \dfrac{1}{2 \cdot 10^2} + \dfrac{1}{3 \cdot 10^3} - \cdots + \dfrac{(-1)^{n-1}}{n \cdot 10^n} + \cdots.$ ANS.   0.0953.

11. $\dfrac{1}{5} + \dfrac{2}{5^2} + \dfrac{3}{5^3} + \cdots + \dfrac{n}{5^n} + \cdots.$ ANS.   0.3125.

12. $\dfrac{1}{1 \cdot 2} + \dfrac{1}{2 \cdot 3} \cdot \dfrac{1}{10} + \dfrac{1}{3 \cdot 4} \cdot \dfrac{1}{10^2} + \cdots + \dfrac{1}{n(n+1)10^{n-1}} + \cdots.$

      ANS.   0.5176.

80. Summation of Power Series

The general problem given a power series, to find the sum of the series in terms of known functions, is naturally incapable of solution. Even if the sum does happen to be expressible in terms of known functions, the actual determination of that sum may be prohibitively difficult.

There are instances in which the application of our knowledge of the basic series in Section 45, page 119, will yield the desired sum.

EXAMPLE (a). Sum the series $\displaystyle\sum_{n=0}^{\infty} \frac{(-1)^n(n+2)x^n}{n!}$.

We start with a known series suggested by the series to be summed. We know that

$$(1) \qquad e^{-x} = \sum_{n=0}^{\infty} \frac{(-1)^n x^n}{n!},$$

for all finite x.

The series to be summed has a factor $(n+2)$ in the numerator. Such a factor can be introduced by differentiation of x^{n+2}. Therefore we first introduce a factor x^2 on both sides of equation (1) to obtain

$$(2) \qquad x^2 e^{-x} = \sum_{n=0}^{\infty} \frac{(-1)^n x^{n+2}}{n!}.$$

Then differentiation of each member of equation (2) yields

$$(3) \qquad e^{-x}(2x - x^2) = \sum_{n=1}^{\infty} \frac{(-1)^n(n+2)^{n+1}}{n!},$$

and the desired sum is obtained by division of both members of (3) by x:

$$(4) \qquad e^{-x}(2 - x) = \sum_{n=0}^{\infty} \frac{(-1)^n(n+2)x^n}{n!},$$

valid for all finite x.

EXAMPLE (b). Sum the series $\displaystyle\sum_{n=0}^{\infty} \frac{(-1)^n x^{2n}}{(n+1)(n+3)}$.

A factor $(n+1)$ can be introduced into the denominator by integrating $x^n\,dx$, a factor $(n+3)$ by integrating $x^{n+2}\,dx$. But in this instance we can start off with a factor $(n+1)$ in the denominator by using the basic series

$$(5) \qquad \ln(1+x) = \sum_{n=1}^{\infty} \frac{(-1)^{n+1}x^n}{n}, \qquad |x| < 1,$$

and shifting index from n to $(n+1)$ to obtain

(6) $$\ln(1+x) = \sum_{n=0}^{\infty} \frac{(-1)^n x^{n+1}}{n+1}.$$

To get the desired power x^{n+2} into the numerator, we multiply throughout by x, obtaining

(7) $$x \ln(1+x) = \sum_{n=0}^{\infty} \frac{(-1)^n x^{n+2}}{n+1}.$$

Then an integration yields

$$\int x \ln(1+x) \, dx = C + \sum_{n=0}^{\infty} \frac{(-1)^n x^{n+3}}{(n+1)(n+3)},$$

or

(8) $$\frac{1}{2}(x^2 - 1) \ln(1+x) - \frac{1}{4}(x-1)^2 = C + \sum_{n=0}^{\infty} \frac{(-1)^n x^{n+3}}{(n+1)(n+3)}.$$

Put $x=0$ to obtain C. Thus we find that $C = -\frac{1}{4}$. Therefore we now have

(9) $$\frac{1}{2}(x^2 - 1) \ln(1+x) - \frac{1}{4}x^2 + \frac{1}{2}x = \sum_{n=0}^{\infty} \frac{(-1)^n x^{n+3}}{(n+1)(n+3)}.$$

To obtain the desired power x^{2n} on the right, we first divide by x^3, exclude $x=0$, and write

(10) $$\frac{x^2-1}{2x^3} \ln(1+x) - \frac{1}{4x} + \frac{1}{2x^2} = \sum_{n=0}^{\infty} \frac{(-1)^n x^n}{(n+1)(n+3)}.$$

Finally we replace x by x^2, thus obtaining the desired sum

$$\frac{x^4-1}{2x^6} \ln(1+x^2) - \frac{1}{4x^2} + \frac{1}{2x^4} = \sum_{n=0}^{\infty} \frac{(-1)^n x^{2n}}{(n+1)(n+3)}, \qquad 0 < |x| < 1.$$

Note the implication that the left member, near $x=0$, is an indeterminate form, as $x \to 0$, with limit $\frac{1}{3}$ ($n=0$ term on the right).

Exercises

Sum the given series with the aid of the basic series in Section 45, page 119.

1. $\displaystyle\sum_{n=0}^{\infty} \frac{(n+1)(n+2)x^n}{n!}$.   Start with the series for $x^2 e^x$.

ANS. $e^x(x^2 + 4x + 2)$.

2. $\displaystyle\sum_{n=0}^{\infty} \frac{(-1)^n(n+2)(n+3)x^n}{n!}$.   ANS. $e^{-x}(x^2 - 6x + 6)$.

3. $\displaystyle\sum_{n=0}^{\infty} \frac{x^{n+4}}{n!(n+2)}$.   ANS. $x^2(xe^x + 1 - e^x)$.

4. $\displaystyle\sum_{n=0}^{\infty} \frac{(-1)^n x^{2n+3}}{(2n)!(2n+2)}$.   Start with the series for $x \cos x$.

ANS. $x(x \sin x + \cos x - 1)$.

5. $\displaystyle\sum_{n=0}^{\infty} \frac{(-1)^n x^{2n+5}}{(2n+1)!(2n+3)}$.   ANS. $x^2(\sin x - x \cos x)$.

6. $\displaystyle\sum_{n=0}^{\infty} (n+2)(n+1)x^{n+2}$.   ANS. $\dfrac{2x^2}{(1-x)^3}$.

7. $\displaystyle\sum_{n=0}^{\infty} \frac{(n+3)(n-1)x^{n+1}}{n+1}$.   ANS. $4\ln(1-x) + \dfrac{x}{(1-x)^2}$.

8. $\displaystyle\sum_{n=0}^{\infty} (-1)^n(n+1)(n+2)x^{2n+1}$.   ANS. $\dfrac{2x}{(1+x^2)^3}$.

9. $\displaystyle\sum_{n=0}^{\infty} \frac{(-1)^n(n+4)x^{n+3}}{n!(n+3)}$.   ANS. $2 + e^{-x}(x^3 - x^2 - 2x - 2)$.

10. $\displaystyle\sum_{n=0}^{\infty} \frac{1}{n!(n+3)}$.   Use the method of Exercise 3; then put $x = 1$.

ANS. $e - 2$.

11. $\displaystyle\sum_{n=0}^{\infty} \frac{(-1)^n}{n!(n+3)}$.   See Exercise 10.   ANS. $2 - 5e^{-1}$.

12. $\displaystyle\sum_{n=0}^{\infty} \frac{(-1)^n(n+1)}{4^n(2n)!}$.   ANS. $\cos\tfrac{1}{2} - \tfrac{1}{4}\sin\tfrac{1}{2}$.

CHAPTER 13

Asymptotic Series

81. Two Methods of Approximation

If a function $f(x)$ has a Maclaurin expansion

$$(1) \qquad f(x) = \sum_{n=0}^{\infty} c_n x^n, \qquad |x| < R,$$

with partial sum

$$(2) \qquad S_n(x) = \sum_{k=0}^{n} c_k x^k,$$

then for each fixed x in $|x| < R$,

$$(3) \qquad \lim_{n \to \infty} [f(x) - S_n(x)] = 0.$$

That is, for each fixed x, $S_n(x)$ can be made to approximate $f(x)$ as closely as desired by making n sufficiently large. This is the underlying character of the convergence of the power series to the function.

We now turn our attention to power series with partial sums $s_n(x)$ that, for each fixed n, can be made to approximate $f(x)$ as closely as desired by choosing x sufficiently close to zero. Indeed, we shall stipulate that not only does

$$(4) \qquad f(x) - s_n(x) \to 0, \qquad \text{as } x \to 0,$$

but that it does so more rapidly than x^n does, in the sense that

(5)
$$\frac{|f(x) - s_n(x)|}{|x^n|} \to 0, \qquad \text{as } x \to 0.$$

The condition (5) requires that $s_n(x)$ approximate $f(x)$ but in a different way from the requirement in the condition (3). This time $x \to 0$ and n is held fixed.

Since nothing is said in (5) about the behavior of $s_n(x)$ as $n \to \infty$, the series may, or may not, converge. Convergence and divergence simply have no bearing on the concept now being introduced, that of an asymptotic series. A formal definition is presented in the next section.

82. Definition of an Asymptotic Expansion

We write*

(1)
$$f(x) \sim \sum_{n=0}^{\infty} a_n x^n, \qquad \text{as } x \to 0 \text{ in a region } A,$$

if and only if, for each fixed n,

(2)
$$\lim_{x \to 0 \text{ in } A} \frac{|f(x) - s_n(x)|}{|x^n|} = 0,$$

where $s_n(x)$ is the partial sum

(3)
$$s_n(x) = \sum_{k=0}^{n} a_k x^k.$$

When the series in (1) has the property (2), we call the series an asymptotic expansion for $f(x)$ as $x \to 0$ in the region A. It makes no sense to say a series is asymptotic without describing what point the variable is approaching and in what manner it approaches the point. We shall soon introduce series asymptotic as $x \to \infty$ in some region, and also as $x \to x_0$ in a specified manner.

First, we show that asymptotic series exist by exhibiting one in the example below. In later sections we shall develop some simple properties of asymptotic series.

* The symbol $\sim$ is used here in a different sense from the meaning it had in our work on Fourier series. Since the right-hand member in (1) is a power series, the two uses of the symbol should cause no confusion. Unfortunately, the symbol $\sim$ is also used with other meanings in mathematical literature. Care should be taken to determine what is meant by this symbol each time it is encountered.

Asymptotic series are of great value in many computations. They play an important role in the solution of linear differential equations about irregular singular points. Such series were used by astronomers more than a century ago, long before the pertinent mathematical theory was developed.

EXAMPLE. Show that

(4) $$\int_0^\infty \frac{e^{-t}\,dt}{1-xt} \sim \sum_{n=0}^\infty n!\,x^n, \qquad x\to 0 \text{ in } \mathrm{Re}(x) \leq 0.$$

Let us put

$$s_n(x) = \sum_{k=0}^n k!\,x^k.$$

In the region $\mathrm{Re}(x) \leq 0$, the integral on the left in (4) is absolutely and uniformly convergent. To see this, note that $t \geq 0$ so that $\mathrm{Re}(1-xt) \geq 1$. Hence $|1-xt| \geq 1$, and we have

$$\left| \int_0^\infty \frac{e^{-t}\,dt}{1-xt} \right| \leq \int_0^\infty e^{-t}\,dt = 1.$$

For k a non-negative integer,

(5) $$\int_0^\infty e^{-t} t^k\,dt = \Gamma(k+1) = k!.$$

Hence

$$\int_0^\infty \frac{e^{-t}\,dt}{1-xt} - s_n(x) = \int_0^\infty \frac{e^{-t}\,dt}{1-xt} - \sum_{k=0}^n \int_0^\infty e^{-t} t^k x^k\,dt$$

$$= \int_0^\infty e^{-t} \left[\frac{1}{1-xt} - \sum_{k=0}^n (xt)^k \right] dt.$$

From elementary algebra we have

$$\sum_{k=0}^n r^k = \frac{1-r^{n+1}}{1-r}, \qquad r \neq 1.$$

Therefore

$$\int_0^\infty \frac{e^{-t}\,dt}{1-xt} - s_n(x) = \int_0^\infty \frac{e^{-t}(xt)^{n+1}\,dt}{1-xt},$$

from which, since $|1-xt| \geq 1$, we obtain

$$\left| \int_0^\infty \frac{e^{-t}\,dt}{1-xt} - s_n(x) \right| \leq |x|^{n+1} \int_0^\infty e^{-t} t^{n+1}\,dt, \qquad \text{in } \mathrm{Re}(x) \leq 0.$$

We may conclude that

$$(6) \qquad \left| \int_0^\infty \frac{e^{-t}\,dt}{1-xt} - s_n(x) \right| \leq (n+1)!\,|x|^{n+1}, \qquad \text{in } \mathrm{Re}(x) \leq 0.$$

From (6) it follows at once that the condition (2), page 223, is satisfied, which concludes the proof. Actually (6) gives more information than that. Let $E_n(x)$ be the error made in computing the sum function by discarding all terms after the term $n!x^n$. Then $|E_n(x)|$ is the left member of (6), and the inequality (6) shows that $|E_n(x)|$ is smaller than the magnitude of the first term omitted. This property, although not possessed by all asymptotic series, is one of frequent occurrence.

For finite x_0, we say that

$$(7) \qquad f(x) \sim \sum_{n=0}^{\infty} a_n(x - x_0)^n, \qquad \text{as } x \to x_0 \text{ in } A,$$

if and only if, for each fixed n,

$$(8) \qquad \lim_{x \to x_0 \text{ in } A} \frac{|f(x) - s_n(x)|}{|x - x_0|^n} = 0,$$

with

$$(9) \qquad s_n(x) = \sum_{k=0}^{n} a_k(x - x_0)^k.$$

83. Asymptotic Expansions About Infinity

Asymptotic series are used most often for large absolute values of the variable. We define

$$(1) \qquad f(x) \sim \sum_{n=0}^{\infty} \frac{A_n}{x^n}, \qquad \text{as } x \to \infty \text{ in a region } B,$$

if and only if, for each fixed n,

$$(2) \qquad \lim_{x \to \infty \text{ in } B} |x^n\{f(x) - s_n(x)\}| = 0,$$

in which

$$(3) \qquad s_n(x) = \sum_{k=0}^{n} \frac{A_k}{x^k}.$$

Very often we replace the region B by the real axis, restrict x to real values, and let $x \to \infty$ or $x \to -\infty$, as the case may be.

Of course, $f(x)$ may have no asymptotic expansion about a point, finite or infinite, by the definitions of this and the preceding section. In some instances, the desired expansion can be obtained by introducing a modification of the above definitions. For example, we say that

(4) $$f(x) \sim h(x) + g(x) \sum_{n=0}^{\infty} a_n x^{-n}, \qquad \text{as } x \to \infty \text{ in } B,$$

if and only if

(5) $$\frac{f(x) - h(x)}{g(x)} \sim \sum_{n=0}^{\infty} a_n x^{-n}, \qquad \text{as } x \to \infty \text{ in } B,$$

and similarly for asymptotic expansions about a point in the finite plane.

EXAMPLE. Obtain, for real x, as $x \to \infty$, an asymptotic expansion of the error function

(6) $$\operatorname{erf}(x) = \frac{2}{\sqrt{\pi}} \int_0^x \exp(-t^2) \, dt.$$

From the fact that $\Gamma(\tfrac{1}{2}) = \sqrt{\pi}$, it follows at once that the error function has the property

$$\lim_{x \to \infty} \operatorname{erf}(x) = 1$$

Let us write

$$\operatorname{erf}(x) = \frac{2}{\sqrt{\pi}} \int_0^{\infty} \exp(-t^2) \, dt - \frac{2}{\sqrt{\pi}} \int_x^{\infty} \exp(-t^2) \, dt$$

$$= 1 - \frac{2}{\sqrt{\pi}} \int_x^{\infty} \exp(-t^2) \, dt.$$

Now consider the function

$$B(x) = \int_x^{\infty} \exp(-t^2) \, dt$$

and integrate by parts to get

$$B(x) = -\tfrac{1}{2} \left[t^{-1} \exp(-t^2) \right]_x^{\infty} - \tfrac{1}{2} \int_x^{\infty} t^{-2} \exp(-t^2) \, dt$$

$$= \tfrac{1}{2} x^{-1} \exp(-x^2) - \tfrac{1}{2} \int_x^{\infty} t^{-2} \exp(-t^2) \, dt.$$

Iteration of the integration by parts soon yields

$$B(x) =$$
$$\exp(-x^2)\left[\frac{1}{2x} - \frac{1}{2^2x^3} + \frac{1\cdot 3}{2^3x^5} - \frac{1\cdot 3\cdot 5}{2^4x^7} + \cdots + \frac{(-1)^n 1\cdot 3\cdot 5\cdots(2n-1)}{2^{n+1}x^{2n+1}}\right]$$
$$+ \frac{(-1)^{n+1} 1\cdot 3\cdot 5\cdots(2n+1)}{2^{n+1}} \int_x^\infty t^{-2n-2}\exp(-t^2)\,dt,$$

(7) $\quad B(x) = \frac{1}{2}\exp(-x^2)\sum_{k=0}^{n}\frac{(-1)^k(\frac{1}{2})_k}{x^{2k+1}}$

$$+ (-1)^{n+1}\left(\frac{1}{2}\right)_{n+1}\int_x^\infty t^{-2n-2}\exp(-t^2)\,dt.$$

Let

$$s_n(x) = \frac{1}{2}\sum_{k=0}^{n}\frac{(-1)^k(\frac{1}{2})_k}{x^{2k+1}}.$$

Then, from (7),

$$\exp(x^2)B(x) - s_n(x) = (-1)^{n+1}(\tfrac{1}{2})_{n+1}\exp(x^2)\int_x^\infty t^{-2n-2}\exp(-t^2)\,dt.$$

The variable of integration is never less than x. We replace the factor t^{-2n-2} in the integrand by tx^{-2n-3} and thus obtain

$$\left|\exp(x^2)B(x) - s_n(x)\right| < \frac{(\tfrac{1}{2})_{n+1}\exp(x^2)}{x^{2n+3}}\int_x^\infty t\exp(-t^2)\,dt,$$

from which it follows that

(8) $$\left|\exp(x^2)B(x) - s_n(x)\right| < \frac{(\tfrac{1}{2})_{n+1}}{2x^{2n+3}}.$$

Hence

$$x^{2n+2}[\exp(x^2)B(x) - s_n(x)] \to 0, \qquad \text{as } x \to \infty,$$

which permits us to write the asymptotic expansion

$$\exp(x^2)B(x) \sim \sum_{n=0}^{\infty}\frac{(-1)^n(\frac{1}{2})_n}{2x^{2n+1}}, \qquad x \to \infty.$$

But $\operatorname{erf}(x) = 1 - \dfrac{2}{\sqrt{\pi}}B(x)$. Hence

(9) $\quad \operatorname{erf}(x) \sim 1 - \dfrac{1}{\sqrt{\pi}}\exp(-x^2)\sum_{n=0}^{\infty}\dfrac{(-1)^n(\frac{1}{2})_n}{x^{2n+1}}, \qquad x \to \infty.$

Note also the useful bound in (8).

84. Algebraic Properties

Asymptotic expansions behave like convergent power series in many ways. To illustrate this behavior, we shall prove some theorems about asymptotic series in which $x \to \infty$ in B. The reader can easily parallel the proofs and obtain results as x approaches any finite x_0.

THEOREM 76. *If, as $x \to \infty$ in B,*

$$(1) \qquad\qquad f(x) \sim \sum_{n=0}^{\infty} a_n x^{-n}$$

and

$$(2) \qquad\qquad g(x) \sim \sum_{n=0}^{\infty} b_n x^{-n},$$

then

$$(3) \qquad\qquad f(x) + g(x) \sim \sum_{n=0}^{\infty} (a_n + b_n) x^{-n}$$

and

$$(4) \qquad\qquad f(x)g(x) \sim \sum_{n=0}^{\infty} \sum_{k=0}^{n} a_k b_{n-k} x^{-n}.$$

The right member of (4) is the Cauchy product of the series in (1) and (2).

PROOF. Let

$$(5) \qquad\qquad S_n(x) = \sum_{k=0}^{n} a_k x^{-k}, \qquad T_n(x) = \sum_{k=0}^{n} b_k x^{-k}.$$

We are given by (1) and (2), that, for each fixed n, as $x \to \infty$ in B,

$$(6) \qquad\qquad x^n[f(x) - S_n(x)] \to 0$$

and

$$(7) \qquad\qquad x^n[g(x) - T_n(x)] \to 0.$$

The partial sum of the series in (3) is

$$\sum_{k=0}^{n} (a_k + b_k) x^{-k} = S_n(x) + T_n(x).$$

By (6) and (7),

$$x^n[f(x) + g(x) - S_n(x) - T_n(x)] \to 0, \qquad \text{as } x \to \infty \text{ in } B,$$

which concludes the proof of (3).

Now consider (4). Let the partial sum of the series in (4) be

$$
(8) \qquad Q_n(x) = \sum_{k=0}^{n} \sum_{s=0}^{k} a_s b_{k-s} x^{-k}.
$$

Form the product of the finite series S_n and T_n of (5). Each term in the product is of the form

$$
a_i b_j x^{-i-j}.
$$

Group the terms by powers of x and separate those with exponents 0 to $(-n)$ from those with exponents $(-n-1)$ to $(-2n)$. Thus we have

$$
S_n(x) T_n(x) = \sum_{k=0}^{n} \sum_{s=0}^{k} a_s b_{k-s} x^{-k} + R_n(x),
$$

or, by (8),

$$
(9) \qquad S_n(x) T_n(x) = Q_n(x) + R_n(x),
$$

in which

$$
(10) \qquad x^n R_n(x) \to 0, \qquad \text{as } x \to \infty.
$$

Define the functions $\delta_n(x)$ and $\varepsilon_n(x)$ by

$$
(11) \qquad f(x) - S_n(x) = x^{-n} \delta_n(x)
$$

and

$$
(12) \qquad g(x) - T_n(x) = x^{-n} \varepsilon_n(x),
$$

and note that, because of (6) and (7),

$$
(13) \qquad \delta_n(x) \to 0 \quad \text{and} \quad \varepsilon_n(x) \to 0, \qquad \text{as } x \to \infty.
$$

Equations (11) and (12) yield

$$
f(x) g(x) = S_n(x) T_n(x) + x^{-n} T_n(x) \delta_n(x) + x^{-n} S_n(x) \varepsilon_n(x) + x^{-2n} \delta_n(x) \varepsilon_n(x).
$$

Using equation (9), we rewrite the above equation as

$$
f(x) g(x) = Q_n(x) + R_n(x) + x^{-n} [T_n(x) \delta_n(x) + S_n(x) \varepsilon_n(x) + x^{-n} \delta_n(x) \varepsilon_n(x)].
$$

It follows that

$$
(14) \quad x^n [f(x) g(x) - Q_n(x)]
$$
$$
= x^n R_n(x) + T_n(x) \delta_n(x) + S_n(x) \varepsilon_n(x) + x^{-n} \delta_n(x) \varepsilon_n(x).
$$

Each term on the right in (14) $\to 0$ as $x \to \infty$. Hence

$$
(15) \qquad x^n [f(x) g(x) - Q_n(x)] \to 0, \qquad \text{as } x \to \infty,
$$

which concludes the proof of the validity of (4).

85. Term-by-Term Integration

Suppose that for real x we have

(1) $$f(x) \sim \sum_{n=0}^{\infty} a_n x^{-n}, \qquad x \to \infty.$$

Surely we are interested here in large x, so that an integral which it is natural to consider is $\int_y^{\infty} f(x)\, dx$. But $\int_y^{\infty} a_0\, dx$ and $\int_y^{\infty} a_1 x^{-1}\, dx$ do not exist. Therefore we restrict ourselves to the consideration of an expansion

(2) $$g(x) \sim \sum_{n=2}^{\infty} a_n x^{-n}, \qquad x \to \infty,$$

and seek $\int_y^{\infty} g(x)\, dx$. Of course $g(x) = f(x) - a_0 - a_1 x^{-1}$.

Let

$$s_n(x) = \sum_{k=2}^{n} a_k x^{-k}.$$

Then, by (2),

(3) $$x^n [g(x) - s_n(x)] \to 0, \qquad \text{as } x \to \infty.$$

Define $\varepsilon_n(x)$ by

(4) $$g(x) - s_n(x) = x^{-n} \varepsilon_n(x).$$

Then, for each fixed $n \geq 2$, $\varepsilon_n(x) \to 0$ as $x \to \infty$, and

(5) $$y^{n-1} \int_y^{\infty} \frac{|\varepsilon_n(x)|\, dx}{x^n} \to 0, \qquad \text{as } y \to \infty.$$

Since

$$\left| \int_y^{\infty} g(x)\, dx - \int_y^{\infty} s_n(x)\, dx \right| \leq \int_y^{\infty} |g(x) - s_n(x)|\, dx,$$

we may conclude from (4) and (5) that, for $n \geq 2$,

$$y^{n-1} \left| \int_y^{\infty} g(x)\, dx - \int_y^{\infty} s_n(x)\, dx \right| \to 0, \qquad \text{as } y \to \infty.$$

But

$$\int_y^{\infty} s_n(x)\, dx = \sum_{k=2}^{n} a_k \int_y^{\infty} x^{-k}\, dx = \sum_{k=2}^{n} \frac{a_k y^{-k+1}}{(k-1)}.$$

Hence

(6)
$$\int_y^\infty g(x)\, dx \sim \sum_{n=2}^\infty \frac{a_n y^{-n+1}}{n-1}, \qquad y \to \infty,$$

the desired result.

86. Uniqueness

Since $x^n e^{-x} \to 0$, as $x \to \infty$, for every fixed n, whole classes of functions have the same asymptotic expansion. From

$$f(x) \sim \sum_{n=0}^\infty a_n x^{-n}, \qquad \text{as } x \to \infty,$$

and

$$e^{-x} \sim \sum_{n=0}^\infty 0 x^{-n}, \qquad \text{as } x \to \infty,$$

it follows that, for any constant c,

$$F(x) = f(x) + c e^{-x} \sim \sum_{n=0}^\infty a_n x^{-n}, \qquad \text{as } x \to \infty.$$

Other examples are easily concocted, replacing e^{-x} by $\exp(-x^2)$, $e^{-x}\cos 2x$, etc.

On the other hand, a given function cannot have more than one asymptotic expansion as $x \to \infty$ in a specific region or direction, as stated in the theorem below

THEOREM 77. *If*

(1)
$$f(x) \sim \sum_{n=0}^\infty a_n x^{-n}, \qquad \text{as } x \to \infty \text{ in } B,$$

and

(2)
$$f(x) \sim \sum_{n=0}^\infty b_n x^{-n}, \qquad \text{as } x \to \infty \text{ in } B,$$

then, for every n, $b_n = a_n$.

PROOF. Let

(3)
$$A_n(x) = \sum_{k=0}^n a_k x^{-k}, \qquad B_n(x) = \sum_{k=0}^n b_k x^{-k}.$$

We know, by (1) and (2), that

$$x^n[f(x) - A_n(x)] \to 0, \qquad \text{as } x \to \infty,$$

and

$$x^n[f(x) - B_n(x)] \to 0, \qquad \text{as } x \to \infty.$$

It follows that

(4) $$x^n[A_n(x) - B_n(x)] \to 0, \qquad \text{as } x \to \infty.$$

Using (3), we see that (4) becomes

(5) $$\sum_{k=0}^{n} (a_k - b_k)x^{n-k} \to 0, \qquad \text{as } x \to \infty.$$

The left member of (5) is a polynomial in x. The only way a polynomial in x can approach zero, as $x \to \infty$, is for each coefficient to be zero. Hence $a_k = b_k$ for every k, so $a_n = b_n$ as stated in Theorem 77. The asymptotic power series associated with $f(x)$ as $x \to \infty$ in a specified region or direction is unique. Of course, $f(x)$ may have two different asymptotic expansions as $x \to \infty$ in different regions.

Exercises

1. Let

$$f(x) = \int_0^\infty \frac{e^{-xt}\, dt}{1 + t^2}.$$

    Show that

$$f(x) - \sum_{k=0}^{n} (-1)^k (2k)!\, x^{-2k-1} = (-1)^{n+1} \int_0^\infty \frac{e^{-xt} t^{2n+2}\, dt}{1 + t^2},$$

    and thus obtain not only

$$\int_0^\infty \frac{e^{-xt}\, dt}{1 + t^2} \sim \sum_{n=0}^{\infty} \frac{(-1)^n (2n)!}{x^{2n+1}}, \qquad \text{as } x \to \infty,$$

    but also a bound on the error made in computing with the series involved.

2. Use integration by parts to establish that for real $x \to \infty$,

$$\int_x^\infty e^{-t} t^{-1}\, dt \sim e^{-x} \sum_{n=0}^{\infty} (-1)^n n!\, x^{-n-1}.$$

3. Use integration by parts to show that if $\text{Re}(\alpha) > 0$, and if x is real,

$$\int_x^\infty e^{-t} t^{-\alpha}\, dt \sim x^{1-\alpha} e^{-x} \sum_{n=0}^{\infty} \frac{(-1)^n (\alpha)_n}{x^{n+1}}, \qquad x \to \infty,$$

    of which Exercise 2 is the special case $\alpha = 1$.

87. Computations with Asymptotic Series

In computing with convergent positive term series, the more terms we use, the nearer the partial sum is to the actual sum of the series. For any convergent series, we can approximate the sum as closely as we wish by using enough terms of the series. Asymptotic series exhibit a behavior essentially different from the behavior of convergent ones in this respect. Many asymptotic series diverge and, from some n-value on, approximations get worse, not better, as we use more terms.

Let the function expanded in the example on page 224 be called $\varphi(x)$,

$$(1) \qquad \varphi(x) = \int_0^\infty \frac{e^{-t}}{1 - xt} \, dt, \qquad \mathrm{Re}(x) \leqq 0.$$

We showed that φ has the asymptotic expansion

$$(2) \qquad \varphi(x) \sim \sum_{n=0}^\infty n! x^n, \qquad \text{as } x \to 0 \text{ in } \mathrm{Re}(x) \leqq 0.$$

Suppose that we wish to compute φ at $x = -0.1$. The partial sum

$$(3) \qquad s_n(x) = \sum_{k=0}^n k! x^k$$

yields the desired approximation to $\varphi(x)$. Defining the error made by the relation

$$(4) \qquad E_n(x) = \varphi(x) - s_n(x),$$

we found that

$$(5) \qquad |E_n(x)| \leqq (n+1)! |x|^{n+1}.$$

For $x = -0.1 = -10^{-1}$, our series is

$$(6) \quad \varphi(-10^{-1}) \sim 1 - 1 \cdot 10^{-1} + 2!(10)^{-2} - 3!(10)^{-3} + 4!(10)^{-4} + \cdots$$
$$+ (-1)^n n! 10^{-n} + \cdots.$$

Each term in (6) can be obtained from the term preceding it by changing the sign and multiplying the previous term by the index n and dividing by 10. Of course, the magnitude of the term for $n = 10$ will be equal the magnitude of the term for $n = 9$. For $n > 10$, the magnitude of the term increases steadily, and indeed $\to \infty$, as $n \to \infty$. In rough language, the approximation gets worse steadily as we use terms beyond that for $n = 10$. All that we can say precisely is that, at $x = -0.1$, our inequality for E_n in (5) is less and less useful as n increases, for $n > 10$.

Denote the general term of the series in (6) by a_n. Then

$$a_0 = +1.000\ 000$$
$$a_1 = -0.100\ 000$$
$$a_2 = +0.020\ 000$$
$$a_3 = -0.006\ 000$$
$$a_4 = +0.002\ 400$$
$$a_5 = -0.001\ 200$$
$$a_6 = +0.000\ 720$$
$$a_7 = -0.000\ 504$$
$$a_8 \doteq +0.000\ 403$$
$$a_9 = -0.000\ 363$$
$$a_{10} = +0.000\ 363$$
$$a_{11} = -0.000\ 399$$
$$a_{12} = +0.000\ 479, \quad \text{etc.}$$

The best we can do here is to use $n = 8$. Then

$$|E_8(-0.1| \leq |a_9|,$$

so

$$|E_8(-0.1)| \leq 0.000\ 363.$$

We can compute $\varphi(-0.1)$ by (6) to three decimal places. From the numerical values above we obtain $s_8(-0.1) = 0.915\ 819$. Then

$$\varphi(-0.1) = 0.916.$$

What the definition of asymptotic expansions guarantees is that we can, for any fixed n, compute our function $\varphi(x)$ as closely as desired by taking the x-value sufficiently close to 0, staying in the region $\text{Re}(x) \leq 0$. If we choose to compute $\varphi(x)$ for $x = -0.01$, a value closer to the critical one, $x = 0$, we get much more accuracy.

Since

(7) $$\varphi(-0.01) \sim \sum_{n=0}^{\infty} (-1)^n n! 10^{-2n},$$

the terms decrease in magnitude for $n < 100$, and increase in magnitude for $n > 100$. Let b_n denote the general term in (7). Then

$$b_0 = +1.000\ 000\ 000$$
$$b_1 = -0.010\ 000\ 000$$
$$b_2 = +0.000\ 200\ 000$$
$$b_3 = -0.000\ 006\ 000$$
$$b_4 = +0.000\ 000\ 240, \quad \text{etc.}$$

With $n = 3$, using only four terms, we obtain six decimal place accuracy,

$$\varphi(-0.01) = 0.990\ 194.$$

The purpose of an asymptotic expansion about $x = x_0$, finite or infinite, is to provide a tool for the study of the function in the immediate vicinity of x_0. Behavior of the series as $x \to x_0$ properly (in the region) is beautiful to behold. Behavior away from x_0 is not pertinent.

Exercises

1. For the $\varphi(x)$ of this section, compute $\varphi(-0.001)$ to ten decimal places
    ANS.   0.999 001 994 0.

2. Define $f(x)$ by

    $$f(x) = e^x \int_x^\infty e^{-t} t^{-1}\, dt, \qquad x > 0.$$

    Refer to Exercise 2, page 232, in which we found that

    $$f(x) \sim \sum_{n=0}^\infty (-1)^n n!\, x^{-n-1}, \qquad \text{as } x \to \infty.$$

    Compute $f(100)$ to six decimal places.
    ANS.   0.009 902.

3. For the $f(x)$ of Exercise, 2 compute $f(1000)$ to six decimal places.
    ANS.   0.000 999.

CHAPTER 14

Infinite Products

88. Definition of an Infinite Product

A product symbol $\prod$ is used in much the same way as the summation symbol, except that the elements are multiplied instead of being added.

We let

$$\prod_{k=1}^{n}(1+a_k)$$

denote the product of n factors

$$(1+a_1)(1+a_2)(1+a_3)\cdots(1+a_n),$$

and then proceed to define an infinite product in a manner similar to the way we attached a meaning to an infinite series.

Consider the sequence with elements

(1) $$P_n = \prod_{k=1}^{n}(1+a_k).$$

If $\{P_n\}$ converges but is not a null sequence, we say that the infinite product

(2) $$\prod_{n=1}^{\infty}(1+a_n)$$

converges. That is, if

(3) $$\lim_{n\to\infty} P_n = P \neq 0,$$

we say the product (2) converges to P and we write

(4)
$$P = \prod_{n=1}^{\infty} (1 + a_n).$$

If at least one of the factors of the product (2) is zero, if only a finite number of factors of (2) are zero, and if the product with the zero factors deleted converges to $P \neq 0$, we say that the infinite product (2) *converges to zero*.

If the infinite product is not convergent, it is said to be divergent. If the divergence is not due to the failure of the limit in (3) to exist, but to the fact that the limit is zero, the product is said to *diverge to zero*. We make no attempt to treat products with an infinity of zero factors.

The peculiar role which the number zero plays in multiplication is the reason for the slight difference between the definition of convergence of an infinite product and the analogous definition of convergence of an infinite series.

We know that if a series converges, its general term must approach zero as the index approaches infinity. For an infinite product to converge, it is necessary that the general factor approach unity as the index approaches infinity.

THEOREM 78. *If* $\prod_{n=1}^{\infty} (1 + a_n)$ *converges,* $\lim_{n \to \infty} a_n = 0$.

PROOF. If the product converges to $P \neq 0$,

$$1 = \frac{P}{P} = \frac{\lim_{n \to \infty} \prod_{k=1}^{n} (1 + a_k)}{\lim_{n \to \infty} \prod_{k=1}^{n-1} (1 + a_k)} = \lim_{n \to \infty} (1 + a_n).$$

Hence $\lim_{n \to \infty} a_n = 0$, as desired. If the product converges to zero, remove the zero factors and repeat the argument.

89. The Associated Series of Logarithms

Any infinite product without zero factors has associated with it the infinite series of logarithms of the separate factors. For simplicity, let us restrict our products to those with positive factors so $\ln(1 + a_n)$ will have its usual elementary meaning.*

THEOREM 79. *If no $a_n = -1$,* $\prod_{n=1}^{\infty}(1 + a_n)$ *and* $\sum_{n=1}^{\infty} \ln(1 + a_n)$ *converge or diverge together.*

PROOF. Let the partial product and the partial sum be defined by

$$(1) \qquad\qquad P_n = \prod_{k=1}^{n}(1 + a_k) \quad \text{and} \quad S_n = \sum_{k=1}^{n} \ln(1 + a_k).$$

Then

$$(2) \qquad\qquad\qquad \exp S_n = P_n$$

and

$$(3) \qquad\qquad\qquad \lim_{n \to \infty} \exp S_n = \exp(\lim_{n \to \infty} S_n).$$

Hence $\{P_n\}$ converges if and only if $\{S_n\}$ converges, and $\{P_n\}$ cannot converge to zero because the exponential function cannot take on the value zero. Note that, by (2), $P_n \to 0$ would imply $S_n \to -\infty$.

90. Absolute Convergence of Products

Assume that the product has had its zero factors, if any, deleted. We say that the product

$$\prod_{n=1}^{\infty}(1 + a_n)$$

is absolutely convergent if and only if

$$\sum_{n=1}^{\infty} \text{Ln}(1 + a_n)$$

is absolutely convergent.

THEOREM 80. *The product* $\prod_{n=1}^{\infty}(1 + a_n)$ *with all zero factors deleted, is absolutely convergent if and only if* $\sum_{n=1}^{\infty} a_n$ *is absolutely convergent.*

---

* If $(1 + a_n)$ is allowed to be any nonzero complex number, $\ln(1 + a_n)$ should be replaced by the principal value $\text{Ln}(1 + a_n)$, a specified choice from the infinity of values taken on by $\ln(1 + a_n)$. For the principal value of a logarithm see books on complex variables, for example, R. V. Churchill, *Complex Variables and Applications*, New York, McGraw-Hill Book Co., 2nd ed., 1960, p. 56.

PROOF. First throw out any a_n's which are zero; they contribute only unit factors in the product and zero terms in the sum and thus have no bearing on convergence.

We know that if either the series or the product in the theorem converges, $\lim_{n\to\infty} a_n = 0$. Let us then consider n large enough, $n > n_0$, so that $|a_n| < \frac{1}{2}$ for all $n > n_0$. We may now write

(1)
$$\frac{\mathrm{Ln}(1 + a_n)}{a_n} = \sum_{k=0}^{\infty} \frac{(-1)^k a_n^k}{k+1},$$

from which it follows that

$$\left| \frac{\mathrm{Ln}(1 + a_n)}{a_n} - 1 \right| \leqq \sum_{k=1}^{\infty} \frac{|a_n|^k}{k+1} < \sum_{k=1}^{\infty} \frac{1}{2^{k+1}} = \frac{1}{2}.$$

Thus we have

$$\frac{1}{2} < \left| \frac{\mathrm{Ln}(1 + a_n)}{a_n} \right| < \frac{3}{2},$$

from which

$$\left| \frac{\mathrm{Ln}(1 + a_n)}{a_n} \right| < \frac{3}{2} \quad \text{and} \quad \left| \frac{a_n}{\mathrm{Ln}(1 + a_n)} \right| < 2.$$

By a comparison test it follows that the absolute convergence of either of $\sum_{n=1}^{\infty} \mathrm{Ln}(1 + a_n)$ or $\sum_{n=1}^{\infty} a_n$ implies the absolute convergence of the other. We then use the definition of absolute convergence of the product to complete the proof of Theorem 80.

Because of Theorem 79 it follows at once that an infinite product which is absolutely convergent is also convergent.

EXAMPLE (a) Show that the following product converges and find its value:

$$\prod_{n=1}^{\infty} \left[1 + \frac{1}{(n+1)(n+3)} \right].$$

The series of positive numbers

$$\sum_{n=1}^{\infty} \frac{1}{(n+1)(n+3)}$$

is known to be convergent. It can easily be tested by the polynomial test or by comparison with the series $\sum\limits_{n=1}^{\infty} \dfrac{1}{n^2}$. Hence our product is absolutely convergent by Theorem 80.

The partial products are often useful in evaluating an infinite product. When the following method is employed, there is no need for the separate testing for convergence made in the preceding paragraph. Consider the partial products

$$P_n = \prod_{k=1}^{n} \left[1 + \frac{1}{(k+1)(k+3)} \right] = \prod_{k=1}^{n} \frac{(k+2)^2}{(k+1)(k+3)}$$

$$= \frac{[3\cdot4\cdot5\cdots(n+2)]^2}{[2\cdot3\cdot4\cdots(n+1)][4\cdot5\cdot6\cdots(n+3)]} = \frac{n+2}{2} \cdot \frac{3}{n+3}.$$

At once $\lim\limits_{n\to\infty} P_n = \frac{3}{2}$, from which we conclude both that the infinite product converges and that its value is $\frac{3}{2}$.

EXAMPLE (b). Show that if z is not a negative integer,

$$\lim_{n\to\infty} \frac{(n-1)!\, n^z}{(z+1)(z+2)(z+3)\cdots(z+n-1)}$$

exists.

We shall form an infinite product for which the expression

$$P_n = \frac{(n-1)!\, n^z}{(z+1)(z+2)(z+3)\cdots(z+n-1)}$$

is a partial product, prove that the infinite product converges, and thus conclude that $\lim\limits_{n\to\infty} P_n$ exists.

If $z = 0$ or $z = 1$, $P_n \equiv 1$, so $\{P_n\}$ converges. If z is not zero, or unity, or a negative integer, write

$$P_{n+1} = \frac{n!\,(n+1)^z}{(z+1)(z+2)\cdots(z+n)}$$

$$= \frac{n!}{(z+1)(z+2)\cdots(z+n)} \cdot \frac{2^z}{1^z} \cdot \frac{3^z}{2^z} \cdot \frac{4^z}{3^z} \cdots \frac{(n+1)^z}{n^z}$$

$$= \prod_{k=1}^{n} \left[\frac{k}{z+k} \cdot \frac{(k+1)^z}{k^z} \right] = \prod_{k=1}^{n} \left[\left(1 + \frac{z}{k} \right)^{-1} \left(1 + \frac{1}{k} \right)^z \right].$$

Consider now the product

(2)
$$\prod_{n=1}^{\infty}\left[\left(1+\frac{z}{n}\right)^{-1}\left(1+\frac{1}{n}\right)^{z}\right].$$

Since

$$\lim_{n\to\infty} n^{2}\left[\left(1+\frac{z}{n}\right)^{-1}\left(1+\frac{1}{n}\right)^{z}-1\right],$$

$$= \lim_{\beta\to 0}\frac{(1+z\beta)^{-1}(1+\beta)^{z}-1}{\beta^{2}} = \lim_{\beta\to 0}\frac{(1+\beta)^{z}-1-z\beta}{\beta^{2}}$$

$$= \lim_{\beta\to 0}\frac{z[(1+\beta)^{z-1}-1]}{2\beta} = \lim_{\beta\to 0}\frac{z(z-1)(1+\beta)^{z-2}}{2} = \tfrac{1}{2}z(z-1),$$

we conclude with the aid of a comparison test and the convergence of $\sum_{n=1}^{\infty}\frac{1}{n^{2}}$ that the product (2) converges. Therefore $\lim_{n\to\infty} P_n$ exists.

91. Uniform Convergence of Products

Now let the factors in the product

$$\prod_{n=1}^{\infty}[1+a_n(z)]$$

be dependent upon a complex variable z. Let R be a closed region in the z-plane. If the product converges in such a way that, given any $\varepsilon > 0$, there exists an n_0 independent for z for all z in R such that

$$\left|\prod_{k=1}^{n_0+p}[1+a_k(z)] - \prod_{k=1}^{n_0}[1+a_k(z)]\right| < \varepsilon$$

for all positive integral p, we say that the product $\prod_{n=1}^{\infty}[1+a_n(z)]$ is *uniformly convergent* in the region R.

Again the convergence properties parallel those of infinite series. We need a Weierstrass M-test.

THEOREM 81. *If there exist positive constants M_n such that $\sum_{n=1}^{\infty} M_n$ is convergent and $|a_n(z)| < M_n$ for all z in the closed region R, the product $\prod_{n=1}^{\infty}[1+a_n(z)]$ is uniformly convergent in R.*

PROOF. *Since* $\sum\limits_{n=1}^{\infty} M_n$ is convergent and $M_n > 0$, $\prod\limits_{n=1}^{\infty}(1 + M_n)$ is con-

vergent and $\lim\limits_{n\to\infty} \prod\limits_{k=1}^{n}(1 + M_k)$ exists. Therefore, given any $\varepsilon > 0$, there
exists an n_0 such that

$$\prod_{k=1}^{n_0+p}(1 + M_k) - \prod_{k=1}^{n_0}(1 + M_k) < \varepsilon$$

for all positive integers p. For all z in R, each $a_k(z)$ is such that $|a_k(z)| < M_k$.
Hence

$$\left| \prod_{k=1}^{n_0+p}[1 + a_k(z)] - \prod_{k=1}^{n_0}[1 + a_k(z)] \right|$$

$$= \left| \prod_{k=1}^{n_0}[1 + a_k(z)] \right| \cdot \left| \prod_{k=n_0+1}^{n_0+p}[1 + a_k(z)] - 1 \right|$$

$$< \prod_{k=1}^{n_0}(1 + M_k)\left[\prod_{k=n_0+1}^{n_0+p}(1 + M_k) - 1 \right]$$

$$< \prod_{k=1}^{n_0+p}(1 + M_k) - \prod_{k=1}^{n_0}(1 + M_k) < \varepsilon,$$

which was to be proved.

Exercises

1. Show that the following product converges, and find its value:

$$\prod_{n=1}^{\infty}\left[1 + \frac{6}{(n+1)(2n+9)}\right].$$ ANS. $\dfrac{21}{8}$.

2. Show that $\prod\limits_{n=2}^{\infty}\left(1 - \dfrac{1}{n^2}\right) = \dfrac{1}{2}$.

3. Show that $\prod\limits_{n=2}^{\infty}\left(1 - \dfrac{1}{n}\right)$ diverges to zero.

4. Investigate the product $\prod\limits_{n=0}^{\infty}(1 + z^{2^n})$ in $|z| < 1$.

ANS.   Abs. conv. to $\dfrac{1}{1 - z}$.

5. Show that $\prod\limits_{n=1}^{\infty} \exp\left(\dfrac{1}{n}\right)$ diverges.

6. Show that $\prod\limits_{n=1}^{\infty} \exp\left(-\dfrac{1}{n}\right)$ diverges to zero.

7. Test $\displaystyle\prod_{n=1}^{\infty}\left(1-\frac{z^2}{n^2}\right)$.   ANS. Abs. conv. for all finite z.

8. Show that $\displaystyle\prod_{n=1}^{\infty}\left[1+\frac{(-1)^{n+1}}{n}\right]$ converges to unity.

9. Test for convergence: $\displaystyle\prod_{n=2}^{\infty}\left(1-\frac{1}{n^p}\right)$ for real $p\neq 0$.

          ANS. Conv. for $p>1\cdot$div. for $p\leq 1$.

10. Show that $\displaystyle\prod_{n=1}^{\infty}\frac{\sin(z/n)}{z/n}$ is absolutely convergent for all finite z with the usual convention at $z=0$. Hint: Show first that

$$\lim_{n\to\infty}n^2\left[\frac{\sin(z/n)}{z/n}-1\right]=-\frac{z^2}{6}.$$

11. Show that if c is not a negative integer,

$$\prod_{n=1}^{\infty}\left[\left(1-\frac{z}{c+n}\right)\exp\left(\frac{z}{n}\right)\right]$$

is absolutely convergent for all finite z. Hint: Show first that

$$\lim_{n\to\infty}n^2\left[\left(1-\frac{z}{c+n}\right)\exp\left(\frac{z}{n}\right)-1\right]=z\left(c-\frac{1}{2}z\right).$$

92. Euler's Product for the Gamma Function

In Section 58, page 153, we defined the Gamma function by means of an integral,

$$(1)\qquad\qquad \Gamma(z)=\int_{0}^{\infty}e^{-t}t^{z-1}\,dt,\qquad \mathrm{Re}(z)>0.$$

In this section we shall obtain Euler's infinite product representation for $\Gamma(z)$.

It is convenient to establish a series of lemmas and from them to get the desired theorem.

LEMMA 12. *If z is neither zero nor a negative integer,*

$$(2)\qquad \frac{1}{z}\prod_{n=1}^{\infty}\left[\left(1+\frac{1}{n}\right)^z\left(1+\frac{z}{n}\right)^{-1}\right]=\lim_{n\to\infty}\frac{n!\,n^z}{z(z+1)(z+2)\cdots(z+n)}.$$

PROOF. In Example (b), page 240, we showed that the product on the left in (2) converges and that

(3) $$\prod_{n=1}^{\infty}\left[\left(1+\frac{1}{n}\right)^{z}\left(1+\frac{z}{n}\right)^{-1}\right]=\lim_{n\to\infty}\frac{n!\,(n+1)^{z}}{(z+1)(z+2)\cdots(z+n)}.$$

Since

$$\lim_{n\to\infty}\left(\frac{n+1}{n}\right)^{z}=1,$$

equation (2) follows from (3) and the fact that division by z is legitimate because $z\neq 0$.

LEMMA 13. *If n is integral and $\mathrm{Re}(z)>0$,*

(4) $$\lim_{n\to\infty}\int_{0}^{n}\left(1-\frac{t}{n}\right)^{n}t^{z-1}\,dt=\frac{1}{z}\prod_{n=1}^{\infty}\left[\left(1+\frac{1}{n}\right)^{z}\left(1+\frac{z}{n}\right)^{-1}\right].$$

PROOF. In the integral on the left in (4) put $t=n\beta$ and thus obtain the equation

(5) $$\int_{0}^{n}\left(1-\frac{t}{n}\right)^{n}t^{z-1}\,dt=n^{z}\int_{0}^{1}(1-\beta)^{n}\beta^{z-1}\,d\beta.$$

An integration by parts gives us the reduction formula

$$\int_{0}^{1}(1-\beta)^{n}\beta^{z-1}\,d\beta=\frac{n}{z}\int_{0}^{1}(1-\beta)^{n-1}\beta^{z}\,d\beta,$$

iteration of which yields

$$\int_{0}^{1}(1-\beta)^{n}\beta^{z-1}\,d\beta=\frac{n(n-1)(n-2)\cdots 1}{z(z+1)(z+2)\cdots(z+n-1)}\int_{0}^{1}\beta^{z+n-1}\,d\beta$$

$$=\frac{n!}{z(z+1)(z+2)\cdots(z+n)}.$$

Now (5) becomes

$$\int_{0}^{n}\left(1-\frac{t}{n}\right)^{n}t^{z-1}\,dt=\frac{n!\,n^{z}}{z(z+1)(z+2)\cdots(z+n)}$$

so that

$$\lim_{n\to\infty}\int_{0}^{n}\left(1-\frac{t}{n}\right)^{n}t^{z-1}\,dt=\lim_{n\to\infty}\frac{n!\,n^{z}}{z(z+1)\cdots(z+n)}$$

and therefore Lemma 13 follows from Lemma 12.

LEMMA 14. *If $0\leq\alpha<1$, $1+\alpha\leq\exp(\alpha)\leq(1-\alpha)^{-1}$.*

PROOF. Compare the three series

$$1+\alpha=1+\alpha, \quad \exp(\alpha)=1+\alpha+\sum_{n=2}^{\infty}\frac{\alpha^n}{n!}, \quad (1-\alpha)^{-1}=1+\alpha+\sum_{n=2}^{\infty}\alpha^n.$$

LEMMA 15. *If $0\leq\alpha<1$, $(1-\alpha)^n\geq 1-n\alpha$, for n a positive integer.*

PROOF. For $n=1$, $1-\alpha=1-1\cdot\alpha$, as desired. Next assume that

$$(1-\alpha)^k\geq 1-k\alpha,$$

and multiply each member by $(1-\alpha)$ to obtain

$$(1-\alpha)^{k+1}\geq(1-\alpha)(1-k\alpha)=1-(k+1)\alpha+k\alpha^2,$$

so that

$$(1-\alpha)^{k+1}\geq 1-(k+1)\alpha.$$

Lemma 15 now follows by induction.

LEMMA 16. *If $0\leq t<n$, n a positive integer,*

$$0\leq e^{-t}-\left(1-\frac{t}{n}\right)^n\leq\frac{t^2 e^{-t}}{n}.$$

PROOF. Use $\alpha=t/n$ in Lemma 14 to get

$$1+\frac{t}{n}\leq\exp\left(\frac{t}{n}\right)\leq\left(1-\frac{t}{n}\right)^{-1}$$

from which

(6)
$$\left(1+\frac{t}{n}\right)^n\leq e^t\leq\left(1-\frac{t}{n}\right)^{-n}$$

or

$$\left(1+\frac{t}{n}\right)^{-n}\geq e^{-t}\geq\left(1-\frac{t}{n}\right)^{n},$$

so that

(7)
$$e^{-t}-\left(1-\frac{t}{n}\right)^n\geq 0.$$

But also

$$e^{-t}-\left(1-\frac{t}{n}\right)^n=e^{-t}\left[1-e^t\left(1-\frac{t}{n}\right)^n\right]$$

and, by (6), $e^t \geq \left(1 + \dfrac{t}{n}\right)^n$. Hence

(8) $$e^{-t} - \left(1 - \frac{t}{n}\right)^n \leq e^{-t}\left[1 - \left(1 - \frac{t^2}{n^2}\right)^n\right].$$

Now Lemma 15 with $\alpha = t^2/n^2$ yields

$$\left(1 - \frac{t^2}{n^2}\right)^n \geq 1 - \frac{t^2}{n}$$

which may be used in (8) to obtain

(9) $$e^{-t} - \left(1 - \frac{t}{n}\right)^n \leq e^{-t}\left[1 - 1 + \frac{t^2}{n}\right] = \frac{t^2 e^{-t}}{n}.$$

The inequalities (7) and (9) constitute the result stated in Lemma 16.

We are now in a position to obtain the desired product representation for $\Gamma(z)$.

THEOREM 82. *If* $\mathrm{Re}\,(z) > 0$,

(10) $$\Gamma(z) = \frac{1}{z} \prod_{n=1}^{\infty} \left[\left(1 + \frac{1}{n}\right)^z \left(1 + \frac{z}{n}\right)^{-1}\right].$$

PROOF. For the time being let the right member of (10) be called $f(z)$. We need to show that $\Gamma(z) = f(z)$. From

(11) $$\Gamma(z) = \int_0^{\infty} e^{-t} t^{z-1}\, dt$$

and Lemma 13, we obtain

$$\Gamma(z) - f(z) = \lim_{n \to \infty} \left[\int_0^{\infty} e^{-t} t^{z-1}\, dt - \int_0^n \left(1 - \frac{t}{n}\right)^n t^{z-1}\, dt\right]$$

$$= \lim_{n \to \infty} \left[\int_0^n \left\{e^{-t} - \left(1 - \frac{t}{n}\right)^n\right\} t^{z-1}\, dt + \int_n^{\infty} e^{-t} t^{z-1}\, dt\right].$$

From the convergence of the integral on the right in (11) it follows that

$$\lim_{n \to \infty} \int_n^{\infty} e^{-t} t^{z-1}\, dt = 0.$$

Hence

(12) $$\Gamma(z) - f(z) = \lim_{n \to \infty} \int_0^n \left[e^{-t} - \left(1 - \frac{t}{n}\right)^n\right] t^{z-1}\, dt.$$

But, by Lemma 16 and the fact that $|t^z| = t^{\mathrm{Re}(z)}$,

$$\left| \int_0^n \left[e^{-t} - \left(1 - \frac{t}{n}\right)^n \right] t^{z-1}\, dt \right| \leqq \int_0^n \frac{t^2 e^{-t}}{n} \cdot t^{\mathrm{Re}(z)-1}\, dt \leqq \frac{1}{n} \int_0^n e^{-t} t^{\mathrm{Re}(z)+1}\, dt.$$

Now $\int_0^\infty e^{-t} t^{\mathrm{Re}(z)+1}\, dt$ converges, so $\int_0^n e^{-t} t^{\mathrm{Re}(z)+1}\, dt$ is bounded. Therefore it follows that

$$\lim_{n \to \infty} \int_0^n \left[e^{-t} - \left(1 - \frac{t}{n}\right)^n \right] t^{z-1}\, dt = 0,$$

and we may conclude from equation (12) that

$$\Gamma(z) = f(z),$$

which is what is stated in Theorem 82.

The Euler product in Theorem 82 can be used to give the function $\Gamma(z)$ meaning for all complex z except for zero and the negative integers.

93. The Weierstrass Product

In Section 52, page 141, we proved the existence of the Euler, or Mascheroni, constant γ. We showed that

$$\lim_{n \to \infty} (H_n - \ln n) = \gamma,$$

in which H_n is the finite harmonic sum. Since

$$\lim_{n \to \infty} \ln \frac{n+1}{n} = 0,$$

we may write

(1) $$\lim_{n \to \infty} [H_n - \ln(n+1)] = \gamma.$$

Now

(2) $$\sum_{k=1}^n \ln \frac{k+1}{k} = \ln(n+1)$$

because the finite series telescopes. Combining (1) and (2) we obtain

$$\lim_{n \to \infty} \left[H_n - \sum_{k=1}^n \ln \frac{k+1}{k} \right] = \gamma.$$

Then

(3)
$$\lim_{n \to \infty} \exp\left[-H_n z + z \sum_{k=1}^{n} \ln \frac{k+1}{k}\right] = \exp(-\gamma z).$$

Since

$$\exp(-z H_n) = \prod_{k=1}^{n} \exp\left(-\frac{z}{k}\right)$$

and

$$\exp\left[z \sum_{k=1}^{n} \ln \frac{k+1}{k}\right] = \prod_{k=1}^{n} \left(\frac{k+1}{k}\right)^z,$$

equation (3) may be put in the form

(4)
$$\lim_{n \to \infty} \prod_{k=1}^{n} \left[\left(1 + \frac{1}{k}\right)^z \exp\left(-\frac{z}{k}\right)\right] = \exp(-\gamma z).$$

From Theorem 82, page 246, we obtain

(5)
$$z\Gamma(z) = \lim_{n \to \infty} \prod_{k=1}^{n} \left[\left(1 + \frac{1}{k}\right)^z \left(1 + \frac{z}{k}\right)^{-1}\right].$$

Comparison of (4) and (5) encourages us to rewrite (5) as

(6)
$$z\Gamma(z) = \lim_{n \to \infty} \prod_{k=1}^{n} \left[\left(1 + \frac{1}{k}\right)^z \exp\left(-\frac{z}{k}\right)\left(1 + \frac{z}{k}\right)^{-1} \exp\left(\frac{z}{k}\right)\right].$$

Using the result (4) on the right in (6) yields

(7)
$$z\Gamma(z) = \exp(-\gamma z) \lim_{n \to \infty} \prod_{k=1}^{n} \left[\left(1 + \frac{z}{k}\right)^{-1} \exp\left(\frac{z}{k}\right)\right],$$

from which it follows, by inverting each member, that

(8)
$$\frac{1}{z\Gamma(z)} = \exp(\gamma z) \lim_{n \to \infty} \prod_{k=1}^{n} \left[\left(1 + \frac{z}{k}\right) \exp\left(-\frac{z}{k}\right)\right].$$

From (8) we obtain the result in (9) below, the Weierstrass product for $\dfrac{1}{\Gamma(z)}$.

THEOREM 83. *If z is neither zero nor a negative integer,*

(9)
$$\frac{1}{\Gamma(z)} = z \exp(\gamma z) \prod_{n=1}^{\infty} \left[\left(1 + \frac{z}{n}\right) \exp\left(-\frac{z}{n}\right)\right].$$

94. Evaluation of Certain Infinite Products

The Weierstrass infinite product for $\Gamma(z)$ yields a simple evaluation of all infinite products whose factors are rational functions of the index n. The most general such product must take the form

$$(1) \qquad P = \prod_{n=1}^{\infty} \frac{(n+a_1)(n+a_2)\cdots(n+a_s)}{(n+b_1)(n+b_2)\cdots(n+b_s)}$$

$$= \prod_{n=1}^{\infty} \frac{\prod\limits_{k=1}^{s}\left(1+\dfrac{a_k}{n}\right)}{\prod\limits_{k=1}^{s}\left(1+\dfrac{b_k}{n}\right)}$$

because convergence requires that the nth factor approach unity as $n \to \infty$, which in turn forces the numerator and denominator polynomials to be of the same degree and to have equal leading coefficients. Now the nth factor in the right member of (1) may be put in the form

$$1 + \frac{1}{n}\left(\sum_{k=1}^{s} a_k - \sum_{k=1}^{s} b_k\right) + \frac{\theta_n}{n^2},$$

in which θ_n is bounded. We must therefore also insist, to obtain convergence, that

$$(2) \qquad \sum_{k=1}^{s} a_k = \sum_{k=1}^{s} b_k.$$

If (2) is not satisfied, the product in (1) diverges; we get absolute convergence or no convergence.

We now have an absolutely convergent product (1) in which the a's and b's satisfy the condition (2).

Since

$$\exp\left(\frac{1}{n}\sum_{k=1}^{s} a_k\right) = \exp\left(\frac{1}{n}\sum_{k=1}^{s} b_k\right),$$

we may, without changing the value of the product (1), insert the appropriate exponential factors to write

$$(3) \qquad P = \prod_{n=1}^{\infty} \frac{\prod\limits_{k=1}^{s}\left[\left(1+\dfrac{a_k}{n}\right)\exp\left(-\dfrac{a_k}{n}\right)\right]}{\prod\limits_{k=1}^{s}\left[\left(1+\dfrac{b_k}{n}\right)\exp\left(-\dfrac{b_k}{n}\right)\right]}.$$

The Weierstrass product for $1/\Gamma(z)$ yields

$$\prod_{n=1}^{\infty}\left[\left(1+\frac{z}{n}\right)\exp\left(-\frac{z}{n}\right)\right]=\frac{1}{z\exp(\gamma z)\Gamma(z)}=\frac{1}{\Gamma(z+1)\exp(\gamma z)}.$$

Thus we obtain from (3) the result

$$P=\prod_{k=1}^{s}\frac{\Gamma(1+b_k)\exp(\gamma b_k)}{\Gamma(1+a_k)\exp(\gamma a_k)}$$

$$=\exp\left[\gamma\left(\sum_{k=1}^{s}b_k-\sum_{k=1}^{s}a_k\right)\right]\prod_{k=1}^{s}\frac{\Gamma(1+b_k)}{\Gamma(1+a_k)}$$

$$=\prod_{k=1}^{s}\frac{\Gamma(1+b_k)}{\Gamma(1+a_k)}.$$

THEOREM 84. *If* $\sum_{k=1}^{s}a_k=\sum_{k=1}^{s}b_k$, *and if no* a_k *or* b_k *is a negative integer,*

$$\prod_{n=1}^{\infty}\frac{(n+a_1)(n+a_2)\cdots(n+a_s)}{(n+b_1)(n+b_2)\cdots(n+b_s)}=\frac{\Gamma(1+b_1)\Gamma(1+b_2)\cdots\Gamma(1+b_s)}{\Gamma(1+a_1)\Gamma(1+a_2)\cdots\Gamma(1+a_s)}.$$

EXAMPLE. Evaluate

$$\prod_{n=1}^{\infty}\frac{(c-a+n-1)(c-b+n-1)}{(c+n-1)(c-a-b+n-1)}.$$

Since $(c-a-1)+(c-b-1)=(c-1)+(c-a-b-1)$, we may employ Theorem 84 if no one of the quantities c, $c-a$, $c-b$, $c-a-b$ is either zero or a negative integer. With those restrictions we obtain

$$(4)\qquad\prod_{n=1}^{\infty}\frac{(c-a+n-1)(c-b+n-1)}{(c+n-1)(c-a-b+n-1)}=\frac{\Gamma(c)\Gamma(c-a-b)}{\Gamma(c-a)\Gamma(c-b)}.$$

Exercises

1. Use the Euler product in Theorem 82, page 246, to prove that

$$\Gamma(z+1)=z\Gamma(z).$$

2. Use the Euler product for $\Gamma(z)$ to show that $\Gamma(1)=1$.

3. In the Weierstrass product formula for $\dfrac{1}{\Gamma(z)}$ on page 248, take logs of both members to get

$$\ln\Gamma(z)=-\text{Ln }z-\gamma z-\sum_{n=1}^{\infty}\left[\text{Ln}\left(1+\frac{z}{n}\right)-\frac{z}{n}\right].$$

Differentiate both members of the above equation, showing uniform convergence of the resulting series and conclude that

$$\frac{\Gamma'(z)}{\Gamma(z)} = -\gamma - \frac{1}{z} - \sum_{n=1}^{\infty} \left(\frac{1}{z+n} - \frac{1}{n} \right).$$

4. Use the results in Exercises 2 and 3 to show that

$$\Gamma'(1) = -\gamma.$$

5. Combine Theorem 82, page 246, and Lemma 12, page 243, and a little manipulation, to prove that

$$\lim_{n \to \infty} \frac{(n-1)!\, n^z}{(z)_n} = \Gamma(z).$$

6. Let

$$a_n = \left| \frac{(\alpha)_n (\beta)_n}{(\gamma)_n\, n!} \right|$$

and let $\delta = \frac{1}{2} \operatorname{Re}(\gamma - \alpha - \beta)$. Recall that for complex x

$$|n^x| = n^{\operatorname{Re}(x)}.$$

Show that

$$n^{1+\delta} a_n = \left| \frac{(\alpha)_n}{(n-1)!\, n^\alpha} \cdot \frac{(\beta)_n}{(n-1)!\, n^\beta} \cdot \frac{(n-1)!\, n^\gamma}{(\gamma)_n} \cdot \frac{n^\delta}{n^{\gamma-\alpha-\beta}} \right|$$

and thus conclude that, if $\operatorname{Re}(\gamma - \alpha - \beta) > 0$,

$$\lim_{n \to \infty} n^{1+\delta}\, a_n = 0.$$

7. Use the result in Exercise 6 and a comparison theorem to show that if $\operatorname{Re}(\gamma - \alpha - \beta) > 0$, the series

$$F(\alpha, \beta; \gamma; x) = 1 + \sum_{n=1}^{\infty} \frac{(\alpha)_n (\beta)_n x^n}{n!\, (\gamma)_n}$$

is absolutely convergent for all $|x| = 1$.

Tables

Table of Power Series

In some series the following symbols are used:
$(a)_n = a(a+1)(a+2)\cdots(a+n-1)$, page 151;
B_n = Bernoulli number, page 144;
E_n = Euler number, page 147;
H_n = Harmonic sum, page 141.

1. $\dfrac{1}{1-x} = \displaystyle\sum_{n=0}^{\infty} x^n, \qquad |x| < 1.$

2. $\dfrac{1}{(1-x)^2} = \displaystyle\sum_{n=0}^{\infty} (n+1)x^n, \qquad |x| < 1.$

3. $\dfrac{1}{(1-x)^3} = \tfrac{1}{2}\displaystyle\sum_{n=0}^{\infty} (n+1)(n+2)x^n, \qquad |x| < 1.$

4. $(1-x)^{-a} = \displaystyle\sum_{n=0}^{\infty} \dfrac{(a)_n x^n}{n!}, \qquad |x| < 1.$

5. $\ln(1+x) = \displaystyle\sum_{n=1}^{\infty} \dfrac{(-1)^{n+1}x^n}{n}, \qquad -1 < x \leq 1.$

6. $\tfrac{1}{2}\ln\dfrac{1+x}{1-x} = \displaystyle\sum_{n=0}^{\infty} \dfrac{x^{2n+1}}{2n+1}, \qquad |x| < 1.$

7. $\dfrac{\ln(1+x)}{1+x} = \displaystyle\sum_{n=1}^{\infty} (-1)^{n+1}H_n x^n, \qquad |x| < 1.$

8. $\tfrac{1}{2}\ln^2(1+x) = \displaystyle\sum_{n=1}^{\infty} \dfrac{(-1)^{n+1}H_n x^{n+1}}{n+1}, \qquad |x| < 1.$

9. $e^x = \sum_{n=0}^{\infty} \frac{x^n}{n!}, \qquad |x| < \infty.$

10. $\sin x = \sum_{n=0}^{\infty} \frac{(-1)^n x^{2n+1}}{(2n+1)!}, \qquad |x| < \infty.$

11. $\cos x = \sum_{n=0}^{\infty} \frac{(-1)^n x^{2n}}{(2n)!}, \qquad |x| < \infty.$

12. $\tan x = \sum_{n=1}^{\infty} \frac{(-1)^{n+1} 2^{2n}(2^{2n}-1) B_{2n} x^{2n-1}}{(2n)!}, \qquad |x| < \tfrac{1}{2}\pi.$

13. $x \csc x = \sum_{n=0}^{\infty} \frac{(-1)^{n+1}(2^{2n}-2) B_{2n} x^{2n}}{(2n)!}, \qquad |x| < \pi.$

14. $\sec x = \sum_{n=0}^{\infty} \frac{(-1)^n E_{2n} x^{2n}}{(2n)!}, \qquad |x| < \tfrac{1}{2}\pi.$

15. $x \cot x = \sum_{n=0}^{\infty} \frac{(-1)^n 2^{2n} B_{2n} x^{2n}}{(2n)!}, \qquad |x| < \pi.$

16. $\sin^2 x = \sum_{n=0}^{\infty} \frac{(-1)^n 2^{2n+1} x^{2n+2}}{(2n+2)!}, \qquad |x| < \infty.$

17. $\cos^2 x = 1 + \sum_{n=1}^{\infty} \frac{(-1)^n 2^{2n-1} x^{2n}}{(2n)!}, \qquad |x| < \infty.$

18. $\tan^2 x = \sum_{n=1}^{\infty} \frac{(-1)^n 2^{2n+1}(2^{2n+2}-1) B_{2n+2} x^{2n}}{(n+1)(2n)!}, \qquad |x| < \tfrac{1}{2}\pi.$

19. $\sec^2 x = 1 + \sum_{n=1}^{\infty} \frac{(-1)^n 2^{2n+1}(2^{2n+2}-1) B_{2n+2} x^{2n}}{(n+1)(2n)!}, \qquad |x| < \tfrac{1}{2}\pi.$

20. $x^2 \csc^2 x = 1 + \sum_{n=1}^{\infty} \frac{(-1)^{n+1}(2n-1) 2^{2n} B_{2n} x^{2n}}{(2n)!}, \qquad |x| < \pi.$

21. $x^2 \cot^2 x = 1 - \tfrac{2}{3}x^2 + \sum_{n=2}^{\infty} \frac{(-1)^{n+1}(2n-1) 2^{2n} B_{2n} x^{2n}}{(2n)!}, \qquad |x| < \pi.$

22. $\sec x \tan x = \sum_{n=1}^{\infty} \frac{(-1)^n E_{2n} x^{2n-1}}{(2n-1)!}, \qquad |x| < \tfrac{1}{2}\pi.$

23. $\sec^3 x = \sum_{n=0}^{\infty} \frac{(-1)^{n+1}(E_{2n+2} - E_{2n}) x^{2n}}{2(2n)!}, \qquad |x| < \tfrac{1}{2}\pi.$

24. $\sin^3 x = \tfrac{3}{4} \sum_{n=1}^{\infty} \frac{(-1)^{n+1}(3^{2n}-1) x^{2n+1}}{(2n+1)!}, \qquad |x| < \infty.$

25. $\cos^3 x = \tfrac{1}{4} \sum_{n=0}^{\infty} \frac{(-1)^n (3^{2n}+3) x^{2n}}{(2n)!}, \qquad |x| < \infty.$

26. $\sec^2 x \tan x = \sum_{n=1}^{\infty} \frac{(-1)^n 2^{2n}(2^{2n+2}-1) B_{2n+2} x^{2n-1}}{(n+1)(2n-1)!}, \qquad |x| < \tfrac{1}{2}\pi.$

27. $x^3 \csc^2 x \cot x = 1 + \sum_{n=2}^{\infty} \frac{(-1)^n(2n-1)(n-1)2^{2n}B_{2n}x^{2n}}{(2n)!}$, $\qquad |x| < \pi.$

28. $\ln(\sec x + \tan x) = \sum_{n=0}^{\infty} \frac{(-1)^n E_{2n}x^{2n+1}}{(2n+1)!}$, $\qquad |x| < \tfrac{1}{2}\pi.$

29. $\ln \cos x = \sum_{n=1}^{\infty} \frac{(-1)^n 2^{2n-1}(2^{2n}-1)B_{2n}x^{2n}}{n(2n)!}$, $\qquad |x| < \tfrac{1}{2}\pi.$

30. $\ln \dfrac{\tan x}{x} = \sum_{n=1}^{\infty} \frac{(-1)^{n+1}2^{2n}(2^{2n-1}-1)B_{2n}x^{2n}}{n(2n)!}$, $\qquad |x| < \tfrac{1}{2}\pi.$

31. $\ln \dfrac{\sin x}{x} = \sum_{n=1}^{\infty} \frac{(-1)^n 2^{2n-1}B_{2n}x^{2n}}{n(2n)!}$, $\qquad |x| < \pi.$

32. $\ln \dfrac{1 + \cos x}{2} = \sum_{n=1}^{\infty} \frac{(-1)^n(2^{2n}-1)B_{2n}x^{2n}}{n(2n)!}$, $\qquad |x| < \pi.$

33. $\dfrac{1}{\sqrt{1-x^2}} = \sum_{n=0}^{\infty} \frac{(\frac{1}{2})_n x^{2n}}{n!}$, $\qquad |x| < 1.$

34. $\operatorname{Arcsin} x = \sum_{n=0}^{\infty} \frac{(\frac{1}{2})_n x^{2n+1}}{(2n+1)n!}$, $\qquad |x| < 1.$

35. $\dfrac{1}{\sqrt{1-x^2}} \operatorname{Arcsin} x = \sum_{n=0}^{\infty} \frac{n!\, x^{2n+1}}{(\frac{3}{2})_n}$, $\qquad |x| < 1.$

36. $(\operatorname{Arcsin} x)^2 = \sum_{n=0}^{\infty} \frac{n!\, x^{2n+2}}{(n+1)(\frac{3}{2})_n}$, $\qquad |x| < 1.$

37. $\sqrt{1-x^2}\, \operatorname{Arcsin} x = x - \tfrac{1}{2}\sum_{n=0}^{\infty} \frac{n!\, x^{2n+3}}{(\frac{3}{2})_{n+1}}$, $\qquad |x| < 1.$

38. $\operatorname{Arctan} x = \sum_{n=0}^{\infty} \frac{(-1)^n x^{2n+1}}{2n+1}$, $\qquad |x| \leqq 1.$

39. $\sinh x = \sum_{n=0}^{\infty} \frac{x^{2n+1}}{(2n+1)!}$, $\qquad |x| < \infty.$

40. $\cosh x = \sum_{n=0}^{\infty} \frac{x^{2n}}{(2n)!}$, $\qquad |x| < \infty.$

41. $\tanh x = \sum_{n=1}^{\infty} \frac{2^{2n}(2^{2n}-1)B_{2n}x^{2n-1}}{(2n)!}$, $\qquad |x| < \tfrac{1}{2}\pi.$

42. $x \operatorname{csch} x = -\sum_{n=0}^{\infty} \frac{(2^{2n}-2)B_{2n}x^{2n}}{(2n)!}$, $\qquad |x| < \pi.$

43. $\operatorname{sech} x = \sum_{n=0}^{\infty} \frac{E_{2n}x^{2n}}{(2n)!}$, $\qquad |x| < \tfrac{1}{2}\pi.$

44. $x \coth x = \sum_{n=0}^{\infty} \frac{2^{2n}B_{2n}x^{2n}}{(2n)!}$, $\qquad |x| < \pi.$

45. $\cos x \cosh x = \sum\limits_{n=0}^{\infty} \dfrac{(-1)^n 2^{2n} x^{4n}}{(4n)!}$, $\quad |x| < \infty$.

46. $\sin x \sinh x = \sum\limits_{n=0}^{\infty} \dfrac{(-1)^n 2^{2n+1} x^{4n+2}}{(4n+2)!}$, $\quad |x| < \infty$.

47. $\sin x \cosh x = \sum\limits_{n=0}^{\infty} \dfrac{(-1)^{\alpha(n)} 2^n x^{2n+1}}{(2n+1)!}$,

in which $\alpha(n) = $ greatest integer $\leq \frac{1}{2} n$, $\quad |x| < \infty$.

48. $\cos x \sinh x = \sum\limits_{n=0}^{\infty} \dfrac{(-1)^{\beta(n)} 2^n x^{2n+1}}{(2n+1)!}$,

in which $\beta(n) = $ greatest integer $\leq \frac{1}{2} n + \frac{1}{2}$, $\quad |x| < \infty$.

49. $\ln(x + \sqrt{1+x^2}) = \sum\limits_{n=0}^{\infty} \dfrac{(-1)^n (\frac{1}{2})_n x^{2n+1}}{(2n+1) n!}$, $\quad |x| < 1$.

50. $\dfrac{\ln(x + \sqrt{1+x^2})}{\sqrt{1+x^2}} = \sum\limits_{n=0}^{\infty} \dfrac{(-1)^n n! \, x^{2n+1}}{(\frac{3}{2})_n}$, $\quad |x| < 1$.

51. $\ln^2(x + \sqrt{1+x^2}) = \sum\limits_{n=0}^{\infty} \dfrac{(-1)^n n! \, x^{2n+2}}{(n+1)(\frac{3}{2})_n}$, $\quad |x| < 1$.

52. $\sqrt{1+x^2} \ln(x + \sqrt{1+x^2}) = x + \frac{1}{2} \sum\limits_{n=0}^{\infty} \dfrac{(-1)^n n! \, x^{2n+3}}{(\frac{3}{2})_{n+1}}$, $\quad |x| < 1$.

53. $\exp(x \cos \theta) \cos(x \sin \theta) = \sum\limits_{n=0}^{\infty} \dfrac{x^n \cos n\theta}{n!}$, $\quad |x| < \infty$.

54. $\exp(x \cos \theta) \sin(x \sin \theta) = \sum\limits_{n=1}^{\infty} \dfrac{x^n \sin n\theta}{n!}$, $\quad |x| < \infty$.

55. $\cosh(x \cos \theta) \cos(x \sin \theta) = \sum\limits_{n=0}^{\infty} \dfrac{x^{2n} \cos 2n\theta}{(2n)!}$, $\quad |x| < \infty$.

56. $\cosh(x \cos \theta) \sin(x \sin \theta) = \sum\limits_{n=0}^{\infty} \dfrac{x^{2n+1} \sin(2n+1)\theta}{(2n+1)!}$, $\quad |x| < \infty$.

57. $\sinh(x \cos \theta) \cos(x \sin \theta) = \sum\limits_{n=0}^{\infty} \dfrac{x^{2n+1} \cos(2n+1)\theta}{(2n+1)!}$, $\quad |x| < \infty$.

58. $\sinh(x \cos \theta) \sin(x \sin \theta) = \sum\limits_{n=1}^{\infty} \dfrac{x^{2n} \sin 2n\theta}{(2n)!}$, $\quad |x| < \infty$.

59. $\dfrac{1 - x \cos \theta}{1 - 2x \cos \theta + x^2} = \sum\limits_{n=0}^{\infty} \cos(n\theta) \, x^n$, $\quad |x| < 1$.

60. $\dfrac{x \sin \theta}{1 - 2x \cos \theta + x^2} = \sum\limits_{n=1}^{\infty} \sin(n\theta) \, x^n$, $\quad |x| < 1$.

Table of Fourier Series

Items 1–19 give the sums of certain Fourier series that occur frequently. Items 20–45 give Fourier expansions for some simple functions. Consult Chapter 11 for a description of the sum of the series outside the basic interval.

1. $\displaystyle\sum_{n=1}^{\infty} \frac{1}{n} \sin \frac{n\pi x}{c} = \frac{\pi(c-x)}{2c},\qquad 0 < x \leq c.$

2. $\displaystyle\sum_{n=1}^{\infty} \frac{(-1)^{n+1}}{n} \sin \frac{n\pi x}{c} = \frac{\pi x}{2c},\qquad 0 \leq x < c.$

3. $\displaystyle\sum_{n=1}^{\infty} \frac{1}{n^3} \sin \frac{n\pi x}{c} = \frac{\pi^3 x(c-x)(2c-x)}{12c^3},\qquad 0 \leq x \leq c.$

4. $\displaystyle\sum_{n=1}^{\infty} \frac{(-1)^{n+1}}{n^3} \sin \frac{n\pi x}{c} = \frac{\pi^3 x(c^2-x^2)}{12c^3},\qquad 0 \leq x \leq c.$

5. $\displaystyle\sum_{n=1}^{\infty} \frac{1}{n^5} \sin \frac{n\pi x}{c} = \frac{\pi^5 x(c-x)(2c-x)[7c^2-3(c-x)^2]}{720c^5},\qquad 0 \leq x \leq c.$

The right member in Item 5 can be put in the form

$$\pi^5\left[\frac{1}{90}\left(\frac{x}{c}\right) - \frac{1}{36}\left(\frac{x}{c}\right)^3 + \frac{1}{48}\left(\frac{x}{c}\right)^4 - \frac{1}{240}\left(\frac{x}{c}\right)^5\right].$$

6. $\displaystyle\sum_{n=1}^{\infty} \frac{(-1)^{n+1}}{n^5} \sin \frac{n\pi x}{c} = \frac{\pi^5 x(c^2-x^2)(7c^2-3x^2)}{720c^5},\qquad 0 \leq x \leq c.$

7. $\displaystyle\sum_{k=0}^{\infty} \frac{1}{2k+1} \sin \frac{(2k+1)\pi x}{c} = \frac{\pi}{4},\qquad 0 < x < c.$

8. $\displaystyle\sum_{k=0}^{\infty} \frac{(-1)^k}{(2k+1)^2} \sin \frac{(2k+1)\pi x}{c} = \frac{\pi^2 x}{4c},\qquad 0 \leq x \leq \tfrac{1}{2}c,$

$$= \frac{\pi^2(c-x)}{4c},\qquad \tfrac{1}{2}c \leq x \leq c.$$

9. $\displaystyle\sum_{k=0}^{\infty} \frac{1}{(2k+1)^3} \sin \frac{(2k+1)\pi x}{c} = \frac{\pi^3 x(c-x)}{8c^2},\qquad 0 \leq x \leq c.$

10. $\displaystyle\sum_{k=0}^{\infty} \frac{(-1)^k}{(2k+1)^4} \sin \frac{(2k+1)\pi x}{c} = \frac{\pi^4 x(3c^2-4x^2)}{96c^3},\qquad 0 \leq x \leq \tfrac{1}{2}c,$

$$= \frac{\pi^4(c-x)[3c^2-4(c-x)^2]}{96c^3},\qquad \tfrac{1}{2}c \leq x \leq c.$$

11. $\displaystyle\sum_{k=0}^{\infty} \frac{1}{(2k+1)^5} \sin \frac{(2k+1)\pi x}{c} = \frac{\pi^5 x(c-x)(c^2+cx-x^2)}{96c^4},\qquad 0 \leq x \leq c.$

12. $\displaystyle\sum_{n=1}^{\infty} \frac{1}{n^2} \cos \frac{n\pi x}{c} = \frac{\pi^2[3(c-x)^2-c^2]}{12c^2},\qquad 0 \leq x \leq c.$

13. $\displaystyle\sum_{n=1}^{\infty} \frac{(-1)^{n+1}}{n^2} \cos \frac{n\pi x}{c} = \frac{\pi^2(c^2 - 3x^2)}{12c^2}$, $\qquad 0 \leq x \leq c.$

14. $\displaystyle\sum_{n=1}^{\infty} \frac{1}{n^4} \cos \frac{n\pi x}{c} = \frac{\pi^4[-15(c-x)^4 + 30c^2(c-x)^2 - 7c^4]}{720c^4}$, $\qquad 0 \leq x \leq c.$

The right member in Item 14 can be put in the form

$$\pi^4\left[\frac{1}{90} - \frac{1}{12}\left(\frac{x}{c}\right)^2 + \frac{1}{12}\left(\frac{x}{c}\right)^3 - \frac{1}{48}\left(\frac{x}{c}\right)^4\right].$$

15. $\displaystyle\sum_{n=1}^{\infty} \frac{(-1)^{n+1}}{n^4} \cos \frac{n\pi x}{c} = \frac{\pi^4(15x^4 - 30c^2x^2 + 7c^4)}{720c^4}$, $\qquad 0 \leq x \leq c.$

16. $\displaystyle\sum_{k=0}^{\infty} \frac{(-1)^k}{2k+1} \cos \frac{(2k+1)\pi x}{c} = \tfrac{1}{4}\pi,$ $\qquad 0 \leq x < \tfrac{1}{2}c,$

$\qquad\qquad\qquad\qquad\qquad\qquad = 0, \qquad\qquad x = \tfrac{1}{2}c,$

$\qquad\qquad\qquad\qquad\qquad\qquad = -\tfrac{1}{4}\pi, \qquad \tfrac{1}{2}c < x \leq c.$

17. $\displaystyle\sum_{k=0}^{\infty} \frac{1}{(2k+1)^2} \cos \frac{(2k+1)\pi x}{c} = \frac{\pi^2(c-2x)}{8c}$, $\qquad 0 \leq x \leq c.$

18. $\displaystyle\sum_{k=0}^{\infty} \frac{(-1)^k}{(2k+1)^3} \cos \frac{(2k+1)\pi x}{c} = \frac{\pi^3(c^2 - 4x^2)}{32c^2}$, $\qquad 0 \leq x \leq \tfrac{1}{2}c,$

$$= \frac{\pi^3[4(c-x)^2 - c^2]}{32c^2}, \qquad \tfrac{1}{2}c \leq x \leq c.$$

19. $\displaystyle\sum_{k=0}^{\infty} \frac{1}{(2k+1)^4} \cos \frac{(2k+1)\pi x}{c} = \frac{\pi^4(4x^3 - 6cx^2 + c^3)}{96c^3}$, $\qquad 0 \leq x \leq c.$

20. $\displaystyle 1 = \frac{4}{\pi}\sum_{k=0}^{\infty} \frac{1}{2k+1} \sin \frac{(2k+1)\pi x}{c}$, $\qquad 0 < x < c.$

21. $\displaystyle x = \frac{2c}{\pi}\sum_{n=1}^{\infty} \frac{(-1)^{n+1}}{n} \sin \frac{n\pi x}{c}$, $\qquad -c < x < c.$

22. $\displaystyle x = \tfrac{1}{2}c - \frac{4c}{\pi^2}\sum_{k=0}^{\infty} \frac{1}{(2k+1)^2} \cos \frac{(2k+1)\pi x}{c}$, $\qquad 0 \leq x \leq c.$

23. $\displaystyle x^2 = 2c^2\sum_{n=1}^{\infty}\left[\frac{(-1)^{n+1}}{n\pi} - \frac{2\{1 - (-1)^n\}}{n^3\pi^3}\right] \sin \frac{n\pi x}{c}$, $\qquad 0 \leq x < c.$

24. $\displaystyle x^2 = \frac{c^2}{3} + \frac{4c^2}{\pi^2}\sum_{n=1}^{\infty} \frac{(-1)^n}{n^2} \cos \frac{n\pi x}{c}$, $\qquad -c \leq x \leq c.$

25. $\displaystyle x^3 = \frac{2c^3}{\pi^3}\sum_{n=1}^{\infty} \frac{(-1)^{n+1}(n^2\pi^2 - 6)}{n^3} \sin \frac{n\pi x}{c}$, $\qquad -c < x < c.$

26. $\displaystyle x^3 = \frac{c^3}{4} + 6c^3\sum_{n=1}^{\infty}\left[\frac{(-1)^n}{n^2\pi^2} + \frac{2\{1 - (-1)^n\}}{n^4\pi^4}\right] \cos \frac{n\pi x}{c}$, $\qquad 0 \leq x \leq c.$

27. $x^4 = \dfrac{c^4}{5} + 8c^4 \displaystyle\sum_{n=1}^{\infty} \dfrac{(-1)^n(n^2\pi^2-6)}{n^4\pi^4} \cos\dfrac{n\pi x}{c}, \qquad -c \leqq x \leqq c.$

28. $x^4 = 2c^4 \displaystyle\sum_{n=1}^{\infty} \left[(-1)^{n+1}\left(\dfrac{1}{n\pi} - \dfrac{12}{n^3\pi^3}\right) + \dfrac{24\{1-(-1)^n\}}{n^5\pi^5} \right] \sin\dfrac{n\pi x}{c},$

$$0 \leqq x < c.$$

29. $e^{ax} = \dfrac{\sinh ac}{ac} + 2\sinh ac \displaystyle\sum_{n=1}^{\infty} \dfrac{(-1)^n}{a^2c^2+n^2\pi^2}\left[ac\cos\dfrac{n\pi x}{c} - n\pi\sin\dfrac{n\pi x}{c} \right],$

$$-c < x < c.$$

30. $e^{ax} = \displaystyle\sum_{n=1}^{\infty} \dfrac{2n\pi[1-(-1)^n e^{ac}]}{a^2c^2+n^2\pi^2} \sin\dfrac{n\pi x}{c}, \qquad 0 < x < c.$

31. $e^{ax} = \dfrac{e^{ac}-1}{ac} + 2ac \displaystyle\sum_{n=1}^{\infty} \dfrac{(-1)^n e^{ac}-1}{a^2c^2+n^2\pi^2} \cos\dfrac{n\pi x}{c}, \qquad 0 \leqq x < c.$

32. $\sinh ax = 2\sinh ac \displaystyle\sum_{n=1}^{\infty} \dfrac{(-1)^{n+1}n\pi}{a^2c^2+n^2\pi^2} \sin\dfrac{n\pi x}{c}, \qquad -c < x < c.$

33. $\sinh ax = \dfrac{\cosh ac-1}{ac} + 2ac \displaystyle\sum_{n=1}^{\infty} \dfrac{(-1)^n\cosh ac-1}{a^2c^2+n^2\pi^2} \cos\dfrac{n\pi x}{c},$

$$0 \leqq x < c.$$

34. $\cosh ax = \dfrac{\sinh ac}{ac} + 2ac\sinh ac \displaystyle\sum_{n=1}^{\infty} \dfrac{(-1)^n}{a^2c^2+n^2\pi^2} \cos\dfrac{n\pi x}{c},$

$$-c < x < c.$$

35. $\cosh ax = \displaystyle\sum_{n=1}^{\infty} \dfrac{2n\pi[1-(-1)^n\cosh ac]}{a^2c^2+n^2\pi^2} \sin\dfrac{n\pi x}{c}, \qquad 0 < x < c.$

36. If $\dfrac{ac}{\pi} \neq$ integer,

$$\sin ax = \sin ac \sum_{n=1}^{\infty} \dfrac{2n\pi(-1)^{n+1}}{n^2\pi^2-a^2c^2} \sin\dfrac{n\pi x}{c}, \qquad -c < x < c.$$

37. If $\dfrac{ac}{\pi} \neq$ integer,

$$\sin ax = \dfrac{1-\cos ac}{ac} - \sum_{n=1}^{\infty} \dfrac{2ac[1-(-1)^n\cos ac]}{n^2\pi^2-a^2c^2} \cos\dfrac{n\pi x}{c}, \qquad 0 \leqq x < c.$$

38. If $m =$ integer, $m > 1$,

$$\sin\dfrac{m\pi x}{c} = \dfrac{1-(-1)^m}{m\pi} - \dfrac{2m}{\pi}\sum_{n=1}^{m-1} \dfrac{1-(-1)^{m+n}}{n^2-m^2} \cos\dfrac{n\pi x}{c}$$

$$- \dfrac{2m}{\pi}\sum_{n=m+1}^{\infty} \dfrac{1-(-1)^{m+n}}{n^2-m^2} \cos\dfrac{n\pi x}{c}, \qquad 0 \leqq x < c.$$

39. $\sin\dfrac{\pi x}{c} = \dfrac{2}{\pi} - \dfrac{4}{\pi}\displaystyle\sum_{k=1}^{\infty}\dfrac{1}{4k^2-1}\cos\dfrac{2k\pi x}{c}, \qquad 0 \leqq x < c.$

40. If $\dfrac{ac}{\pi} \neq$ integer,

$$\cos ax = \dfrac{\sin ac}{ac} - 2\,ac\sin ac\displaystyle\sum_{n=1}^{\infty}\dfrac{(-1)^n}{n^2\pi^2-a^2c^2}\cos\dfrac{n\pi x}{c}, \qquad -c < x < c.$$

41. If $\dfrac{ac}{\pi} \neq$ integer,

$$\cos ax = \displaystyle\sum_{n=1}^{\infty}\dfrac{2n\pi[1-(-1)^n\cos ac]}{n^2\pi^2-a^2c^2}\sin\dfrac{n\pi x}{c}, \qquad 0 < x < c.$$

42. If $m=$ integer, $m>1$,

$$\cos\dfrac{m\pi x}{c} = \dfrac{2}{\pi}\displaystyle\sum_{n=1}^{m-1}\dfrac{n[1-(-1)^{m+n}]}{n^2-m^2}\sin\dfrac{n\pi x}{c}$$

$$+\dfrac{2}{\pi}\displaystyle\sum_{n=m+1}^{\infty}\dfrac{n[1-(-1)^{n+m}]}{n^2-m^2}\sin\dfrac{n\pi x}{c}, \qquad 0 < x < c.$$

43. $\cos\dfrac{\pi x}{c} = \dfrac{8}{\pi}\displaystyle\sum_{k=1}^{\infty}\dfrac{k}{4k^2-1}\sin\dfrac{2k\pi x}{c}, \qquad 0 < x < c.$

44. $f(x) = 1, \qquad 0 < x < x_0,$

$\qquad = 0, \qquad x_0 < x < x_1,$

$f(x) \sim \dfrac{2}{\pi}\displaystyle\sum_{n=1}^{\infty}\dfrac{1}{n}\left(1-\cos\dfrac{n\pi x_0}{x_1}\right)\sin\dfrac{n\pi x}{x_1}, \qquad 0 < x < x_1.$

45. $f(x) = 1, \qquad 0 < x < x_0,$

$\qquad = 0, \qquad x_0 < x < x_1,$

$f(x) \sim \dfrac{x_0}{x_1}+\dfrac{2}{\pi}\displaystyle\sum_{n=1}^{\infty}\dfrac{1}{n}\sin\dfrac{n\pi x_0}{x_1}\cos\dfrac{n\pi x}{x_1}, \qquad 0 < x < x_1.$

Index

A

Abel, N. H., 103
Abel's lemma, 103–104
Absolutely convergent infinite
    series, 110
Absolutely convergent power
    series, 110
Absolutely convergent series,
    61–110
  insertion and removal of paren-
    theses in, 66
  rearrangement of terms of, 67–69

Addition of series, 67
  of power series, 125–126
Alternating series, 73-78
  tests for convergence of, 75
Asymptotic series, 222–235
  algebraic properties of, 228–229
  computation with, 233-235
  definition of, 223
  expansions, 223–227
  integration of, 230
  uniqueness of, 231–232

B

Bernoulli, Jakob, 144
Bernoulli numbers, 144–147
Bessel, F. W., 163
Bessel function, 163–165

  differential equation, 165
  inequality, 173
Beta functions, 155–156

C

Cauchy, A. L., 24
Cauchy criteria, 24
  product of series, 72–73
  radical test, 36–37
Churchill, R. V., 185
Cluster point, of sequence, 22–24

Comparison tests, 35–40; 51–52
Computations, numerical, 215–218
  with asymptotic series, 233–235
Continuity, 94–98
Convergence of infinite products,
  236

of power series, 109–112
of series, 5
Convergence, rapidity of, 214

tests for, 29–46; 51–59; 62–65
uniform, 83–107
Convergent sequence, 14

D

D'Alembert, J., 145
D'Alembert's ratio test, 44, 62, 111
Differentiation of Fourier series,
    207–213

of power series, 137
of series, 102–103
Divergence of series, 5
Divergent sequence, 14

E

Euler, Leonard, 215
Euler numbers, 147–149
    product for gamma function,

243–246
Even function, 145, 176

F

Factorial, simple, 7
    function, 151–152
Fourier coefficients, 183–184
    cosine series, 201–204
    sine series, 196–200

Fourier series, 146, 182–213
    differentiation of, 207–213
    integration of, 205–207
    sum of, 209
    table of, 256–259

G

Gamma function, 153–154
Gauss, C. F., 57

Gauss' test, 57–58

H

Hardy, G. H., 103

Hardy's test for uniform conver-

gence, 103–105
Harmonic series, 33, 40, 141–143
Hypergeometric function, 157–162

with unit argument, 158
Hypergeometric series, 158–159
Hyperharmonic series, 33

I

Integral test, 29–34
Integration of asymptotic series,
   231–232

of Fourier series, 205–207
of power series, 133
of series, 98–102

K

Kernel, 175
Knopp, Konrad, 13, 215
Kummer, E. E., 53

Kummer's criteria, 53
   test, 55

L

Least square property, 170–172

M

Maclaurin, Colin, 118
Maclaurin series, 114–120
Monotone sequence, 15

Multiplication of power series,
   70–72
of series, 125–126

N

Normalization, 170
Null sequence, 14

Numerical computations, 215–218

O

Odd function, 176
Orthogonal sets of functions,
167–181

set of sines and cosines, 178–181
Orthonormal set of functions, 170

P

Power series, 108–166
absolute convergence of, 110
addition of, 125–126
convergence of, 109–112
defined, 108
differentiation of, 137
division of, 129–132
integration of, 133
multiplication of, 125–126
radius of convergence of, 110
summation of, 219

table of, 252–255
uniform convergence of, 110
uniqueness of, 128
Pringsheim, A., 28
Products, infinite, 236–251
absolute convergence of, 238–240
convergence of, 236
definition of, 236
evaluation of, 249–251
uniform convergence of, 241–242

R

Raabe, J. L., 56
Raabe's test, 56
Radius of convergence of power
series, 110

Rapidity of convergence, 214
Ratio tests, 43–46, 51–52, 62
Rolle's theorem, 116

S

Sequence, 10–28
basic properties of, 13–14
cluster point, 22–24

convergence, 14
defined, 10
divergence, 14

general term, 11
least upper bound, 16–17
limit, 11
monotone, 15
null, 14
telescoping, 25–27
Series,
    absolute convergence, 61
    addition of, 125–126
    alternating, 73
    asymptotic, 222–235
    complex terms, 79–80
    divergent, 5
    Fourier, 182–213

geometric, 1
harmonic, 33, 40
hypergeometric, 158–159
hyperharmonic, 33
multiplication of, 70–72
partial sum, 5
power, 108–166
rearrangement of terms, 47–48
sum, 5
Stolz, O., 53
Subsequence, 19–20
Summation of power series, 219–221
Symbolic notation, 144–145

T

Taylor, Brooks, 116
Taylor series, 114–120

Telescoping series, 25–27

U

Uniform convergence, 83–107; 110
    Hardy's test for, 103–105
    infinite products, 241–242
    power series, 110

Weierstrass M-test for, 93, 110
Uniqueness of asymptotic series,
    231–232
    of power series, 128

W

Watson, G. N., 185
Weierstrass, Karl, 93
Weierstrass M-test for uniform con-
    vergence, 93

product, 247–248
Weight function, 167
Whittaker, E. T., 185